SICKNESS is recognized to be the most important and the most common single cause of economic insecurity. The United States of America has lagged behind other progressive countries of the world in the study and adoption of methods to protect the wage-earner and the salaried worker against sickness, disability and invalidity. The Social Security Act of 1935 makes provision for an increased program to prevent disease. It does not, however, deal with insecurity caused by loss of wages on account of disabling sickness or with protection against the costs of medical care.

SECURITY AGAINST SICKNESS is the outgrowth of a three-year study of the burdens created by sickness and of the opportunity for health insurance in the United States. The first part of the book gives a concise account of sickness costs and problems in our own country. The second part is devoted to a careful examination of the health insurance systems of other countries. The systems used in Great Britain, Germany, France, Denmark, and in other countries have been carefully studied. What these systems are and how they operate, how much they cost, and who pays the bill—these and ꞏer details are described in the present In aꞏꞏꞏꞏ the study shows to ꞏan sꞏꞏ ꞏve

SECURITY AGAINST SICKNESS

SECURITY AGAINST SICKNESS

A Study of Health Insurance

BY

I. S. FALK

DOUBLEDAY, DORAN & COMPANY, INC.

GARDEN CITY, NEW YORK

1936

PRINTED AT THE *Country Life Press*, GARDEN CITY, N. Y., U. S. A

TO
EDGAR SYDENSTRICKER
1881–1936

CONTENTS

❧

vii

PART FOUR

APPENDICES

TABLES

❧

PART ONE

☙

THE NEED FOR GROUP PAYMENT OF SICKNESS COSTS IN THE
UNITED STATES

I. INTRODUCTION

II. THE COSTS OF SICKNESS

III. THE GROUP PAYMENT OF SICKNESS COSTS

CHAPTER I

INTRODUCTION

HEALTH is a precious possession, so precious that one does not ordinarily set a money value upon it. It is not exchanged in the market place. It is personal and intimate, something cherished for the pursuit of happiness.

Yet health has material value and, in many circumstances, its maintenance has a price. Man has risen from the mud and slime of former ages by dint of great effort. Life has been prolonged and living made more healthful through the expenditure of vast energy and enormous wealth. If man had not learned how to safeguard the purity of his water supplies, dispose of his wastes, insure wholesome food, and deal more or less effectively with contagious diseases, he would still be living a pastoral life or would be huddled in the pestilential warrens which he once called towns. Without sanitation and medical science, rural life would still be primitive, modern urban living would be impossible, and a Spartan existence would still be the price of health everywhere except in Utopia.

From earliest infancy through adult life, the living being has a value not merely in an esthetic and intangible sense, but even in terms of money. A large capital investment has been made in bringing a child into the world and in carrying it through each year of life. Even though we set no monetary value upon a mother's care or a father's devotion, and though we disregard the worth of love and the comfort of family ties, human life still has a capital value. Indeed, our human capital—the money value of man—is by far the largest capital investment which society possesses.

Life has a capital money value because it can be productive. Hence the money value of a man is primarily a value to those who have a direct interest in his earnings—his dependents, his business or professional associates, and the society of which he is a member. This money value of man, arising from his productive powers, depends largely or entirely upon his health. Thus, from a strictly financial point of view, health has great value and it is sound economy that considerable sums should be spent for its preservation.

However specious or intangible a financial analysis may seem to many people, no one will underrate the human and emotional value of health. There was a time in history when all disease was viewed as a divine dispensation; but man has learned somewhat the extent to which pain and suffering express sanitary or hygienic, rather than moral, sins. He has learned to appreciate the value of healthful living and to recognize the spiritual value of the sound mind in the sound body. *Mens sana in corpore sano* was once the dictum only of a pagan philosophy. Now it is the pragmatic judgment of centuries of effort devoted to the search for a kindlier and happier way of life.

It has become a commonplace to remark upon the transformation which science has caused in the world. Scientific progress has been as rapid and profound in the biological as in the chemical and physical sciences. This has been equally true of the application which has been made of the pure sciences in the fields of practical affairs. Nowhere has the usefulness of scientific advance been so clear as in the medical sciences, where biology has a common meeting ground with chemistry and physics. Nor has progress been less rapid in the application of the medical sciences to the medical arts. It may perhaps be said that there have been greater improvements in the practice of sanitation and medicine in the years since 1882 (when Pasteur published his first report on rabies and Robert Koch described the bacillus of tuberculosis) or in the years since 1895 (when Roentgen described the X-rays) than the world had known previously since the beginning of history. These improvements have had profound effects not merely upon the services rendered by the sanitarian or the physician, but upon the style and the amenities of living. Life has been given a certainty and a safety, and health and human vigor have been given a reality, such as were undreamed of before. The consequences, both good and bad, have been clear in the productivity of an industrial world, in the augmented wealth of nations, in rising standards of living, in a newer pressure of population upon the resources of the world, in political transformations, and in an accelerated spread and movement of mankind over the face of the earth.

Two lines of evolution have proceeded apace. One has been the enormous increase in sanitary and medical knowledge and the vast improvement in the practical techniques of preventive and curative medicine; the other has been the growing public demand for the right to the enjoyment of health. But along with these advances, new problems have arisen. In health service, as in industry, there has developed the problem of *distribution*—how to make the augmented capacities of health service available to the people.

Industry has learned how to apply science to large-scale production and how to reduce the unit costs of its products. But medical care is not a machine-made *thing*; it is primarily a *personal service*. Improvements in the technology of industry may operate to reduce the cost of material *things*; but advances in medical science and improvements in medical technique call for longer periods of training for practitioners, greater skills, and more expensive personal *services*. There are some notable exceptions to the general rule, but it is the rule nevertheless, that the rising level of medical skill brings greater and not lesser costs. Progress which makes medicine more and more valuable to hundreds of millions of people makes payment of the costs more and more difficult.

Nor are medical costs the only important costs of sickness. When ill health befalls the wage-earner and disables him, the consequences may be very serious. When the worker becomes incapable of going about his accustomed labors, he fails to earn an income precisely when his financial needs may be unusually large. There was a time not long ago when he was without protection even against the effects of disability arising out of industrial accidents. The workmen's compensation laws have afforded him a measure of protection against this hazard, although they still have left him unprotected, except in some states, against the financial consequences of occupational disease. But when illness does not arise out of employment, the worker and his family must shoulder as best they can the economic effects of his disability. Loss of income and medical costs may combine to endanger or destroy the economic independence of the family.

Even apart from the effects of illness of the employed person in curtailing income, there has been a steadily growing restlessness and public discontent with medical costs for all the family. Books, magazine articles, newspaper comments, and fireside conversations everywhere yield a steady stream of complaints against the "high cost of sickness." At the same time, physicians protest that their incomes are meager; hospitals show that their annual operations leave them with deficits; and nurses continue to suffer from unemployment.

None of this is new; it is an old story. It was happening during the years when the country was steadily climbing to a higher peak of prosperity than it had ever known before and while national income was establishing a new high record. The failings in the distribution of medical service and the impacts of burdensome costs upon individual families are no consequence of a depression. They were plainly evident in our days of well-being. They are due to some fundamental weakness in the functional and economic relations between medicine and society.

American difficulties in furnishing medical care and problems in paying for the service were not new phenomena; the difficulties had appeared earlier in many countries of the world. Generally they had reached an acute state in Europe a generation or two before they began to receive national recognition in the United States. There are probably many reasons for the lag between European and American experience. But whatever the reasons, when the reality of the problems on the domestic scene became clear, attention was focussed upon the stage abroad. Some observers learned that in Europe solutions to the economic problems of medicine had been sought (and presumably found) in national programs of contributory health or sickness insurance. It seemed highly doubtful that any of the European systems were entirely suited to American needs; but the design of an appropriate American system was made difficult by lack of precise information on the nature of our problems, their causes, their exact definition, and their quantitative characteristics. During the years 1912 to 1920, an active but unsuccessful campaign was carried on by various agencies to enact health or sickness insurance legislation in a number of states and in the federal Congress. Because of national preoccupation with the problems of war-time, and perhaps because the programs were inadequate, the movement failed of any definitive accomplishments.

This, in brief, was the situation prior to 1927 when the Committee on the Costs of Medical Care was created and launched its five-year program of scientific and dispassionate inquiry. This non-official Committee of fifty persons included representative physicians, public health workers, dentists, nurses, hospital and other institutional authorities, educators, economists, sociologists, and citizens long active in the general public welfare. The Committee published in February, 1928, a carefully designed program of study and received financial support from eight philanthropic foundations. Between 1929 and 1933, its Research Staff issued the results of twenty-five fact-finding studies and then summarized the facts and the conclusions derived from all of the studies. Finally, the Committee itself reviewed the facts, drew its own conclusions, and formulated its recommendations.*

The factual information gathered by the Research Staff, the interpretation of the data, and the conclusions which flowed from them, were published with the approval of the members of the Committee.

*All of the publications of the Committee are distributed by The University of Chicago Press, Chicago, Illinois. The summary volume, prepared by the Research Staff, is the Committee's Publication No. 27; the Committee's own report is its Publication No. 28.

The unanimity with which the research studies were received did not, however, apply to the Committee's own recommendations. Thirty-five of a total of forty-eight members—including a majority of all the physicians in the Committee and a majority of the fifteen private practitioners—subscribed to the Majority Report. A minority of nine members (eight physicians and one non-medical member) presented an independent report (Minority Report No. 1). Two dentists submitted another independent report (Minority Report No. 2); and two individual members who signed no report offered personal dissenting statements. The various reports were contained in a volume, MEDICAL CARE FOR THE AMERICAN PEOPLE, issued in November, 1932.

The final report of the Committee received widespread attention. Unfortunately, it was not generally understood that important differences of opinion within the Committee were held in respect to some issues and not in respect to others. Confusion was further confounded by the resolutions passed by some organizations which endorsed one report or condemned another, sometimes in such fashion as to indicate that the few who drafted the resolutions and the many who concurred in them had not read the Committee reports closely, if at all.

In the year which followed publication of the Committee's final volume, public attention was focussed upon the conflict of opinion over recommendations. Comparatively little note was taken of the fundamental facts which had been uncovered by the studies and the substantial unanimity of opinion which had prevailed within the Committee upon the significance of these facts. While disputes over the Committee's recommendations continued, the need for constructive action still remained. Indeed, the need became more and more acute as the economic depression plumbed lower and lower depths and intensified the issues over medical costs. Various national and local groups turned their faces from controversies over recommendations, reëxamined the facts, and evolved their own programs. Unfortunately, no program of sufficient scope was developed in this period to deal adequately with the major problems or even to hold the promise of effective action on a large or national scale.

The studies represented in part by the present volume were therefore undertaken early in 1933 in search of a rational basis for constructive action on certain problems which arise out of illness and its social and economic sequelae. This work was interrupted in the summer of 1934 when the author was invited to join the technical staff of President Roosevelt's Committee on Economic Security to study the risks to economic security arising out of ill health. The present studies were resumed in 1935 after the reports for the President's Committee had been filed.

No attempt is made in the chapters which follow to review systematically the facts collected or compiled by the Committee on the Costs of Medical Care and the agencies which collaborated with them, or by other authors. The reader interested in the detailed data should consult the individual Committee publications or the summary volume prepared by the Committee's Research Staff.* The pertinent facts bearing upon the problems of the present study are introduced in this text only as the needs develop, and are brought together only to define and answer problems or to illustrate a method of computation or the quantitative validity of an argument. Nor has any effort been made to introduce a complete bibliography of other documents; only such studies as have immediate bearing are singled out for citation.

The present task is to define certain problems and to seek out, as objectively and rigorously as possible, the principles upon which constructive action should rest. The starting point for this study is an analysis of the economic burdens which are created by illness. This, we shall see, will involve consideration of loss of earnings by workers who become disabled by sickness, the costs of medical care for themselves and their dependents, the adequacy of medical services, the remuneration of doctors, dentists and nurses, the

*Falk, I. S., Rorem, C. Rufus and Ring, Martha D.: THE COSTS OF MEDICAL CARE. Publication No. 27 of The Committee on the Costs of Medical Care. Chicago, The University of Chicago Press, 1933, 648 pp.

financing of hospitals, and other complex subjects. None of these can, of course, be treated exhaustively within the compass of this volume.

The study of certain European systems of health insurance is an unavoidable task if we would profit in the United States by the experiences of other countries. The survey of health insurance has involved examination of a large variety of documents, both official and non-official, and personal inquiries in eight foreign countries. Each chapter devoted to the system of a particular country has been examined critically by government administrators, physicians and non-medical authorities of that country, in addition to other persons familiar with the subject. The author is greatly indebted to them for counsel and assistance.

When these studies were undertaken, attention was focussed upon the problems which face the American public and their government officers, the private medical and dental practitioners, hospital administrators, philanthropic agencies, and others. Consequently, this has been no cloistered research. After a rough draft of the manuscript was completed in 1934, the principal conclusions were discussed and criticized by a number of medical and non-medical people in many parts of the United States. The author has profited greatly from comments and criticisms which have been expressed publicly or privately, by word of mouth, through correspondence, or published articles. He wishes to record here his indebtedness to critics from whom he has learned much that has been of value and whose expressions have influenced the final development of this volume.

The author wishes also to record his indebtedness to the Milbank Memorial Fund for the generous support which made possible the collection of the factual information recorded in this volume. The interpretation of facts, the comments and the conclusions are, of course, the author's own and do not profess to represent the views or policies of the Fund or its officers.

CHAPTER II

THE COSTS OF SICKNESS

THE toll of illness cannot be measured in money alone. If the full account were added up, the reckoning would have to include the story of human pain and suffering, the frustration of life, and the consequences of premature death. With much of this, which is part of the price of illness, the social scientist cannot deal, except so far as illness can be prevented through the wise ordering of social forces or so far as the anti-social consequences of illness can be prevented or reduced. But social study can recognize the economic consequences of illness and can search out ways to deal with some of the problems. It can measure certain direct and indirect costs of ill health and it can devise ways of dealing with some of the burdens which are created by these costs.

If we neglect the intangible items and consider only the losses which can be measured in dollars and cents, the costs of illness are still tremendous. First, there is the money value of preventable deaths. Careful studies have shown that about one-third of the deaths which occur every year are preventable—in the sense that they occur prematurely—under present conditions through the application of well-established measures of public health and preventive medicine. These preventable deaths represent a capital value of over six billion dollars[1]* and this must be charged against the costs of illness. Second, there is the loss of earnings on account of sickness among employed persons and the loss in education costs due to the sickness of school children. A conservative estimate places these losses between 250 and 500 million dollars a year, even when full

*References and notes appear at the end of each chapter.

11

allowance is made for the fact that even in "good times" there are unemployed persons ready to take the place of some of those who are disabled by illness. Third, there are the expenditures for medical and related services for the prevention and cure of disease. In normal times, these medical expenditures amount to 3.7 billion dollars a year.

Thus, in the aggregate, illness costs the people of the United States about ten billion dollars a year. This is equivalent to about $80 a person in the entire population. The largest part—six billions in the capital loss from premature death—represents sheer waste because it is preventable through the proper expenditure of comparatively small sums in preventive work. It does not ordinarily arouse great economic anxiety, because the money value of human life is not generally recognized and because the loss is indirect rather than direct. Those costs of illness which are personal rather than social, and individual rather than collective, seem more real and arouse more concern because they involve direct and immediate burdens upon the particular individuals who must bear them.

The costs of illness are so large that they deserve great social concern. But "social concern" is not ordinarily anybody's particular concern. Of more immediate importance are the practical issues connected with the direct burdens of illness upon those who pay the costs. These costs are everybody's concern.

The money loss in premature death may seem vague and unreal; but the loss of earnings or the cost of medical care is specific and real. This point does not need laboring, for there are tens of millions of people in the United States over whom sickness hangs like a sword of Damocles. Sickness, disability, loss of earnings through sickness, and the costs of medical care are the most constant and the most frequent threats to their economic security. In good times and in bad times, each year the threat becomes a reality in millions of homes. It is in terms of this reality—illness as an important cause of social and economic insecurity—that we propose to examine the costs of illness. Our objective, however, is twofold: to search out a way of furnishing security against some of the economic risks which arise from illness; and to contribute as much as we can to an understanding of social measures which may be devised to reduce the burdens of sickness costs so that people may be better enabled to purchase adequate medical care. To carry the analysis forward, we propose to examine in some detail the characteristics of the loss of earnings due to illness and of the costs of medical care.

Loss of Earnings

Various studies which have been conducted in the United States indicate that among persons of wage-earning ages there is an average disability of about eight calendar days or nearly seven working days a year. This is equivalent to saying that on an average day of the year 2.25 per cent of the total industrial population of the country are so sick as to be incapacitated for their ordinary pursuits of life. This happens year in and year out in normal times. Multiplying the average disability by the number of gainfully employed persons and by an average daily income gives an estimate of the total loss of earnings due to disabling illness. For a period like the year 1930 the total would be nearly two billion dollars; for a period like the present, when there is widespread unemployment (March, 1936), it would be about one or one and a half billion dollars. Generally, the loss of earnings from disability amounts to about one and a half billion dollars a year, or an average loss of over $30 per gainfully employed person. These figures take no account of the larger losses involved to industry and to society generally.

If the total loss of earnings on account of disability is considered in relation to those among whom it occurs, it appears that most of the burden falls upon people in the lower income brackets. About $900,000,000 is lost to employed persons who are members of families with incomes of less than $2,500[2] and only some $600,000,000 loss occurs among those in the higher brackets. The loss in the upper income classes is comparatively small, first, because there are comparatively fewer persons in these classes and, second, because the higher incomes are derived chiefly from salaries and business and tend to go on without interruption in spite of temporary disability from illness. Among people of modest and small incomes (families with $2,500 a year and under) the loss of earnings is probably distributed about as follows:

Families with Incomes of:	Average Loss per Employed Person	Total Loss
$1,200 to $2,500	$32	$650,000,000
Less than $1,200	25	250,000,000

The workmen's compensation laws provide for partial remuneration of those whose disability arises out of employment, and cover a loss of about $150,000,000 a year.

Costs of Medical Care

Recent studies show that in the United States the total expenditures for medical care in a normal year are about 3.66 billion dollars or $30 per person.* This total includes the following items of expenditure:

Patients	$2,886,000,000
Governments (public health, hospitals, etc.)	509,000,000
Philanthropy	182,000,000
Industry (chiefly medical care under workmen's compensation laws)	79,000,000
TOTAL	$3,656,000,000

In other words, apart from expenditures made for them by governments (federal, state and local), by philanthropy or industry, the people of the United States spend privately, year after year in normal times, nearly three billion dollars ($23 or $24 per person) or about

---

*It is merely a coincidence that both the average loss of earnings and the average medical expenditures amount to about $30. There is, however, an important difference between these two figures: the loss of earnings is about $30 per gainfully employed person; the medical cost is about $30 per person in the entire population.

4 per cent of their total income. Nearly all of this sum is spent for the cure of sickness; private expenditures for preventive care account for only 33 cents per person a year.

Considering only the lower income classes, we have the following:

Families with Incomes of:	Average Cost per Family	Total Cost
$1,200 to $2,500	$86	$1,200,000,000
Less than $1,200	49	300,000,000

These figures include medical costs for entire families and are not restricted to the costs for gainfully occupied persons. From such data as are available, it appears that among families with incomes of $1,200 to $2,500, medical care for the employed persons costs about $15 per person and in the next lower income class (less than $1,200) about $9 per person. These figures measure the average private charges incurred for medical care for the worker. But this is only part of the cost which is faced by the worker, for the medical care of his dependents must also be purchased from his earnings. The family costs more correctly measure the financial burden faced by the people who are in these lower income brackets.

THE COMPARATIVE SIZE OF LOSS OF EARNINGS AND MEDICAL COSTS

If we bring together the two tabulations, we find the following relations between the two kinds of costs which arise out of illness:

Families with Incomes of:	Loss of Earnings	Costs of Medical Care
$1,200 to $2,500	$650,000,000	$1,200,000,000
Less than $1,200	250,000,000	300,000,000

It is obvious that in these lower income brackets the costs of remedial care create larger and more important economic burdens than loss of earnings on account of disability. In the higher income classes, medical costs are even proportionately larger than loss of earnings.

It is not intended to underestimate the importance of loss of earnings on account of illness. It must be recognized, however, that of the two main risks arising out of illness, the costs of medical care is much the larger. This, we shall see in later chapters, is a new condition, different from what prevailed in other times and in other countries when they faced the problems of planning for economic security against sickness. In European countries health insurance programs were developed in a time when medical costs were much smaller than loss of earnings. Hence these programs dealt first with insurance against loss of earnings and came only later to emphasize insurance against medical costs. These facts explain why the present American approach to the subject is different from that which has been traditional in European countries and why American students of the subject are now giving greater emphasis to the costs of medical care than to the loss of earnings.

The Problem Involved in Loss of Earnings through Disability

By and large, the annual loss of earnings caused by disabling sickness amounts to about $30 per gainfully employed person. In the aggregate, this is a large sum. Yet expressed in terms of an average per worker, there is nothing terrifying about it. The financial problems created by eight days of disabling illness a year and the loss of $30, more or less, cannot be made to seem very grave. Workers who earn very small wages, and especially those whose employment is intermittent, would find even a $30 loss during a year very serious, but most employed persons could manage to carry the burden and even budget against the expected loss through small weekly or monthly savings. Thus, consideration of this cost of illness in terms of the average loss per worker leads to the conclusion that it is a matter deserving comparatively little attention.

A moment's reflection, however, will show that such an analysis is without merit. It involves a fictitious assumption, namely, that the loss of earnings on account of disability actually occurs among workers equally and in the average amount. If each worker had the average disability a year and the average loss of earnings a year the problem would be simple. But he doesn't suffer average illness or average loss except by chance. Disabling illnesses are not all of eight days' duration. To the contrary, disabling illness ranges each year from less than a day to the entire year. Whether an illness will be mild and non-disabling, or severe and disabling; whether disability will last a day, a week, a month, or a year depends upon many factors—the preceding health of the individual, the nature of the illness, and its severity in the particular case.

As a general rule there will be, in any ordinary year, about 500 cases of disabling illness among each 1,000 persons in the population. More than one-half the people will not suffer such illness; among the other persons, some will have one attack, some will have two attacks, and some will have even more frequent attacks during the year. Among gainfully occupied persons, considering only wage-earners and salaried workers between the ages of 15 and 65, about 28 per cent will have one or more disabling illnesses during a year. Of these, about 15 per cent will be disabled for 8 days or less; about 10.5 per cent will be disabled for 9 to 45 days; and 2 to 2.5 per cent for 45 to 365 days. That this will happen year after year, in any ordinary group of a thousand or a million employed persons, can be predicted with considerable accuracy. But what will happen to any particular person in the thousand or in the million cannot be predicted.

On the basis of chance alone, it is to be expected that some workers earning average incomes will have disabling illness of average duration and will suffer the average financial loss. Others, with larger or smaller earnings, will have no disabling illness at all or illness of very short duration—perhaps a day or two. But others, with larger or smaller earnings, may suffer illness which will reduce their earnings by anything from 2 per cent to 100 per cent. *And the individual worker cannot know in advance in which class he will fall.* This is the essential reason why the averages are misleading and why disabling sickness is a constant threat to the security of the individual and the family.

It must constantly be borne in mind that these are not merely statistical predictions of what *may* happen; they are statistical summaries of what *does* happen, year in and year out. They are the cold and impersonal figures which summarize the tragedy of economic insecurity, especially for the families of modest and small means. For in ordinary times, about one-third or one-half of all cases of family dependency can be traced directly or indirectly to the effects of illness.

Considered in terms of large groups of people or in terms of averages, loss of earnings because of illness presents a comparatively small risk to income and to security. Considered in terms of the individual worker or the individual family, the risk is uncertain and is capable of producing either mild or catastrophic effects. Obviously, protection against the risk can be afforded by converting the risk of the individual into the average risk of the large group. This means applying the principle of insurance so that each member of the group accepts the cost of the average risk in return for protection against the uncertain event which may befall him.

The Problems Involved in Medical Costs

In an ordinary year, the people of the United States receive medical services and consume medicines worth about three and two-thirds billions of dollars. This sum represents 4 per cent of all the wages, salaries, profits, and other income received by the entire population.[3] Of the total amount spent for all kinds of health and medical services, governments (federal, state and local) provide from tax funds 14 per cent, philanthropy supplies 5 per cent, and industry 2 per cent. The remaining 79 per cent is paid from the private purses of families and individuals. More than a million persons earn their livelihood in the service of furnishing medical care. Six billion dollars are invested in the hospitals, clinics, professional offices and other kinds of plant and equipment used for medical service. Whether measured in terms of invested capital, annual expenditures, or personnel, this "service industry" ranks fifth or sixth in the nation's economy.

These were the figures before the depression, applying to the years 1928 to 1931. During the more recent years there has been great shrinkage in expenditures for medical care, as there has been for commodities or services generally. Various estimates[4] indicate that total expenditures for health and medical services declined to about 2.8 billion dollars in 1932 and to about 2 billions in 1933. But national income also suffered great reductions so that the total medical bill remained between 3 and 4 per cent of income. Both income and medical expenditures increased in 1934 and 1935.

The total expenditures for medical care are divided almost equally between private practitioners and institutions. Ordinarily, about 1.9 billion dollars are spent for the services of over 500,000 private practitioners of all kinds—physicians, dentists, nurses, midwives, optometrists, osteopaths, chiropractors, and others; the remaining 1.7 billion dollars are spent for services rendered in medical institutions, for commodities (chiefly medicines), and for the remuneration of the 530,000 persons engaged in these activities. Of expenditures for private practitioners, the lion's share falls to the 125,000 physicians. Dentistry and nursing are the next largest items. Among the institutions, hospitals consume 856 million dollars, drugs and medicines 665 millions, public health 121 millions, and all other services 90 millions.

The total expenditures for medical care amount to about 4 per cent of all income. This cannot be considered an excessive burden when account is taken of the fact that in the same year in which we customarily spent 3.66 billion dollars for medical care, we spent more than 20 billions for luxuries, amusements, and non-essentials of various sorts. If standards of good medical care call for larger expenditures, an additional billion or two—that is, up to 5 or 6 per cent of all income—could be spent for medical service in normal times, and *if spent on a national basis* would still induce no financial hardship.

Of course, the nation's total cost for medical care is not a national bill, in the sense that it is not a single or central expenditure. It is the composite expenditure of government agencies, industry, philanthropy, commercial organizations, and the year-round private expenditures of thirty million individual families. To refer to the national bill for medical care is merely a statistical figure of speech. It has the convenience of permitting us to deal with gross totals and broad averages. We use it merely as an expression of convenience, without intending to give the impression that it is a unit national cost.

To appreciate the significance of the cost figures which have been cited, they must be expressed in more homely units. For example, if the national bill for medical care (public and private) of an average or so-called "normal" year were equally distributed among the people of this country, the annual charge would be $30 per person. The fraction of the total which is paid from private—as distinguished from public—purses is equivalent to an average annual charge of $23 or $24 per person or $108 for an ordinary white family of two or more persons. This average of $108 per family for the private purchase of medical care is a composite average. It takes into account in proper proportions the averages for families of different economic levels and living in various types of communities. From the poorest to the wealthiest families the average cost increases tenfold, ranging from about $50 per family among those with incomes of less than $1,200 to about $500 per family for those with $10,000 and more. The average cost for families in each income class is in general higher in large cities than in small towns or rural areas. If the average cost for all families combined were distributed among families uniformly according to annual income, each family would have to spend about 4 per cent of its income. If only it were true that these costs were distributed in some such simple way there would be no important problem in respect to medical costs, even if 95 per cent of the people had to shoulder in addition the costs for the 5 per cent who in normal times are indigent or semi-indigent.

Unfortunately, the costs of medical care are not fixed and regular like the costs of food, clothing, or shelter. The purchase of food or clothing and the payment of rent recur regularly; and except for those whose incomes are below the minimum for subsistence, to procure these essentials involves only the common problem of living within one's income. Unlike the costs of food, clothing, and shelter, however, the costs of medical care are determined only to a minor extent by regular, periodic, physiological needs. Medical costs depend almost entirely upon the occurrence of sickness and the receipt of care.

The financial obligation for medical service would create no special problem if the *average* occurrence of sickness applied with compara- tive regularity and certainty to each family or to each individual. In an average population, there are each year about 8 recognized ill- nesses among each ten persons (about 7 among each ten males and about 9 among each ten females). But though these averages may predict what will ordinarily happen in a group of a thousand or a million persons, they may be grossly misleading in respect to an individual or a particular family. How irregular the occurrence actually is appears from the following figures. In a normal year, in a group of 1,000,000 persons:

> 470,000 will suffer no recognized illness
> 320,000 will be sick once
> 140,000 will be sick twice
> 50,000 will be sick three times
> 20,000 will be sick four or more times

Variations like these recur year after year; but no individual can anticipate whether he or his family will be the one to experience a year of life with little or no illness or will be heavily burdened by sickness and the need for medical care.

The figures cited above apply to a composite population like that of an average million persons in the United States and give a fair picture of the situation for families at each level of the economic ladder. The occurrence of illness has little respect for family income. The medical needs of the poor are substantially the same as the medical needs of the rich. Furthermore, the costs of sickness vary even more than the occurrence of sickness, because of variations both in the kinds and the amounts of care needed and received.

In each income class, only about 10 or 15 per cent of the families incur in any particular year medical charges which are approximately equal to the average for all families in their income class. A large proportion of the families normally incurs small charges; and the remaining families incur charges which range from the average to five, ten, or even twenty times the average. For the family so fortunate as to need little or no medical care during a twelve-month period, the costs present no difficult problem. For the families with charges of the average amounts, or twice the average, there is no serious problem except for those with the most meager incomes. But for those whose medical charges are three, four, six, eight, ten times the average—that is, 12 to 40 or 50 per cent of income—medical costs become a burden of the first magnitude. And it must be remembered that the family with small medical costs this year may be the one with large costs next year.

The drain of medical charges upon the family purse is of two quite different kinds. On the one hand, there are the costs of frequent and comparatively inexpensive illnesses or medical needs; and on the other, there is the occasional occurrence of the so-called "high-cost" illness. The difference is of fundamental importance to the family. The occasional, or even frequent, occurrence of minor illness and comparatively small costs for medical care may be easily absorbed in the family budget. But the occurrence of a "high-cost" illness, even when moderate rates are charged for each unit of service, may be a financial catastrophe for the family of small or modest means. At the one extreme, medical care for a "cold" or an attack of some other minor respiratory disease or for a minor digestive disturbance costs, on the average, $6; at the other extreme, a case of pneumonia costs, on the average, $59, a confinement $95, an appendicitis $168, a cancer $342. Even each of these figures is an average among widely varying costs.

Disease is not respectful of persons or considerate of the family exchequer. Large costs may fall upon small purses. Experience shows it is futile to caution people that these uncertainties are certain. The plain fact is that families do not and will not individually budget against a cost which fluctuates within a very broad range and which often attains such a size that it cannot be budgeted. A family's medical cost may, in the extremest case, even exceed annual income. Individual budgeting provides an answer only for wealthy families and for those families of moderate means so fortunate as to have but few illnesses which involve elaborate, costly, or long-continued professional care.

Variations in the occurrence of illness is first among the causes of variation in medical costs. These variations have been studied at great length in many parts of the country and among families of all economic groups. No conclusion has emerged more frequently or more consistently from the studies than that the costs of medical care are felt as a burden more because they are so unevenly distributed among the people than because of their actual amount. The uneven and uncertain occurrence of sickness is part of its very nature and brings an uncertain need for medical care. And this in turn brings an uncertain financial load. This sequence of uncertainty prevents the individual family from budgeting the costs in advance to a degree that is practicable for almost all other large items of family expenditure.

Many families of moderate income who are unable to pay for their medical care in time of sickness are criticized for the fact that they spend relatively large amounts for articles or services which may be considered luxuries. But families of the same income who deny themselves such luxuries find it just as difficult to plan ahead for the costs of illness. The amount of money which these families can save is usually altogether inadequate for an unexpected and expensive medical need.

Which types of medical service are principally responsible for the variations in costs? To what extent would variations in total costs be eliminated in a group of families if the costs of particular types of services were budgeted among groups of families or were paid by taxation or insurance? To these questions it is possible to give exact answers.[3]

It should be kept in mind that the private purchase of medical care is almost entirely for curative, as distinguished from preventive, service. Of the money which the average family spends for medical services from its own income, only 1.4 per cent is, on the average, spent for prevention of disease. Furthermore, in each income class and regardless of the size of the average medical costs for the class, illnesses which involve hospitalization are responsible for one-half the total costs.

A study of variations in the costs of each type of medical service reveals that *in each income level* variations are common in four— the services of the physician, dentist, hospital, and nurse. The *extent* to which variation in costs rests on each type of service has actually been measured from the records of thousands of families. Such an analysis shows that the responsibility for variation in costs is broad and rests upon all the important types of service—physician, dentist, hospital, and nurse. Averaging the costs of any one, or two, or three of these solves part of the problem created by variations in costs. If the costs for families in any particular income level are to be brought within a range which extends only reasonably above and below the average cost for the group, the averaging process (which is the basis of insurance) must include all four. Less than this leaves each family with an appreciable probability that its own annual costs will attain burdensome magnitudes.

Up to this point we have considered only the problems of costs, and have disregarded questions of quality and adequacy of medical care. Many of the findings from recent studies are *prima facie* evidences of moderate, sore, or even wanton neglects, and very few give evidences of pampering medical excesses. When the amount of medical care that is received by representative groups of families is compared with reasonable estimates of the amount of care that is needed, it is found that neither the rich nor the poor obtain the care which they really need. The deficiencies appear in respect to care of all major types (except the purchase of commodities in the drug store) and are especially notable in the receipt of dentistry and of preventive services from physicians. The potential benefits which modern medicine offers are on the whole very inadequately realized.

Nor is the lag between the availability of skill and its utilization determined by costs alone. Other contributing factors include widespread public ignorance of opportunity, deeply-rooted spending habits, the excessive use of self-prescribed medicines, resort to quacks and charlatans, and—particularly among urban people—a helplessness and incapacity to search out the medical service needed from among the confusing supply of practitioners and agencies which are available. Indeed, the complaints of the public against modern medical practice are directed almost as much against the absence of coördination of facilities under trustworthy authority and against the difficulty of making a safe and judicious selection of physician, dentist, or hospital, as against the costs themselves.

Incomes of Medical Practitioners and Institutions

The uneven burden of medical costs upon individuals and families has its counterpart in the uneven distribution of income among the physicians, dentists, and nurses who minister to them. Consider the incomes of doctors in 1929, a year of high prosperity. Among all private practitioners, one-half had *gross* incomes of $7,026 or less. But 42 per cent of gross income is consumed by the professional expenses of private practice. Hence, one-half of the private practitioners had *net* incomes of $4,100 or less. Even when the incomes of the other half are considered, the average *net* income for all was $5,700. These figures include not only general practitioners but also partial and complete specialists who earned more than general practitioners. When the general practitioners are considered alone, the corresponding gross and net incomes were $5,245 and $2,900, respectively. Obviously these are not large incomes for men who carry heavy responsibilities, must occupy important social positions in their communities, and whose professional training has required long and arduous years. Practically everything said about physicians' incomes applies to dentists.

The figures which have been cited, taken by themselves, do not give an adequate picture of professional remuneration because averages or middle incomes give no idea of the large variation which occurs among practitioners in the same or in different communities.

The average income of the physician or dentist no more describes the economic status of the individual practitioner than the average cost of medical care describes the problem of the individual family. If $2,500 is arbitrarily taken as the amount below which net income may be termed inadequate by definition, it is found that even in the heyday of 1929, 33 per cent of the physicians and 22 per cent of the dentists had inadequate incomes (40,000 physicians and 12,500 dentists). If the standard is set as low as $1,500 a year, about 18 per cent of the physicians and about 8 per cent of the dentists fell below even this point. Many people who complain against the high costs of medical care, and especially against the charges of physicians, consider only the large income of the financially successful practitioner. They are not ordinarily aware that for every physician who earned more than $10,000 as an annual net income, there were two who earned less than $2,500. For every dentist who earned more than $10,000, there were four who earned less than $2,500.

This was the unhappy state of affairs in 1929. During the depression the lot of physicians and dentists has, of course, been much worse. Between 1929 and 1932, the cost of living in the United States declined 20 per cent; but the incomes of physicians and dentists declined 40 per cent.[5] In 1932, the average net income of all physicians in private practice was about $3,450 and of all dentists in private practice about $2,800. In 1933 and in 1934 incomes were apparently still lower, though there are as yet no accurate figures except for small or regional groups of practitioners.[6]

The extent of unemployment among physicians is ordinarily so large that even in 1929 the services which they rendered could have been supplied by little more than 50 per cent of those in active practice if each of these had had a reasonably complete quota of patients to provide full use of working time. In the depression years the situation has been much worse.

The private practice of nursing was in desperate economic straits even in 1928 and 1929. The supply of graduate nurses has increased rapidly, from 16 per 100,000 population in 1900 to 240 in 1930. These numbers are exclusive of 77,000 graduate and 80,000 student nurses in American hospitals and 150,000 untrained nurses. Employment for even the well-trained nurse is intermittent and income is inadequate even in good times. Unemployment is increased by the graduation of approximately 25,000 students annually from the 1,500 to 2,000 hospitals which conduct nurses' training schools.

The present situation is unsatisfactory alike to nurses and patients. The graduate nurse finds private duty nursing an overcrowded field, in which she cannot look forward to professional advancement or substantial increase of professional income. The patient cannot afford or objects to the high fees for nursing service ($5 to $8 per day) and goes without needed care which the unemployed nurse would gladly provide. An economic barrier stands between them. How shall they remove it?

The hospitals of the United States are face to face with a financial crisis which has been approaching for several years. Hospital capacity has been adequate for general care, although inadequate for patients afflicted with tuberculosis or mental disease. Although large numbers of people go without needed hospital care because they cannot afford it, general hospitals are on the average occupied to only 65 per cent of capacity.

The present demand for "free service" in both government and private non-profit hospitals has emphasized the need for more adequate and more stable revenue. During the depression years "free service" has risen to such proportions that in many hospitals, especially in the large cities, more than one-half of all patients are in "free beds." Shall the hospitals balance their budgets by charging "pay patients" for service furnished to "free patients"? Shall they be assisted by government grants from tax funds? Shall they hope for charitable gifts? Or will they find some other means of financing the public service which they render?

Of the $656,000,000 spent by hospitals annually for operating costs in a normal year, approximately $302,000,000 is paid by patients through fees, $54,000,000 represents contributions and endowments, and about $300,000,000 is derived from taxation. Most of the $302,000,000 from fees is paid not by the 125 million potential patients but by the 5 million "pay" patients admitted to the non-government institutions for acute medical and surgical conditions. Most of the $300,000,000 spent by governments is used to support hospitals for nervous and mental and for tuberculosis cases, or for the treatment of "indigent" patients requiring general medical or surgical care. Voluntary contributions have greatly declined. The income from endowments, which reached a maximum of $20,000,000 in 1929, has declined greatly since then, and shows little prospect of growth in the near future.

There is a crying need for the stabilization of hospital income. The hospital situation calls for the development of arrangements whereby the economic barrier shall be removed from the path of the individual who needs hospital care, without, at the same time, placing an impossible burden of charity service upon the hospital. To recognize the difficulties which the costs of hospitalization bring to many families, it is important to carry in mind these facts: (1) though only one family in five receives hospital care in any one year, hospital costs are responsible for 13 per cent of all family medical costs; (2) though the average hospital bill is about $50, this is less than 40 per cent of the average cost ($140) of a hospitalized case when professional charges and other costs are added to the hospital bill. Illness which involves hospitalization, it will be recalled, is responsible for 50 per cent of all costs to families. Thus, even though the hospital's bill may of itself be moderate, it usually comes as one more bill in a series which may have been and may continue to be long. The hospital's bill is not uncommonly the proverbial last straw, especially since its payment must usually be made at once. This quality of hospital costs is of the essence in the problem of financing the hospitals of the country. If we are to be practical, we must think of hospital costs and the burdens they involve, not in terms of the average cost of $5.40 per person in the United States, but in terms of $50 per average hospital cost or $140 per average hospitalized case of illness.

If the degree of utilization of physicians, dentists, nurses, and hospitals is the measuring rod, one must conclude that the United States has too many physicians, too many dentists, far too many nurses, and too many general hospital beds. But this conclusion is not fair. The distribution of personnel and facilities follows the dollar, not the need. Where there is spendable money, there are physicians, dentists, and hospitals—usually in excess; where there is little spendable money, there is a dearth. Our metropolitan areas are oversupplied; many rural areas are undersupplied. The measuring rod—current rate of utilization—is one which modern society cannot accept. Acceptance would mean complacence with the forces responsible for the fact that people do not obtain all or much of the medical care which they need.

If the supply of medical personnel and institutional facilities were adequate for the *true* need for medical care, we should need more physicians, far more dentists and dental assistants, more public health nurses, more private duty nurses, and more hospital beds than we now have. This is no plea, however, for hasty expansion of personnel or facilities. Until the public is educated to recognize the full need for—and the full value of—medical care, until the population is more generally able to pay for these services, increasing personnel and facilities would merely increase the so-called "normal" degree of unemployment among physicians, dentists, and nurses, and would increase the number of unoccupied hospital beds. Administrative and economic problems must first be solved before the receipt of medical care can become commensurate with true need and before the demand for care can justify a larger medical equipment for society.

SOME WASTEFUL EXPENDITURES

One of the tragedies revealed by a study of medical costs is the evidence of wasteful expenditures. This would not be of great consequence if non-productive spending merely indicated luxury-spending above and beyond spending for necessities. Unfortunately, wasteful expenditures do not merely *supplement* wise practices; they also *substitute* for wise spending. Extravagance and waste appear in many quarters—in the large overhead of individual private practice; in the luxury of some extravagantly built hospitals; in payments to cultists, quacks, and charlatans; in excessive demands for service; and especially in the enormous outpouring of money for useless or even harmful patent medicines and other self-prescribed remedies.

In ordinary times, the American people spend annually about $665,000,000 for medicines. Even this large figure takes no account of the $50,000,000 spent for the supplies purchased and used by physicians and hospitals. Two-thirds of a billion dollars for medicines is two-thirds the total expenditure for physicians or nearly as much as is spent for hospital care and far more than the annual expenditures for dentistry, private duty nursing or public health. Less than 30 per cent of the medicines consumed annually represent what is used on the prescription of physicians. More than one-half the expenditure for medicines (about $360,000,000) is made for commodities which have secret formulae and which are purchased by the patients direct from retail merchants.

Manufacturers and sellers of medicines are not generally restricted to the code of ethics followed by physicians. Their selling methods tend to exaggerate the healing value of their products, and to encourage the public to diagnose their own ailments and to practise self-treatment.

Though the costs of medicines are very great, they have not aroused the same complaints as have the costs of physicians' services and of hospitalization. There are many reasons for this, but the principal one is that in the individual case the cost of medicines is seldom large enough to be a serious burden upon the family budget.

It would be of only passing interest to demonstrate that the usual retail prices of medicines are high. It is more important to emphasize the principle that medicines should be sold according to the true public need, not according to the greatest financial profit of business promoters. The essential problem in respect to the costs of medicines is not so much to reduce prices as to make the sales subordinate and helpful to the services of physicians.

SOME PROBLEMS IN PROVIDING ADEQUATE MEDICAL CARE

Throughout this brief review it has been constantly assumed that the provision of good medical care is in the interest of the public welfare. From a detailed analysis of professional concepts of "good medical care"[7] it is possible to estimate what the service which meets this standard would cost. Using 1928–1931 cost figures, and making due allowances for the elimination of obvious wastes and for the accumulated neglect of years, reasonably adequate medical care would cost about $36 per person a year for the types of service which are ordinarily purchased privately. This figure is independent of any assumption concerning more efficient organization of medical facilities than ordinarily occurs. With well-designed organization, large economies are possible without sacrifice of quality and with larger and more stable remuneration of the practitioners. Assuming effective organization, the estimated cost can be reduced from $36 to $25–$30 per person for private medical service. If the costs of good public service (for the tuberculous and the mentally diseased and for public health work) are added, good medical care, all told, calls for about $32 to $37 per person. The ordinary expenditures actually made in the United States amount to $30 per person for the entire population. Thus, the costs of a complete program of good medical care are not much larger than the sum we ordinarily spend. *The greatest need is not to find more money for the purchase of medical care, but to find newer and better ways of budgeting the costs and spending the money wisely and effectively.*

One hears and reads a great deal about the "high cost of medical care." From what has already been said it must be evident that though a large sum of money is spent each year for medical care in the United States, even more must be spent if people are to receive the care which they really need and which practitioners and institutions are prepared to furnish them. The costs of medical care are thought to be "high," not so much because the total sum is large or because the average cost is high but because the cost is variable and comes in uncertain and unpredictable amounts. The individual family is not spared the burden of unexpected medical costs even though practitioners and institutions make only "fair" charges; the burden would still be there even if each ethical doctor or dentist and each hospital superintendent did his best to adjust the charges to the patient's ability to pay.

While recognizing that this is true, it should also be recognized that part of the public complaint over "the high cost of medical care" rests on another basis. In a complex and changing society, intimate and continuing relations between doctor and patient are less common than they used to be. The adjustment of medical charges to the patient's ability to pay is vastly more difficult than it was formerly. The city doctor who lacks acquaintance with many of his patients and has only scant knowledge of their ability to pay sometimes makes mistakes in his charges, nowadays more often than formerly. Such mistakes are unavoidable, but they are increasingly irritating occurrences. It is unfortunate that such mistakes made in good faith, increased by the occasions when high charges are made by indifferent or unscrupulous practitioners, give rise to comparatively frequent complaints. It would be unsound to exaggerate the significance of individual cases in which medical costs bear little or no relation to the patient's ability to pay; but it would be equally unsound to ignore such cases.

The medical profession is well aware that when large medical costs fall upon small purses there are complaints and there is development of resentment in the public mind. This may be illustrated from the following quotation, taken not from the remarks of some irresponsible person, but from an address delivered before a medical society by Dr. Olin West, Secretary and General Manager of the American Medical Association:[8]

A young man walked into my office not long ago. It was apparent to me the moment he walked in the door that he was highly indignant about something. He walked over to my desk and laid down upon it what I found to be a statement which had been sent to him by a physician. This young man said, "I have come here to find out what the American Medical Association is going to do about this." I picked up the statement, looked at it, and found it was a doctor's bill for $259 for an operation for appendicitis and for three calls that had been made before the operation. The young man said, "I make exactly $80 a month. I have a wife and three children and my mother to take care of. I have struggled to keep off 'relief.' I went to this doctor when my child became ill and told him my financial condition, showed him my bank account, told him what I had and asked him to please tell me what he was going to charge me and told him that I couldn't pay at once and would have to take a long time to pay it." The doctor told him not to worry, it would be "all right." Two or three days after he operated, he sent the young man a bill for $259, charging three dollars for each of the calls made before the operation and wrote on the bottom, "This bill is past due. Call and make immediate arrangements for payment."

I hesitate to talk about these things even in a group like this, but I am convinced after thinking it over for some time, that the day has arrived when we must talk about them. I know from what men in high positions say to me that they feel the actions of men like the one to whom I referred and the men in the profession who are guilty of other reprehensible actions represent the attitude of the entire medical profession. Within a week, I had a gentleman of high rank in public affairs tell me of an instance similar to that which I have just recited to you. He said, in so many words, that that one instance had convinced him the medical profession today is without any humaneness, that its idealism had been lost, that it had no concern other than what it could get out of the public. It gave me pause when an intelligent citizen, whose name is widely known, told me that he considered this one incident that came under his observation as a true reflection of the attitude of the entire medical profession.

Among some groups it has become almost habitual to lay the blame for the burden of medical costs on the drug store and the cultists. These people frequently imply that most of our troubles would be over if these expenditures were eliminated and other recognized wastes were curtailed. We should not fall into the habit of taking these views too seriously. The obvious savings which are possible would amount to three-quarters of a billion dollars a year, or 20 per cent of the total bill in a normal year. But to effect savings of these kinds would, in the best of circumstances, be a slow, difficult, and arduous task, for spending habits are deeply rooted and ignorance is not easily overcome. Even granting that these savings were effected, the facts in the case indicate conclusively that the major problems of medical costs would still wait on other solutions. There would still remain the need to find solutions for:

A. The uncertain, uneven, and unbudgetable size of medical costs for the individual or the family;

B. The difficulty of knowing how, when, and where to secure good medical care; and

C. The uncertain and inadequate remuneration of practitioners and institutions.

We shall see later that these three problems are, in certain measures, separate and discrete; but we shall also see many evidences that they are interrelated.

REFERENCES AND NOTES

1. Dublin, Louis I.: HEALTH AND WEALTH. New York, Harper & Brothers, 1928, p. 10. *See also* The Cost of Medical Care (cited in reference 3, pp. 12–14; THE MONEY VALUE OF A MAN, by Louis I. Dublin and Alfred J. Lotka. New York, The Ronald Press, 1930; and LENGTH OF LIFE, by Louis I. Dublin and Alfred J. Lotka. New York, The Ronald Press, 1936, 400 pp.

2. Davis, Michael M.: The American Approach to Health Insurance. The Milbank Memorial Fund *Quarterly,* July, 1934, xii, No. 3, pp. 203–217.

3. Falk, I. S., Rorem, C. Rufus and Ring, Martha D.: THE COSTS OF MEDICAL CARE: A SUMMARY OF INVESTIGATIONS ON THE ECONOMIC ASPECTS OF THE PREVENTION AND CARE OF ILLNESS. Publication No. 27 of the Committee on the Costs of Medical Care. Chicago, The University of Chicago Press, 1933, 648 pp. This volume is a general summary. The basic facts concerning family costs appear in more detail in the Committee's Publication No. 26: THE INCIDENCE OF ILLNESS AND THE RECEIPT AND COSTS OF MEDICAL CARE AMONG REPRESENTATIVE FAMILY GROUPS, by I. S. Falk, M. C. Klem and N. Sinai. Chicago, The University of Chicago Press, 1933, 327 pp. A substantial confirmation of the costs from an independent study appears in The Cost of Medical Care, by D. B. Armstrong, L. I. Dublin and E. J. Steele. New York, Metropolitan Life Insurance Company, 1934, 61 pp. *See also* THE DOCTOR'S BILL, by Hugh Cabot. New York, Columbia University Press, 1935, 320 pp.; ECONOMIC PROBLEMS OF MEDICINE, by A. C. Christie. New York, The Macmillan Company, 1935, 242 pp.; Medical Care and Costs in California Families in Relation to Economic Status, by Margaret C. Klem. San Francisco, State Relief Administration of California, 1935, 118 pp.

4. National Income, 1929–32. Senate Document No. 124. Washington, Government Printing Office, 1934; THE MEASUREMENT OF AMERICAN WEALTH, by R. R. Doane, New York, 1933.

5. National Income, 1929–32, *op. cit.,* p. 148.

6. Report of the Committee on Survey of Medical Services and Health Agencies. Michigan State Medical Society (Nathan Sinai, Director of Study), 1933, 193 pp.; Report of the Senate Committee to Investigate the Advisability of a Health Insurance Act to Reduce the High Cost of Sickness. California Legislature, April 12, 1935; Paul A. Dodd (*Discussion of* Illness and the Receipt and Cost of Medical Care among California Families of Low and Moderate Incomes, by M. C. Klem). *Western Hospital Review,* March, 1935, xxiii, p. 8; Our Post-Depression Incomes, by W. A. Richardson. *Medical Economics,* April, 1934, xi, p. 12.

7. Lee, R. I. and Jones, L. W.: THE FUNDAMENTALS OF GOOD MEDICAL CARE. Chicago, The University of Chicago Press, 1933, 325 pp.; *also* THE COSTS OF MEDICAL CARE, *op cit.,* pp. 70–79.

8. West, Olin: Medical Problems of Today and the Future. *Illinois Medical Journal,* October, 1935, lxviii, p. 324.

CHAPTER III

THE GROUP PAYMENT OF SICKNESS COSTS

WHEN it is proposed that newer and better means should be devised to deal with the burdens of medical costs, it is sometimes asked: Why single out (and thereby exaggerate) the imperative necessity of medical care as compared with other things, perhaps equally essential to the preservation of life or of health? Why propose insurance or taxation or some other new method of paying medical costs as against paying the costs of food, clothing or shelter? In the light of the facts presented in the preceding chapter, the answer should be obvious. Though medical care is only one of the four essentials of life, its costs are different in a fundamental respect from the costs of the other three. The costs of food, clothing and shelter are regular and recurring; they can ordinarily be foreseen, fixed, and budgeted according to expected or actual income. But the costs of medical care are uncertain and so variable that though they can be budgeted by a large group of people they cannot be budgeted by the individual or the family.

Let us look at this somewhat more closely. If a family's annual rent is $720, the budgeting of $60 a month will provide housing. But if the average annual cost of medical care for a family is $108, will budgeting $9 a month assure medical care? How can it, if the average conceals the fact that a family's actual costs during the year may be less than $10 or may be $1,000 or more? Setting aside $9 a month will not furnish much protection if even one member of the family suffers a serious accident or develops the need for a major operation or if the members of the family have a series of less serious but

36

repeated illnesses or even a single case of long duration. Budgeting the average amount for something as variable and uncertain as medical costs becomes really effective only after it has been practised over a considerable period of time during which no large medical costs are incurred. This is substantially the same as saying that such budgeting becomes effective after a considerable fund has been accumulated through savings. As an alternative, and with regard to the uncertainties of medical costs, it might be proposed that each family should budget against two, three, four, or five times the average cost for families of its own income level. Yet keeping in mind the pressure of a thousand urges upon the family purse, and how slim is the margin between income and the cost of subsistence for families of small means, and that the average medical costs for a family are about 4 per cent of annual income, one must ask what proportion of families can (or will) budget 8, 12, 16, or 20 per cent of their incomes against an uncertain contingency, especially since illness may cost even far more than 20 per cent and even the most liberal budgeting may be inadequate. The accumulation of savings specifically against future medical costs by a family of small means in a period comparatively free from illness affords less protection against future contingencies than may at first appear. The charges for professional service—especially for specialist services and institutional care—are usually adjusted to ability to pay (taking account of savings as well as income). Hence, part or all of the potential protection afforded by savings must be discounted against the increased charges incurred on account of increased ability to pay. (See page 347.)

The frequency of sickness and the costs of medical care are predictable for a group of people but not for an individual. Budgeting of the costs must be done by groups; for it cannot be done by individuals.[1] *If the costs of medical care are to be deprived of their burdensome qualities, they must be distributed among groups of people and over periods of time.*

There are some who contend that the basic problems of medical costs can be solved only by increasing the incomes of people of small and modest means. Their argument tacitly or explicitly assumes that the people who have difficulty in meeting medical costs are those with "inadequate incomes." The conclusion from this argument is that the problem can be solved appropriately only by an increase of wages for the "underpaid." This is not only a counsel of perfection but also a fallacy. The facts in the case show that medical costs are burdensome for those with family incomes of less than $3,000 or even of less than $5,000. Even in 1928, three families in every four had incomes of less than $3,000 and nine in every ten had incomes of less than $5,000. Must the problems of medical costs wait for a solution until every family has an income of more than $3,000 or $5,000? Even if such adjustment of income were practical, it is almost as though one argued that family protection against the death of the wage-earner should, because of income distribution, be limited to those who earn substantial incomes or who have accumulated large capital. It is as if those who advance the arguments had never understood the elementary principle upon which insurance (life, fire, accident and other forms of insurance) rests: the purchase of mutual protection against a risk which is reasonably certain for the large group though uncertain for the individual, through the pooling of fixed contributions so that the cost of the average risk applies to each member of the group.

In the preceding paragraphs, the discussion has been restricted to the costs of medical care; nothing has been said about the loss of earnings by reason of a wage-earner's disability. A moment's reflection will indicate that nearly everything said about the costs of care applies to the loss of income.

Existing Forms of Group Payment

When it is concluded from a study of the factual information that protection of the individual family against the costs of medical care requires a pooling of the costs by groups of people and over periods of time, the conclusion seems to have qualities of novelty—as though a proposal for the group payment of these costs involved some fundamentally new social technique. Yet, in point of fact, the group payment of medical costs has long been practised in the United States. Some of its forms are well known; others are not always recognized as methods of group payment. It will repay us to consider them in some detail.

As Michael M. Davis[2] has pointed out, the existing forms of group payment may be arranged under four general heads:

1. Charity
2. The sliding scale of medical fees
3. Insurance
4. Taxation

GROUP PAYMENT THROUGH CHARITY

Private charity to assist a sick person or his family or whole groups of sick and their dependents operates, in considerable measure, as a method of group payment of sickness costs. From an economic point of view, charity tends to shift the burden from the sick to the well, and from one social (or economic) group to another.

A large part of charity is today, as it has been from time immemorial, the gift of individuals. Neighbors and groups of neighbors who come to the assistance of those who cannot themselves meet the costs of sickness are, in effect, a group who take over part of the costs of sickness. To an increasing degree, in modern urban communities, charity is given by groups of individuals through organized charitable agencies. In this case, the sickness burdens of the burdened sick have been even more clearly shifted from their own shoulders to those of the people who have contributed to the charitable agencies. Organized charity furnishes a more readily recognized form of group payment than individual charity.

How much money is spent through charity in the group payment of sickness costs cannot be known, for the contributions and services of individual givers cannot be measured. The total volume of charitable gifts through organized agencies in the United States can, however, be estimated and appears to have been not more than $100,000,000 in any year. Only part of this sum is devoted to sickness and only a smaller part to the costs of medical care. The sum involved in this form of group payment of sickness costs is large, yet it is small when measured against the total need. For it must be kept in mind that, in ordinary times, among families with annual incomes of less than $2,500 the costs of medical care of all kinds amount to a sum of one and one-half to two billion dollars a year.

Group Payment through the Sliding Scale

It is well known that physicians give a large volume of service to the poor without charge. This is the extreme of the traditional practice among physicians of adjusting their fees to the ability of the patient to pay. The sliding scale of fees is primarily a method whereby the physician is enabled to make his services available to patients of widely different means. To the extent that he earns larger fees for a specified service from his well-to-do clients, he is enabled to give the same or similar services to his poorer clients at lesser fees and still earn an income which will sustain him in the practice of his profession. In its simplest form, the sliding scale is evident in the practice of many surgeons who have adopted the rule of charging a fixed per cent (say, 10 per cent) of the patient's annual income as a fee for a major operation. The sliding scale is hallowed by centuries of usage; it is commonly recognized by the courts in cases where the fee is in dispute.

This is not the occasion to consider in any detail the extent to which the sliding scale serves or has ceased to serve effectively as a social instrument.[3] Our present concern is with the fact that it is a method of group payment whose justification rests in part on the principle that the well-to-do, individually and as groups, pay in a measure the costs of services rendered to people of smaller means or of no means. This procedure operates not, as in the case cited above, through a charitable agency but through the individual physician, dentist or hospital. The sliding scale also differs in another respect in that not all members of the higher economic group—only the sick among them—pay for the lower group. Furthermore, only the practitioners (or institutions) who reach the upper income classes can make use of this procedure and, in large measure, specialists rather than general practitioners are able to use it to any appreciable extent.

It is difficult to estimate the amount of money involved in group payment through the use of the sliding scale. In an ordinary year, the total gross income of all private practitioners of medicine in the United States was about $1,040,000,000.[4][5] The value of free care rendered annually by physicians has been placed as high as $365,000,000 by one medical writer, but this is probably an excessively high estimate. Many thousands of physicians whose practices were studied gave as their own estimates from their own practice that free care amounted from nothing to 40 per cent and the median value of their own figures was between 4 and 6 per cent. With allowances for fees which had been adjusted downwards, the latter figures would probably be increased to approximately 10 per cent. This would equal about $100,000,000 a year. Similar figures for dentists would add a smaller fraction of their total income (which was about $445,000,000 a year).[6] The amount of money involved in the use of the sliding scale by hospitals is much larger, but this cannot be dealt with so simply because it is complicated by other factors such as organized and individual charitable support of the hospitals, assistance from tax funds, use of less expensive facilities by "free" or "part-pay" patients, the public subscription of the capital funds from which the hospital was built, etc. It may be said, however, that group payment through the sliding scale involves *at least* $100,000,000 and probably very considerably more. Furthermore, in direct or indirect ways, it influences the charges incurred by nearly every person who receives medical services from private practitioners or institutions for the care of the sick.

GROUP PAYMENT THROUGH INSURANCE

It is difficult to assess the scope of group payment through insurance; at so many points it is difficult to draw a sharp line between practices which are clearly insurance and others in which the insurance feature of the plan is not so clear. Arrangements whereby the ability of an individual to pay his medical bills has been increased through a credit agency, using the devices of installment payment, can scarcely be included here; the "insurance" in credit bureaus is "self-insurance" and the payment is individual rather than group. Group payment through insurance involves distribution of the risk (or cost) among groups of people and over a period of time. Installment payment distributes costs over a period of time but not over groups of people. The risk which is distributed by installment payments among groups of people is the risk that the individual who has assumed a specific obligation to pay a specified debt will or will not meet it. This is fundamentally different from distributing among the group the primary risk for which the costs are incurred. The limitations inherent in installment-payment plans have been discussed elsewhere.[7] They do not insure the family against a future risk of sickness; they mortgage future earnings to pay for a calamity which has already occurred. A survey of such plans devised under the auspices of medical societies has recently been published by the American Medical Association; many of these are "proposed" rather than "operating" plans.[8]

Group-payment plans in which the principle of insurance is definitely used have, however, developed in many places and have applied the principle in a hundred ways. The basis of each plan is that the members of the group (the insured persons or the premium contributors) agree to make fixed, periodic (usually weekly or monthly) payments in return for which they or certain other beneficiaries are assured returns or "benefits" which may be cash, services, discounts on fees for medical services, or combinations of these.

Compulsory insurance (legally required) has been developed in the United States only in respect to the injuries and illnesses which arise out of employment. This form of group payment operates under the workmen's compensation laws in forty-six states and in certain areas subject to the federal jurisdiction. According to these laws, the insured "risk" (work accidents and injuries, and occupational diseases) is chargeable against the employment. Hence, with certain minor exceptions, the premiums are paid by the employers rather than by the employees, although the latter are the beneficiaries of the insurance. Workmen's compensation insurance will be discussed in some detail in Chapter XIV. It may be noted here, however, that this form of insurance against sickness involves payments of approximately $400,000,000 a year of which about 20 per cent ($80,-000,000) pays for medical services to injured workmen. The remaining 80 per cent is used for cash benefits in lieu of wages lost on account of illness, disability and deaths, for administration and overhead costs, profits of commercial insurance companies, etc. All other forms of insurance against sickness are voluntary.

We have in the United States sickness insurance operated for profit. Most of this is sold to provide cash benefits through commercial "accident and health policies" and to furnish medical service under individual or group policies. Most of this type of insurance which is written undertakes to furnish only cash benefits; medical services as such are only minor features of this insurance practice. Of a total of about $200,000,000 a year paid in benefits under these policies (by commercial companies, fraternal societies, mutual accident associations and sick benefit associations), less than 10 per cent (i.e., less than $20,000,000 a year) is actually devoted to the medical benefits; the rest is primarily to replace loss of income.

In recent years there have developed, especially on the Pacific Coast, commercial groups which undertake to sell policies to guarantee hospital service or both hospital and medical services. Some of these agencies have tended to bring the entire practice into disrepute because they have been patently dishonest schemes and have lately been prosecuted by public authorities.

The organization of group payment through non-profit insurance has been a far more important development. Many different kinds of groups have utilized group payment through insurance in the provision of medical care for their sick members.[9-12] The most common group has been the employees of a single industry. In 1930, about 540,000 gainfully employed persons in the mining and lumber industries of twenty-one states were eligible to more or less complete medical care on a fixed, periodic, payment basis. About one-third of the Class I steam railroads have organized insurance plans for the medical care of their employees. And several million more employed persons are members of insurance groups which provide complete or partial medical service for these persons or for them and their dependents. In some places, these industrial medical services are financed entirely by industry; in others, the costs are met entirely by the insured persons; but in most, both industry and the employed persons share the costs. Whether a particular plan furnishes complete service (medical, surgical, dental, hospital, nursing, laboratory and other care) or is limited to some particular type of service, the basic principle is always the same. The aggregate cost of furnishing service (or a definite part of the total cost) is divided among the insured persons and the contributions are made through fixed, periodic payments. The arrangements through which the services are furnished to the insured persons are extremely diverse. In some insurance organizations, a hospital and its outpatient clinics may be owned by the non-profit insurance agency, and physicians and other personnel furnish services on a salary basis. In others, the insurance group makes contracts for services to be rendered by local institutions and practitioners. In some, the operating contract may be a guarantee of payment for services rendered to insured persons according to an agreed fee schedule; in others the contract may guarantee only such costs as exceed specified sums. A long catalogue would be required to list the hundreds of schemes through which insurance groups pay for medical services.

In some places, insurance payments may provide only against the costs of nursing care (as in the Brattleboro, Vermont, plan), or of the doctor's service (as in the Dallas, Texas, plan), or of hospital care (as in the plans sponsored by the American Hospital Association and developed by some 100 or 150 hospital groups and communities widely scattered throughout the United States), or of combinations of two or more services (as in the Little Rock, Arkansas, plan), or of complete medical service (as in numerous industrial plans or the Ross-Loos, Los Angeles, private clinic plan). All voluntary plans have suffered the limitations of being capable of serving only especially suitable population groups and particular income classes. Nevertheless, they have succeeded in serving several million persons.

Insurance against hospital care has recently received a great impetus through the development of community hospital (non-profit) insurance plans.[13] In some areas all of the hospitals have entered into an agreement with a central, non-profit agency to furnish hospital care to the insured persons who pay fixed premiums. Such a plan has been developed for the entire state of North Carolina and is now being brought into operation. The insurance agreement usually guarantees the insured person, in return for his premium, hospital care of specified kind for a maximum number of weeks during a twelve-months' period. The non-profit insurance agency usually has contracts with the cooperating hospitals whereby these institutions are guaranteed a fixed remuneration for each day of care rendered to an insured person and payment on an agreed schedule of fees for special services. A recent count (October, 1935) shows that at least 300,000 persons are subscribing members of such plans and the number is increasing.

It may be estimated that all types of voluntary group payment for medical care through insurance, excepting that which operates under the workmen's compensation laws, involve at least $40,000,000 a year.

If this is added to the expenditures for medical care under the compensation laws ($80,000,000), we have in the aggregate about $120,000,000 (or more) a year spent through insurance plans.*

GROUP PAYMENT THROUGH TAXATION

The group payment of sickness costs through taxation is both an older and more extensive practice than such payment through insurance. Traditionally, there has been a sharp contrast between these two methods of group payment. Payment through insurance is a method whereby a group of direct or potential beneficiaries pay for services which they may receive; payment through taxation has been a procedure whereby taxpayers have paid for public health services furnished to the entire community and for individual medical services furnished to the poor and the indigent. Latterly, even before the emergency measures were instituted by federal, state and local governments to care for the victims of the depression, there were many evidences of a tendency to extend the use of tax funds to furnish individual services to those who pay the taxes as well as to the dependent members of society. Tax-supported hospitals, which as a class formerly served only certified indigents, have in many places been opened to "pay" patients;† local governments have increasingly begun to grant subsidies to non-governmental hospitals for services rendered to free or "part-pay" patients; tax funds have been used by states to subsidize local public health and other health or medical services;

---

*The total would be somewhat higher if we could estimate the amount spent by industry for physicians and nurses engaged in services not required by the compensation laws and not part of specific insurance plans and not already otherwise counted.

†The city of Palo Alto, California, has recently inaugurated an interesting plan along these lines. A portion of each resident's hospital bill is paid out of taxation. The sum of $2.50 per day, for a period not to exceed three weeks in any given year, is paid toward the hospital bill of any resident hospitalized in the municipal hospital. The tax payment is not paid toward the charges for rooms which cost more than $8.50 per day. For accommodations which cost less than $5.00 per day the city's contribution is limited to 50 per cent of the hospital bill. The plan was adopted by an overwhelming majority of voters after an experimental trial of about a year. (*Medical Economics*, November, 1935, p. 64; *also* personal communication from the Health Officer of Palo Alto.)

tax-supported health departments have extended their clinic facilities; and in many communities (especially in rural areas and more particularly in Canada than in the United States) tax-supported physicians have been engaged to furnish service to entire communities.

Most of the activities of these kinds which are supported through taxation are financed from general tax funds. In greater or lesser measure, general taxes are levied in accordance with the principle of ability to pay. Accordingly, it will be recognized that medical services which are supported by taxes represent group payment in which the entire population (federal, state or local, as the case may be) is the contributing group and in which the contributors pay not according to the medical services which they may themselves receive but according to their ability to pay taxes. The principle of tax payments through assessment (i.e., equal or graded payments by those who will actually benefit from the use of the tax funds) is used only in very small measure to pay for tax-supported medical services.

Group payment through taxation provides many types of public medical services. Their diversity will be recognized from the following list, prepared in another connection by Michael M. Davis, which deals only with the broad categories:

1. Public health services (health departments, etc.)
2. General medical care for legally dependent persons
3. General medical care for the unemployed and their families under the emergency relief administrations
4. General medical care for entire communities in rural areas (subsidies and subventions to physicians, support of local or neighboring hospitals, etc.)
5. General medical care for certain non-dependent groups for whom special responsibility is assumed by a governmental agency (army, navy, veterans, Indians, seamen, prisoners, students in certain colleges and universities, government employees, etc.)
6. Medical care for persons afflicted with certain diseases or conditions which are "infused with a public interest" (special provisions for the prevention and cure of diphtheria, early diagnosis and prevention of tuberculosis, special provisions

for mothers and children, for those afflicted with venereal diseases, poliomyelitis, etc.)

7. Hospitals and clinics for persons afflicted with acute or chronic diseases

8. Hospitals and clinics for persons afflicted with mental disease or tuberculosis

9. Tax-supported care for certain patients in non-governmental hospitals and clinics

It would take us too far afield to attempt to describe these diverse activities. It will be interesting, however, to indicate the approximate amount of tax money which is spent to support these public undertakings. It was found in the studies conducted by the Research Staff of the Committee on the Costs of Medical Care[14] that in 1929 (and in any "normal" year of recent times) federal, state and local tax funds accounted altogether for health and medical expenditures of about $510,000,000. Of this sum, about $94,000,000 was devoted to public health services; some $416,000,000 a year was spent for public medical services which are almost entirely of the curative type. The total expenditures from tax funds accounted for 14 per cent or about one-seventh of the total sum ($3,660,000,000) spent in the entire country for all kinds of health and medical services and amounted to about $4.10 per person in the entire population. If we exclude the expenditures for public health purposes, tax funds for medical services are in general devoted to services provided to people in the lower income classes. The total expenditures for health and medical services of all kinds for wage-earners and other people with small incomes or no incomes is probably now about $2,000,000,000 a year. It may therefore be estimated that at least one-fourth and perhaps as much as one-third of their needs for service created by sickness are met from tax funds.

Total Expenditures in Group Payment of Medical Costs

Taken altogether, it may be conservatively estimated that the group payment of the costs of sickness—restricting the figures to health and medical services and ignoring loss of income and other costs of sickness—ordinarily involves more than $800,000,000 a year, as follows:

Charity	$100,000,000
Operation of sliding scale	100,000,000
Insurance	120,000,000
Taxation	510,000,000
TOTAL	$830,000,000

Of this total sum representing expenditures made in "normal" years other than through the individual payments of the persons actually served, and equal to nearly one-fourth of the total costs of all health and medical services, tax funds accounted for more than one-half. This last item is, in a sense, a measure of the extent to which so-called *socialized medicine* is an established practice in the United States, apart from the emergency tax expenditures of the present depression period.

To the extent that tax funds are "socialized" funds, tax-supported medical services are "socialized" medical services. The word "socialized" is given many different meanings and its use here is perhaps unfortunate. It should be made clear, however, that tax-supported services—even if they are to be called "socialized" services—are not necessarily all "state medicine." In its accustomed meaning, "state medicine" means medical services not only paid for through public funds but actually furnished by public servants and public institutions—as public education is furnished by teachers employed by the government and paid out of public funds. A substantial part of the tax money enumerated above is not spent in this way, but goes to remunerate private practitioners and private ("voluntary" or non-official) hospitals, and other institutions. A large part of so-called "socialized medicine" is "socialized" in respect to the payment of the costs but not in respect to the furnishing of service. Although about 15 per cent of physicians are salaried practitioners and perhaps one-half of these are employed by public agencies, the "socialization" of medical service is not as extensive as these figures might seem to indicate, because many of these salaried persons in official agencies are in administrative positions and are not primarily active practitioners. The "socialization" of medical service is not nearly so extensive as the "socialization" of medical costs. This point is stressed because it reveals an important characteristic in American medical practices.

THE FUTURE OF GROUP PAYMENT

The brief analysis of the costs of medical care presented in the preceding chapter pointed to the need for group payment of these costs. This is a direct conclusion from the facts in the case and a knowledge of the burdens, the inequities, and the inadequacies which follow from the uncertainties and variations in these costs. Taken of itself, stating such a conclusion tends to give the impression that the development of group payment would be an innovation. The summary of existing forms of group payment presented in the preceding pages shows, however, that group payment, in its various forms, is an old and well-established practice and already involves nearly one-fourth of the total costs of health and medical services. These two conclusions must be brought together, for they are not discrete but simultaneous. Dealing with both together compels the following conclusion: *it is not that there is need for group payment, but that there is need for more group payment than is already practised.*

The practical issue presented by this line of analysis then revolves about the form which expansion of group payment should take. Increase in the burden carried by charity is out of the question and both the public and the professions increasingly object to the operations of the sliding scale. We are left with insurance and taxation as the potential instruments with which to solve an important and pressing social problem. Insurance and taxation are not mutually exclusive forms. Contrariwise, we have seen that they are simultaneously used in the United States, and we shall see later that they are simultaneously used in other countries, even where one or the other has been more extensively developed than in our own country.

At this point it will be recognized that the present study should contemplate careful investigation of the possibilities offered both by insurance and by taxation as methods of dealing with current problems of sickness costs. Even a moment's reflection will indicate that this would involve a very large program in which the two elements would require quite different lines of inquiry and radically different techniques. The possibility inherent in the technique of insurance for further developments may be studied critically in terms of history and experiences, because there are some forty or more countries of the world in which insurance has been developed far more extensively than in the United States. The potentialities inherent in taxation as a method of group payment can be explored in the same way but only in a radically smaller measure. Taxation for medical care, far more than insurance, must be contemplated in terms of theory and "social convictions" rather than in terms of experience. It has therefore seemed wise to conclude that if this study must be limited in scope it should concentrate on a survey of insurance rather than on taxation. It will accordingly be found that the remaining chapters of this volume are mainly devoted to a study of experience with health and sickness insurance at home and abroad. It will also be found, however, that almost everywhere insurance and taxation are complementary and not mutually exclusive practices, and that the line which may be drawn between them is generally arbitrary and tenuous. It is not always clear where one begins and the other leaves off. We shall, however, attempt to draw the distinctions when these are clear and to show somewhat the respective rôles which both insurance and taxation play.

MEDICAL PRACTICE AND PAYMENT FOR MEDICAL CARE

Throughout this analysis of the costs of medical care, *it should be clear that this is not a discussion of the practice of medicine but of the methods of paying for medical care.* When the economics of medicine are examined closely or critically, some physicians take offense; they seem to think that criticism is being leveled at them. Nothing could be further from the point. Taken by and large, the American people are fully aware of the great advances which medicine has made and, in general, have the highest respect for the men and women who practise the professions and for the service which they render. This is quite a different matter from public discontent with medical costs and with the difficulties involved in paying these costs.

A sharp distinction must be made between studies of how to improve the method of paying for medical care and inquiries on how medicine shall be practised. As W. T. Foster has properly said:[15]

> Nobody proposes that lay boards shall tell surgeons how to operate for cancer, or what to prescribe for pneumonia. Nobody suggests any interference with the science of medicine. On the contrary, the aim is to free the *science* of medicine from the present chaos of the *economics* of medicine. What the public does demand is the right to say, not how medicine shall be practiced, but how it shall be purchased and paid for; and who has a better right than those who do the paying? In any event, it is folly to burden physicians any longer with business affairs which they have notoriously mismanaged, for which they are not trained, in which they are not interested, and which interfere with that single-hearted devotion to patients which is the glory of their profession.

FURTHER STUDY OF GROUP PAYMENT

When the economic problems of health and medical care were reviewed in the United States, in the most extensive survey of the subject ever attempted, and the facts were examined closely, four broad conclusions stood out in sharp relief:

1. Medical service should be more largely furnished by groups of physicians and related practitioners, so organized as to maintain high standards of care and to retain the personal relations between patients and physicians.

2. The costs of medical care should be distributed among groups of people and over periods of time.

3. Methods of preventing disease should be more extensively and more effectively applied, as measures both of service and economy; and should be so financed as to minimize the economic deterrents to their extension.

4. The facilities and services for medical care should be coördinated by appropriate agencies on a community basis.

There is little which is either new or novel in these conclusions. They were first presented in this form in the volume which summarized all of the studies conducted by the Research Staff of the Committee on the Costs of Medical Care,[16] and were published without dissent from any member of that Committee.

The study presented in the following chapters may be said to take its origin in these four basic conclusions. In a certain sense, this volume deals primarily with the implications of the second conclusion and only secondarily with the consequences of the other three. Though this second conclusion is adequate as a starting point for the inquiry, it is perhaps excessively restricted. Flowing from a study of the costs of medical care, it recognizes only these particular costs entailed by sickness. Yet the problem being studied is the economic risk which arises as a consequence of ill health. This risk includes not only the costs of medical care for the prevention, diagnosis and treatment of illness, but also the loss of income caused by disabling illness among those who are gainfully employed. Both features of the risk must be taken into account in searching for a way to furnish protection against economic insecurity caused by illness.

The present approach to the subject of "health insurance" is primarily through a study of the costs of medical care. It has already been pointed out that this is not the traditional approach. In European countries, "health insurance" first evolved out of efforts to "insure" against loss of income; insurance against the costs of medical care was at first only a minor phase but became more and more important with the march of time. In the United States the reversal of emphasis has, as we have seen, a sound basis in the fact that the costs of medical care among people in the lower income brackets exceed the wages lost on account of illness.

The approach to "health insurance" from considerations of medical costs also rests on other grounds. The dissatisfaction with individual payment of medical costs is widespread among people of modest means (those with annual incomes of, say, $2,000 to $3,000 or to $5,000) for whom loss of income because of illness is a less consequential risk. Also, there is growing conviction among authorities in other countries who have had experience under "health insurance" and among American students of the subject that insurance against wage-loss should be separated administratively from insurance against the costs of medical care. The proposal is now frequently advanced that insurance against wage-loss on account of disability should be provided in a comprehensive program of social insurance, but that it should be coupled administratively with insurance against wage-loss from other causes, i.e., with "unemployment compensation," rather than with "health insurance." Whatever validity there may be in this proposal—and we shall have opportunity to examine it in later chapters—it emphasizes further the soundness of the approach through group payment for medical care.

REFERENCES AND NOTES

1. Reed, Louis S.: THE ABILITY TO PAY FOR MEDICAL CARE. Chicago, The University of Chicago Press, 1933, 107 pp.

2. Davis, Michael M.: Sickness Insurance and Medical Care. The Milbank Memorial Fund *Quarterly*, October, 1934, xii, No. 4, pp. 287–305.

3. Davis, Michael M.: PAYING YOUR SICKNESS BILLS. Chicago, The University of Chicago Press, 1931, 276 pp.

4. Falk, I. S., Rorem, C. Rufus and Ring, Martha D.: THE COSTS OF MEDICAL CARE. Chicago, The University of Chicago Press, 1933, 648 pp.

5. Leven, Maurice: THE INCOMES OF PHYSICIANS: AN ECONOMIC AND STATISTICAL ANALYSIS. Chicago, The University of Chicago Press, 1932, 135 pp.

6. Leven, Maurice: THE PRACTICE OF DENTISTRY AND THE INCOMES OF DENTISTS IN TWENTY STATES: 1929. Chicago, The University of Chicago Press, 1932, 250 pp.

7. THE COSTS OF MEDICAL CARE, *op. cit.*, p. 439.

8. Special Report of the Bureau of Medical Economics of the American Medical Association. *American Medical Association Bulletin,* June, 1935, xxx, No. 6.

9. THE COSTS OF MEDICAL CARE, *op. cit.*, pp. 459–491.

10. Williams, Pierce (and I. C. Chamberlain): THE PURCHASE OF MEDICAL CARE THROUGH FIXED PERIODIC PAYMENT. New York, National Bureau of Economic Research, Inc., 1932, 308 pp.

11. Clark, Evans: HOW TO BUDGET HEALTH. New York, Harper & Brothers, 1933, 328 pp.

12. NEW PLANS OF MEDICAL SERVICE. Chicago, The Julius Rosenwald Fund, 1936, 76 pp.

13. Rorem, C. Rufus: Hospital Care in the Family Budget, *Bulletin of the American Hospital Association,* July, 1933; revised November, 1933.

14. THE COSTS OF MEDICAL CARE, *op. cit.,* p. 9.

15. Foster, W. T.: Doctors, Patients and the Community. *In* The Medical Profession and the Public. Philadelphia, The American Academy of Political and Social Science, 1934; *also* Transactions of the College of Physicians and Surgeons of Philadelphia, 1934.

16. THE COSTS OF MEDICAL CARE, *op. cit.,* pp. 582–591.

PART TWO

☙

CHAPTER IV

SOME GENERAL OBSERVATIONS ON SICKNESS INSURANCE IN EUROPE

ALL forms of insurance are outgrowths of the human quest for security. Human beings seek an escape from the "slings and arrows of outrageous fortune." Insurance against the burdens of sickness is part of the larger field of social insurance—insurance against death, invalidity, old age, accident, unemployment, and other contingencies in life and living. It is therefore not surprising that the stimuli to create insurance against sickness and against other threats to social or economic security are indissolubly blended with changing forces in the life of society.

Before the industrial revolution the uncertainties and calamities of life were generally due to natural causes. With the coming of the machine age and the urbanization of populations, new uncertainties appeared. Large classes of people who were without property and who earned small wages found themselves without the means of establishing individual financial reserves against emergencies. They sought relief from some of the hazards of life by banding together. They pooled their meager resources into common funds which were to provide guarantees against individual needs. Employers, some fearful that "distress breeds a dangerous temper," some actuated by social motives, and some stimulated by both fear and social responsibility, organized welfare and relief schemes.

For a long while governments followed a policy of "hands off"; but in the last years of the nineteenth century they began to take an

active interest in the social and economic protection of labor. The
state at first encouraged mutual aid by authorizing schemes of welfare and by regulating the nature of contracts; later it provided
assistance through the financial subvention of worthy groups. The
further course of events may be summarized by the following ex-
tracts, quoted from a monumental study of sickness insurance published by the International Labour Office.[1]

> Thus encouraged and supported by the public authorities, the
> mutual aid movement has greatly increased its scope in the
> course of the last half century. It has been able to create in many
> countries thousands, and even tens of thousands, of institutions
> with a membership which is counted in millions. Nevertheless,
> while admiration is due for the efforts and achievements of this
> splendid work of voluntary solidarity, one cannot consider it as
> an adequate solution of the problem of the insecurity of the
> working class.
>
> The membership has remained at a low figure: after fifty
> years of effort, the friendly societies in many countries have only
> succeeded in bringing in a small proportion of the working class.
> Many workers fail to insure, some by improvidence and others
> through lack of means. In particular, those earning low wages
> do not join the societies: forced as they are to apply the greater
> part or the whole of their earnings for the satisfaction of im-
> mediate needs, they are both less able to save and more fre-
> quently ill.
>
> Again, the number of societies is excessive: tiny societies
> abound. Their small membership endangers their financial sound-
> ness and renders them unsuitable for undertaking insurance
> against prolonged sickness or invalidity. There is little order in
> their distribution about the country: in the cities they are to be
> found by hundreds, while in sparsely-populated rural districts
> they are sometimes altogether lacking. The scattered member-
> ship and divided effort result in gaps and overlapping, which
> weaken the social effectiveness of a nation's mutual aid system.
>
> Moreover, friendly societies always suffer from narrowness of
> means. The contributions which members are willing to pay
> are rather low, and, even if they are supplemented by public

subsidies, they do not allow the provision of benefits adequate to cover the risk.

. . . .

In spite of its valuable achievements, the voluntary insurance movement has been found insufficient, and it has become clear that the way to secure general and effective protection against the risk is by making insurance compulsory.

The modern State, as guardian of public health and national prosperity, considers it both a right and a duty to impose compulsion. Even the devotees of individualism admit that in a well-organized community a person should not be free to indulge in improvidence which leads to his becoming a charge on the rates, and that insurance is a social duty the performance of which the State may, in the general interest, enforce.

Germany in 1883, without making lengthy experiments with the voluntary method, was the first to make sickness insurance compulsory for industrial workers; shortly afterwards, in 1885, the scheme was extended to commerce and in 1886 to agriculture.

. . . .

The example of Germany was followed rather slowly by a few industrial States. Austria and Hungary in 1888 and 1891 introduced the system of compulsory sickness insurance applying to wage-earners in industry, transport, and commerce. At the beginning of the twentieth century, however, development became more rapid. Luxemburg in 1901, Norway in 1909, Serbia in 1910, Great Britain and Russia in 1911, and Roumania in 1912 all accepted the principle of compulsion. . . .

The movement of legislation, held up during the war, was resumed with fresh vigour on the conclusion of peace.

The European States created by the Peace Treaties have endeavoured to perfect the insurance schemes which they have inherited. Thus, Czechoslovakia in 1919, Poland in 1920, Austria in 1921, and the Serb-Croat-Slovene Kingdom in 1922 have made sickness insurance compulsory for all wage-earners. Bulgaria, which in 1918 had adopted the compulsory principle, applied it in 1924 to all classes of workers. Portugal in 1919 and Greece in 1922 likewise accepted the principle. Soviet Russia abandoned

the system of public assistance established in 1918 for compulsory insurance, the plan of which was incorporated in the
1922 Labour Code when the new economic policy was inaugurated.

Still more recently, changes and expansion have come rapidly
Lithuania brought into operation a sickness insurance law passed in
1925. Ireland, which was covered by the National Insurance Act,
1911, of Great Britain, had been exempted from the medical benefit
provisions. But in 1930 Northern Ireland incorporated the British
medical benefit plan into its system of social insurance. The Nether-
lands changed from a voluntary to a compulsory basis for cash benefits, and France adopted a compulsory plan in the same year.
Denmark, long considered outstanding for her success with voluntary insurance, shifted in 1933 from a voluntary to a partially compulsory plan. Japan greatly enlarged the scheme of compulsory health
insurance by an Act of March 26, 1934, which became effective January 1, 1935. In Canada, where health insurance has been held to be
a provincial function, a Royal Commission for the Province of British
Columbia and a Legislature Commission for the Province of Alberta
each recently recommended compulsory plans for the provinces. The
Alberta plan has since been enacted into law (April 23, 1935). Early
in 1935 the Government of British Columbia submitted for study a
draft bill for compulsory health insurance which, after a number of
revisions, was passed by the legislature (March 31, 1936), the benefits being restricted to medical care. A compulsory health insurance
bill was introduced and recommended by a Commission of the California Senate early in 1935, but has since been put over to the next
legislature. *All systems of health insurance adopted since the World
War have contained compulsory features.*

Two movements are evident in the course of recent events: expansion of the scope of health insurance (in respect to the persons
who are insured and the benefits which are furnished) and extension
of compulsory rather than voluntary forms. Recent compilations[2]
indicate the following situation:

Countries Having Health Insurance Which Is Entirely or Principally Compulsory

Austria	Greece	Northern Ireland
Bulgaria	Hungary	Norway
Chile	Irish Free State	Poland
Czechoslovakia	Italy*	Portugal
Denmark*	Japan	Roumania
Esthonia	Latvia	Russia
France	Lithuania	Switzerland*
Germany	Luxemburg	Yugoslavia
Great Britain	Netherlands	

Countries Having Health Insurance Which Is Entirely or Principally Voluntary

Argentina	Denmark*	Spain
Australia	Finland	Sweden
Belgium	Italy*	Switzerland*
Brazil†	New Zealand	Union of South Africa
Canada	Palestine	Uruguay

It would take us too far afield to attempt a review of the voluminous literature which describes the various national systems and their operation.[3] But analysis of American problems and needs will gain perspective from reference to experience in European countries.

In Europe, as in the United States, the provision of medical service is mainly in the hands of individual practitioners rather than groups of physicians or professional organizations. The essential difference between European and American practice is not in the way in which medical service is furnished but in the way in which the cost is paid. For a large part of the European population, the

*Countries having both systems, applying to different fractions of the population. In addition to her own voluntary system, Italy retained after the war the compulsory systems which had existed in former Austrian and Hungarian provinces. In addition, Italy has a compulsory system of insurance against tuberculosis which applies to the entire country. In Switzerland, the systems are quite different in the various cantons. In Denmark, registration ("passive insurance") is compulsory but active membership in insurance is voluntary (see Chapter XII).

†Medical benefit is made compulsory in recent old-age and invalidity pension acts.

financial arrangements between physicians and their patients are different from those which prevail in the United States in that payment does not rest on individual purchase but on the principle of group payment through some form of insurance. In some localities clinics and hospitals are used to provide medical service in conjunction with group payment through insurance or through taxation; but in the main, despite group payment, individual rather than group practice predominates in the provision of medical service abroad.

Excepting only Holland and perhaps one or two other countries, the provision of hospital care in Europe is much more largely a governmental function than in the United States. In Great Britain hospital service under government auspices has been rapidly extended in recent years so that far more hospital beds are provided by local government authorities than by voluntary agencies. In addition, voluntary insurance for hospital care has come to include more than twelve million persons. In most European countries hospitals are mainly supported through taxes supplemented by payments from the sickness insurance societies of which the patients are members. These insurance payments to the hospitals usually meet only a fraction of the total cost of the care rendered. Only a very small proportion of the prosperous members of a community enter tax-supported hospitals (except the hospitals for communicable diseases) as paying patients in the American sense. A limited number of private hospitals or so-called "nursing homes" are available for such persons. The medical staff of the typical European hospital includes only a small number of physicians, largely on salary, who are not engaged in any private practice inside or outside the hospital. They are supplemented, of course, by private practitioners who serve in the hospitals, but the number of such non-salaried attending physicians is small by comparison with the current American practice. Thus, only a comparatively small proportion of the medical profession has direct contact with hospital service or reaps the benefit of practising with the aid of hospital facilities.

So far as payment for medical service is concerned, it can be said that, apart from hospital care and professional services in hospitals financed out of tax funds, in most European countries a large part of the population purchases medical service not through fees paid direct to the practitioners who furnish the service, but through regular, periodic payments made to a benefit society or to a local "fund." These societies or "funds" are formed from the employees of a given establishment, or consist of all insured persons of a locality, or of the members of a fraternal or friendly society who may be scattered throughout the country, or of workers engaged in a particular occupation, or otherwise. The insurance societies are self-administered, non-profit organizations and are under government supervision. The scope of official supervision varies in different countries. The insured persons are, as a rule, in the low income classes only; in some countries manual workers are insured without regard to their incomes. The membership dues paid by a wage-earner are usually (though not always) supplemented by payments made by his employer and, in some countries, by appropriations from tax funds. The total sum from all sources is available to pay the expenses of medical service and to furnish other benefits, chiefly cash to replace part of the wages lost on account of disabling sickness.

The scope of the medical service provided by insurance varies widely in different countries. No insurance scheme provides complete medical care of all forms, although the medical benefits are very comprehensive in some.

As is the case in the United States, taxes are always enlisted for the complete or partial support of hospital care and public health work, and sometimes for other forms of medical service; but generally speaking, health insurance is not financed from tax funds but from the contributions of employed persons and their employers. In general, tax funds pay only a small portion of the costs of insurance benefits. Furthermore, medical benefits provided through health insurance are furnished by private practitioners. In these respects health insurance is not "state medicine" or "public medicine." Indeed, in many European countries the provision of medical service under a contributory system of health insurance is regarded by the medical professions "as a bulwark against the really socialistic movement to provide it by means of a whole-time salaried service."[4] Excepting care for hospital patients, "public medical service" through government-employed practitioners exists on a national scale only in Russia.

The scope of service provided by insurance ranges from care for tuberculosis only, as for one class of insured persons in Italy, to the services of a general practitioner, as in Great Britain, and to a fairly complete medical service, as in Germany. Many insurance societies in Germany provide benefits which are not required by law but which the societies are permitted to furnish to their members when the financial reserves which have accumulated are sufficient to afford the costs; the sum of required plus "additional" benefits—especially in some of the cities—is equal to an approximately complete program of medical care. The Russian Soviets are rapidly developing a program of complete health and sickness service financed entirely through government (or government-controlled) funds.[5]

In most countries of Europe employed persons earning less than a specified income are legally required to insure. Medical care of specified scope must be provided (usually by the insurance society) in return for this insurance. Care of a wider scope than is required by law may be furnished if the workers and employers who contribute the funds voluntarily assess themselves larger premiums for additional benefits or if the non-profit insurance societies accumulate surplus funds in excess of reasonable contingent reserves. Cash benefits in partial replacement of wages lost during illness are always included in these insurance plans.

Even from these brief comments at least six points should be clear:

1. Health insurance in Europe is usually (though not always) restricted to the poor and does not embrace entire populations—European systems are commonly "poor-man's systems";

2. The medical care which is furnished as an insurance benefit is in some countries of limited scope and must be supple-

mented by private, individual purchase of service or by supplementary insurance arrangements;

3. Cash benefits for wage-loss are always provided in addition to medical benefits;

4. The costs are met primarily from contributions rather than from tax funds (U.S.S.R. excepted because of the difficulty of defining the funds in this country);

5. Administration, though supervised by government, is in the hands of non-profit associations of insured persons; and

6. Medical service is furnished by private practitioners who are remunerated from the insurance funds.

In American discussion of the subject, health insurance is often indicted on the ground that it leads to "the socialization of medicine." This rests upon a failure to understand health insurance practice. In Europe those who would "socialize" medicine berate health insurance as a great (perhaps the greatest) obstacle in their path.

Health insurance is merely a procedure of pooling funds which are contributed by insured persons (and their employers) and using the pooled contributions to pay cash benefits and to remunerate private practitioners and public or private institutions furnishing medical service. In some countries, and not in others, tax funds supplement contributions; but in no country (again, U.S.S.R. excepted) is any large fraction of the costs raised through taxation, though a substantial share of the cost is met from tax funds in Great Britain (about 15 to 17 per cent) and in Denmark (about 25 per cent). So far as medical benefits are concerned, health insurance is a far cry from the "socialization of medicine." Health insurance in Europe is primarily a system of mutualizing costs to pay cash benefits and to remunerate private medical practitioners. The very fact that health insurance operates through individual private practitioners is its greatest strength in the opinion of those who oppose the "socialization of medicine" and its greatest weakness in the opinion of those who would make the provision of medical services a public function.

The supplementing relations which commonly exist between health insurance and public (tax-paid) medical service may be illustrated by the arrangements which are practised in Italy. Sickness insurance is compulsory only for seamen and airmen, and for certain classes of employed persons in the new provinces where Italy inherited the old Austrian or Hungarian systems of sickness insurance. In 1930, some 38,000 and 187,000 persons, respectively, were covered by these two systems of compulsory insurance. In addition, however, there is compulsory maternity insurance (1930: 963,000 insured persons), compulsory tuberculosis insurance (1930: 5,631,000 insured persons; 1935: 6,500,000 insured persons with partial benefits to their dependents or, altogether about 15,000,000 persons), compulsory as well as voluntary invalidity and old-age insurance (covering about 6,000,000 persons), compulsory unemployment insurance, and several types of partly voluntary-partly compulsory sickness insurance which in 1930 covered about 745,000 industrial workers and 168,000 commercial employees. In addition, insurance has recently been developed for transport and for agricultural workers. All of this taken together is still far from sickness insurance of broad scope for the gainfully occupied population of Italy. It may be suspected that an important reason for this situation is the fact that Italy has an extensive and long-established system of tax-paid medical care for the indigent and the poor.

The "condotta" doctor, responsible for medical care, is an Italian institution going back to the Middle Ages. It received formal status as far back as 1806 and its present legal character in 1888. The "condotta" doctor must attend any person in need of treatment or advice. If the patient can afford to pay for medicines, he does so; otherwise the local government pays. If the patient needs hospital care, this is furnished at the expense of the local government. No disgrace attaches to being the "condotta" doctor or being served by him. The "full condotta" is a whole-time salaried officer of the district authorities and serves rich and poor without direct fee; the "residential condotta" serves the poor without fee and is remunerated for this service by the community, and others for a private fee. The "full condotta" has almost disappeared while the "residential condotta" has developed. The "condotta" doctors are appointed after competitive examinations (under the Provincial Medical Council) for a probationary period of two years and then for a permanent period on a fixed salary with a retiring pension. By 1930, the number of "condotta" doctors had increased to 11,600 with an average population of 3,600 persons per doctor.

In addition to the provision of "condotta" doctors and, of course, of public health services, public medical services in Italy include medical assistance for the aged, infirm and incurable. In the aggregate, medical benefits of these classes (exclusive of public health) involve the expenditure of over 600,000,000 lire a year. Thus, it is seen that the health insurance provisions cannot be properly evaluated except with regard to these other measures of public assistance and protection against sickness.

In Czechoslovakia, for another example, with a total population of 15,000,000, about 7,000,000 people are covered by sickness insurance (about 2,000,000 insured persons covered by compulsory insurance and their 4,000,000 dependents, and—in addition—about 1,000,000 self-employed persons and miners). In addition, there are about 2,000 local doctors paid out of tax funds on a part-time basis for medical care rendered to indigent and poor persons. Nearly all hospitals in Czechoslovakia are public (state or provincial and local) institutions. Each chartered or public hospital gives free care to people without means and is reimbursed from tax funds, the provincial government paying 80 per cent and the local government 20 per cent of the cost.

It may suffice for our purposes to review in greater detail the essential characteristics of four European systems: (1) the German system, selected because it is the oldest of the large national schemes and because it supplied the pattern for the systems which were developed in many other countries; (2) the British system, selected because it was adopted in more recent times after long study of conditions which are in many respects like those which obtain in the United States; (3) the French system (though adopted very recently and not yet thoroughly tried), chosen because some of its most important features were dictated by a strong political organization of physicians; and (4) the Danish system, because it is commonly cited as the best example of a successful "voluntary" plan.

From a review of these four we may hope to visualize the forms which group payment of sickness costs have taken in many countries of the world. Their circumstances may not coincide with ours; but their experiences may none the less provide valuable lessons from which we may profit as the United States fashions the signposts for whatever road it may choose to follow. Later we shall also review the workmen's compensation system in the United States, our only existing form of compulsory sickness insurance, and shall take note of the recent considerations given to health insurance by our federal and state governments.

REFERENCES AND NOTES

1. COMPULSORY SICKNESS INSURANCE, Series M (Social Insurance) No. 6. Geneva, International Labour Office, 1927, p. 9 *et seq.*

2. Adapted from: MEDICAL EDUCATION AND RELATED PROBLEMS IN EUROPE, a report of the Commission on Medical Education. New Haven, April, 1930, 200 pp.; Health Insurance, Monograph No. 3 (in a series on social insurance). New York, Metropolitan Life Insurance Company, 1931; THE WAY OF HEALTH INSURANCE, by A. M. Simons and Nathan Sinai. Chicago, The University of Chicago Press, 1932, 250 pp.; and many miscellaneous sources, especially publications of the International Labour Office, Geneva.

3. The most comprehensive treatment of the subject which is available in English appears in COMPULSORY SICKNESS INSURANCE, *op. cit.,* 810 pp., and in VOLUNTARY SICKNESS INSURANCE, Series M (Social Insurance) No. 7. Geneva, International Labour Office, 1927, 520 pp. The work of the International Labour Organization has recently been summarized in the report, THE INTERNATIONAL LABOUR ORGANISATION AND SOCIAL INSURANCE, Series M (Social Insurance) No. 12. Geneva, International Labour Office, 1936, 228 pp. For references to the literature and a critical commentary, *see* the recent book by Simons and Sinai, *op. cit.* For a comprehensive but lucid review, *cf.* INTERNATIONAL STUDIES ON THE RELATION BETWEEN THE PRIVATE AND OFFICIAL PRACTICE OF MEDICINE, WITH SPECIAL REFERENCE TO THE PREVENTION OF DISEASE (3 vols.), and MEDICINE AND THE STATE, by Sir Arthur Newsholme. London, George Allen & Unwin, Ltd. and Baltimore, Williams & Wilkins Co., 1931 and 1932, 250 pp.; 250 pp.; 558 pp. and 320 pp. *Also* NATIONAL HEALTH INSURANCE, by G. F. McCleary. London, H. K. Lewis & Co., Ltd., 1932, 195 pp.

4. The Method of Medical Care (editorial). *British Medical Journal,* April 7, 1934, No. 3822, pp. 626–627.

5. Newsholme, Sir Arthur and Kingsbury, John A.: RED MEDICINE: SOCIALIZED HEALTH IN SOVIET RUSSIA. New York, Doubleday, Doran & Company, Inc., 1933, 344 pp.

CHAPTER V

A DESCRIPTION OF COMPULSORY SICKNESS
INSURANCE IN GERMANY

NOTE

THE description of sickness insurance in Germany presents a dilemma. Our purpose is to study the experience of Germany since the inception of compulsory insurance on a national scale in 1883–1884. When the drafting of this and the two succeeding chapters was first undertaken early in 1933, it was planned to describe the insurance system as it stood at that time and to examine its evolution and experiences over a period of nearly fifty years (1884–1932). Since then about three years have elapsed and a description of the system in operation in Germany must take account of the National Socialist revolution (January, 1933) which brought changes in the organization of sickness (as well as in other forms of social) insurance. A description of sickness insurance which emphasized the present organization would therefore picture an administrative system with a number of features upon which no substantial experience has as yet accumulated and which have no direct or necessary bearing upon the factual information of preceding years. Furthermore, some of the changes decreed in 1933 and 1934 are of less importance for our purposes than may at first appear because they have not yet actually gone into effect: many are proposals rather than actual revisions; the decrees still wait upon the ministerial announcement of the date upon which they become effective.

To solve the dilemma, both description of the system and the analysis of experience could be treated in two broad categories, dealing, respectively, with insurance in the periods 1883–1932 and 1933–1936. This would not, however, be altogether sound for two reasons: (1) the changes effected in the last two and one-half years have not profoundly altered either the administrative arrangements or the basic operating techniques; and (2) with one exception (introduction of the "leadership" principle), the changes which have been made are logical outgrowths of, and are foreshadowed by, the preceding history of sickness insurance. It has therefore seemed more appropriate to deal with the history of sickness insurance in Germany as an integral whole while drawing attention to the differences between the system of 1932 and that of 1933–1936.

Sickness insurance is not a fixed or unchanging, but a living, social institution. Statistics which attempt to describe its operations must always be related in point of time to the arrangements under which these operations occurred. It is therefore impossible to present an accurate description except as of a particular instant or period of time. In order best to relate description to the statistics of operation over a long period of years, a balance has been sought in the following pages between the fixed and the changing characteristics, so that the description fits—as closely as possible—the circumstances which existed in the particular periods of time for which statistics are cited. Administrative and other changes which have been made so recently that they do not yet apply to any substantial past experience will be described but will not be given at any length except to indicate the course and direction of evolutionary changes.

INTRODUCTION

The principle of obligatory insurance was first clearly established in Prussia by a law of 1854. Local authorities were empowered to require the existing guilds to form insurance societies and to compel employers to make contributions. This law also required the formation of guilds for all employees in mines, mills, salt-works, etc., and the provision of insurance against disability resulting from sickness or accident.[1]

The first national compulsory sickness insurance law in Germany, passed in 1883, applied to wage-earners and managing employees of mines, quarries, factories and other industrial concerns whose annual wages were not in excess of 2,000 marks (about $500).[2] At this time voluntary sickness insurance was already well-developed. All succeeding legislation has extended the system, both in the number of persons covered and in the range of benefits provided.

Only employed persons are required to be insured. As elsewhere in Europe, cash benefits to replace a portion of the wages lost by reason of disability during sickness are provided for insured persons. Medical benefits for the insured persons include not only the service of general practitioners, but also that of specialists, and hospital care. Medical attendance must be furnished to the dependents of insured persons. Sickness insurance organizations have usually voted, as the law permits, to extend benefits to the members of the families of insured persons beyond this statutory obligation. About two-thirds of the population are now covered by the insurance plan.

In some localities, especially in the large cities, the interrelationship between sickness insurance and organized public health work has become extensive.

The administrative responsibility for the system rests primarily with the sickness insurance societies or funds (*Krankenkassen*). There are seven types of funds of which the *Ortskrankenkassen* are the most important. These are organized on a regional basis and include all insured persons in a given locality who are not members of another type of *Krankenkasse*. In addition to the *Ortskrankenkassen*, another important type is illustrated by the industrial funds, each of which is made up of the employees of a large business establishment or industry (*Betriebskrankenkassen*). Some of the funds or societies are outgrowths of the mutual aid associations, institutions founded many years ago by local authorities, townships, proprietors of factories, guilds, trade unions, etc.; others are more modern organizations created for the specific purpose of serving as insurance societies.*

*There is some confusion as to the terms used in English when referring to the insurance carriers. It has been customary to translate the word *Kasse* by the English word *fund*. The *Krankenkasse* has also been referred to as the sickness insurance society. The suggestion made by Davis and Kroeger (*New England Journal of Medi-*

(Continued on page 74)

Control of the sickness insurance fund has, in each case, been vested in a body of representatives, two-thirds of whom are elected by the insured persons and one-third by the employers.[3] (Changes made in 1934 will be cited later.) Employers and employees contribute to the cost. No direct contributions to the sickness insurance benefits are made from tax funds, although tax funds pay approximately one-half the cost of services rendered to insured persons in public hospitals. The government provides certain supervisory measures to see that the laws concerning benefits and financial safeguards are observed.

Different localities generally show variations in the details of benefits provided and in the manner in which arrangements are made for medical service. A free choice of doctor from among all who engage in insurance practice has been customary. This has been limited, however, by: (a) the restrictions in some large cities upon the number of physicians permitted to engage in insurance practice; and (b) the instances in which salaried physicians have been employed for certain areas in which the insured persons could choose only among those staff physicians supplied by the local insurance authorities. The most common method of remunerating physicians has been according to an established fee schedule for services rendered, although both annual salary and annual per-capita bases have been in use in some places. Specialized services are frequently provided through clinics rather than by arrangements with individual specialists, although the specialists are in some instances employed on a part-time or a full-time basis. No single statement will define the arrangements which have been used, because the law has permitted the funds considerable latitude in negotiating and in entering into contracts with physicians.

Voluntary sickness insurance has been extending rapidly, especially

cine, May 30, 1935, ccxii, p. 1037) that the local agencies be called *locals* is further confusing unless this proposed word is restricted to the *Ortskrankenkasse*. The word *society* should perhaps be restricted to the *Ersatzkasse*. These distinctions are, however, ignored and the words *fund* and *society* are used freely and interchangeably in this and the next two chapters, following customary usage in the English literature of this subject. I would express my regret, however, that the words *society* and *benefits*, as well as the word *contributions*, remain from the days of mutual benefit societies to color the vocabulary of modern social insurance.

since the World War, among persons who are above the financial limits of the compulsory insurance system. Some of these voluntary associations are organized on a national and some on a local basis; some are operated by non-profit associations and some by commercial groups. Some provide a fairly complete medical service for specified periodic payments. Not infrequently the contracts provide that the insured person must make certain additional payments at the beginning of an illness or must pay a certain percentage of an established fee schedule, with the intent of preventing unnecessary calls for service or restricting unnecessary purchase of medicines. Within the field of social insurance, there are no special insurance carriers which undertake voluntary insurance exclusively. All persons who, according to the Federal Insurance Code, are entitled to insure voluntarily or to continue their insurance on ceasing to be compulsorily insured may insure with the same funds as are authorized to administer compulsory insurance. The legally recognized funds are not permitted to accept other persons.

Nearly all German hospitals are supported in greater or lesser measure by tax funds. Many are partially supported through the contributions of insurance funds. Municipalities pay for the hospital treatment of the very poor, and uninsured persons pay according to their means. About 65 per cent of the patients served in hospitals are members of insurance societies, but the payments made by the societies to the hospitals commonly do not cover more than one-half the cost of service rendered to the insured patients. Usually hospital doctors are salaried and do not engage in private practice. The very poor receive non-institutional care from specially appointed physicians who are reimbursed by the local governments. There are in addition private hospitals for the well-to-do and institutions wholly owned and operated by the sickness (and invalidity) insurance organizations.

Scope of the Insurance System

The provisions of the German insurance system have been changing to meet new social and economic conditions as they develop. For our present purposes it is most profitable to visualize them as they stood at the close of 1932 or early in 1933.[4] The laws required insurance for all wage-earners, apprentices, and domestic servants, and for all industrial (works) officials and salaried workers earning less than a specified maximum income. The latter requirement applied to manual workers in responsible positions and to non-manual workers earning less than 3,600 Rm. ($858) per year.[2] Formerly, the income limit for non-manual workers in the last class had been 2,700 Rm. ($643) per year. Gainfully occupied persons in certain other classes may insure voluntarily. The laws fix the minimum benefits and the maximum contributions, and specify the additional benefits which may be furnished under specified conditions, leaving further details to the non-profit insurance societies (the *funds* or *Kassen*).

The practical work of administering sickness insurance is entrusted to the societies and the laws allow them broad powers and discretions. Yet they are public corporations, not administrative bodies, and they may sue and be sued in the courts of law. They are supervised and regulated by the state through a series of public offices or tribunals: the local and regional insurance offices (*Versicherungsämter*), the superior insurance offices (*Oberversicherungsämter*), and finally the Federal Insurance Office (*Reichsversicherungsamt*) which, conjointly with the Minister of Labor, is the highest authority.

During the early years of social insurance development, a large number of *Kassen* or *funds* came into existence. Although many were well managed, enjoyed large membership, and attained positions of enviable financial strength, others were small, inefficient and unstable. The Federal Insurance Code dissolved many of the smaller funds (1924, 1925); though there were nearly 19,000 funds in 1885 and over 23,000 in 1907, the first reorganization (beginning with 1911) saw the number reduced to 10,000 in 1914, and the second to 7,800 in 1925. Since then there has been further steady consolidation; there were 6,662 in 1932; 6,427 in 1933, and 6,191 in 1934. Further declines were being registered in 1935. Reduction of the number of funds has led to the elimination of weak organizations and further consolidation of the strong ones. As will soon appear, the majority of insured persons are members of the *local* (geographical) rather than of the *occupational* funds. Progressive concentration of membership in local funds has vastly simplified administrative problems because these are regional units and, in addition, it has facilitated the provision of medical service which, for practical purposes, must be furnished on a geographical basis if it is to be furnished efficiently and economically. Occupational funds often enjoy certain advantages if their primary purpose is insurance for cash benefits—because they have homogeneity in the financial means, industrial risks, and in the trade-union characteristics of the membership; but local funds benefit from administrative advantages, especially from closer relations between officers and members, and from the opportunity to provide medical service through practitioners and institutions largely or wholly devoted to a geographically concentrated population. A rural area may be served by a single fund, but a city may be served by many. However, the confusion is not so great in the large cities as might appear, because each large city now has a single local sickness fund (*Ortskrankenkasse*) which embraces all persons obliged to insure who are not exempt to join a legal sickness fund of another class or by reason of membership in a substitute fund (*Ersatzkasse*).

In its first enactment, the sickness insurance law applied only to industrial wage-earners (1883). Two years later, workers in commerce and transportation were added, and the following year many groups of agricultural workers. Since then the scope of the law has been steadily enlarged, so that by 1928 three classes of insured persons had been established:

A. *Unconditional Compulsory Insurance*—manual workers, apprentices, domestic servants, etc. *These must insure.* Because their wages are highly variable, no wage limit is specified for persons in this class.

B. *Conditional Compulsory Insurance*—salaried employees and officials (factory officials, foremen, shop assistants, actors, musicians, teachers, social workers, persons engaged in home industry, crews of German vessels, etc.). *These must insure if*

*they are in manual or non-manual trades and occupations, and
earn less than 3,600 Rm. ($858) per year.* (The limit of 3,600
Rm. has only recently been made to apply uniformly to all persons in this class; for non-manual workers it has been changed
a number of times—it was 2,700 Rm. from January, 1925, to
October, 1927.)

    C. *Voluntary Insurance*—persons in classes A and B whose
earnings exceed the specified maximum and who are self-
employed persons or family dependents who work without a
contract of labor. *These may voluntarily insure.*

    In consequence of the successive liberalizing acts, the scope of sick-
ness insurance in Germany steadily increased. When first inaugurated
(1885), there were 4,290,000 insured persons or 10 per cent of Germany's population. By 1900 the number of insured persons had increased to 9,520,000; by 1914 to 16,916,000; by 1925 to 20,180,000; and
by 1929 to 22,413,000 or one-third of the entire population. Of especial
interest is the fact that the increase in membership was proportionately far greater among women than among men: in 1885 there
were 22.2 female members per 100 male members; in 1925 there were
61.6 females per 100 males; in 1929, 63.8 and in 1932, 62.3 females per
100 males. Coincidently with this development, benefits applicable to
females became of increasing importance. Membership reached its
peak in 1929. During the four succeeding years of unemployment
and increasingly unfavorable economic conditions, the number declined steadily. Since then the numbers of insured persons have been
increasing:

1929	22,413,000
1930	21,908,000
1931	20,616,000
1932	18,712,000
1933	18,540,000
1934	19,949,000

During the first quarter of the year 1935, the membership in the legal
sickness funds increased further by 400,000 members.

TABLE 1

MEMBERSHIP IN GERMAN SICKNESS FUNDS, AVERAGES FOR THE YEAR 1934*

TYPE OF FUND[a]	NUMBER OF FUNDS	INSURED PERSONS		
		Total	Per Cent	Per Fund
I. Local	1,857	12,124,000	60.8	6,528
II. Rural	408	1,802,000	9.0	4,416
III. Industry (Works)	3,135	3,002,000	15.0	957
IV. Guild (Trade)	710	529,000	2.7	745
V. Seamen's	1	50,000	0.3	50,000
VI. Miner's	33	564,000	2.8	17,090
ALL "LEGAL" FUNDS	6,144	18,071,000	90.6	2,941
VII. Substitute	47	1,878,000	9.4	39,957
ALL FUNDS	6,191	19,949,000	100.0	3,222

*Compiled from Die Ortskrankenkasse, August 11, 1935, p. 775.
[a] The German names of the seven types of funds are: I. Ortskrankenkasse; II. Landkrankenkasse; III. Betriebskrankenkasse; IV. Innungskrankenkasse; V. Seekrankenkasse; VI. Knappschaftskrankenkasse; and VII. Ersatzkasse.

The distribution of insured persons in 1934 among the several types of funds is shown in Table 1. It will be noted that over 60 per cent of the membership is carried in the local funds and approximately nine-tenths in all the legal sickness funds combined. Declines in membership between 1929 and 1933 occurred in all classes of funds except the substitute funds (Ersatzkassen), the industrial funds (Betriebs-, Innungs-, and Knappschaftskassen) being the heaviest losers. The proportionate decline in the rural funds (Landkrankenkassen) was only about two-thirds that which occurred in all legal sickness funds combined. In the substitute funds, the number of insured persons increased as follows:

1929	1,457,000
1930	1,564,000
1931	1,618,000
1932	1,636,000
1933	1,713,000
1934	1,878,000

In the years in which the number of compulsorily insured persons declined, the number of voluntarily insured persons increased steadily, attaining the total of 3,438,000 in 1932.

The progressive concentration of membership in fewer and larger funds has had another effect besides increasing the financial strength and reducing the administrative costs; it has brought about more uniform distribution of the insurance risk by restricting the segregation of selected risks in particular funds or societies. (We shall see later that the law of July 5, 1934, further dealt with this problem by laying the basis for the establishment of a "re-insurance" fund for the partial equalization of risks through the pooling of a fraction of the income of each fund.)

In addition to over 22,400,000 members in the insurance funds in 1929, an approximately equal number of dependents of insured persons had become eligible to enjoy benefits provided by the insurance system. The authorities may extend to the individual funds the privilege of insuring dependents, or of furnishing benefits to them beyond the medical attendance required by law, when the financial strength, administrative efficiency, etc., of the fund attain appropriate levels. In 1914, 37 per cent of the legal sickness funds provided benefits for 4,700,000 dependents. By 1925, 85.4 per cent of the funds, having 94 per cent of all members, made provision for family benefits to 14,300,000 dependents.[5] In October, 1934, when there were 20,316,000 insured persons, there were in addition 16,350,000 family dependents or 80.5 per 100 insured persons.[6] The proportion of dependents to insured persons varied from 57.5 in the guild or trade funds (*Innungskrankenkassen*) to 187.5 in the miner's funds (*Knappschaftskrankenkassen*). This great expansion in the provision of benefits for dependents came in response to a widespread recognition that insurance against the social and economic consequences of sickness should not be restricted to single persons and gainfully employed members of families, but should apply to all persons in families of small or modest means. Various estimates for the years 1928–1932 are in substantial agreement that German sickness insurance covered nearly as many dependents as insured persons during this period, or, all told, 42,000,000 to 44,000,000 persons in 1929 and about 36,700,000 in 1934, nearly two-thirds of the entire population of the country.

CONTRIBUTIONS

The source of insurance funds is the contributions of workers and their employers. Under the original act, the total contributions varied from 1.5 to 6 per cent of the basic daily wage,* depending upon the wage and the industry. The government made no direct contributions. The insured persons pay two-thirds and their employers one-third of the contributions. (Under the law of July 5, 1934, the contributions of employers and of employees are to be equal. But this part of the new law has not yet gone into effect. The proportions cited above still obtain.) Under the law, total contributions were not permitted to exceed 7.5 per cent of earnings, and in most cases they could not exceed 6 per cent. Contributions in excess of 5 per cent must be voted in each insurance fund (*Kasse*) by the contributors. No contributions are required from employee or employer during the unemployment of an insured person; the unemployment insurance fund pays these contributions. The government formerly paid one-half the cost of maternity benefits for the uninsured wives of insured persons, because these benefits were designed as much in the interest of national maternity hygiene as in the interest of providing relief. Otherwise the state makes no contributions except in providing supervision for the operation of the insurance societies (and except for its share of the government-operated hospitals, etc.). The government contributions toward cash benefit for dependents made in the years 1928–1932 were discontinued in 1933. Since then the in-

*The basic wage is fixed by the societies according to procedures which, in principle, are specified by law. In general, it is a close approximation to the average remuneration per day. The maximum basic daily wage is fixed by law at 10 Rm. and is taken at this amount for workers who earn more. There are ten basic daily wages, ranging from less than 1.50 to 10 Rm. per day. Basic wage may be fixed according to actual wages, wage classes, or member classes. Some 80 per cent of the funds with 93 per cent of the members use the wage classes.

come of the sickness funds has included no money from taxes. Changes in the regular contribution rates may be ordered by the Federal Insurance Office upon the request or with the approval of the Minister of Labor; changes requested by the societies must be approved by the authorities.

Contributions had been increasing in recent years and reached their highest values in the middle of 1930; since then they have been declining, as appears in the following average rates for the last six years:

Year	*Average Contribution Rate* *(In per cent of the basic wages)*
1929	6.46
1930	5.75
1931	5.65
1932	5.46
1933	5.25
1934	5.10

The decline has occurred in every type of sickness fund. In May, 1935, the average monthly contribution per insured person amounted to 5 Rm. Inasmuch as the weighted average contribution rate is about 5 per cent, it follows that the weighted average annual income of the insured persons is about 1,200 Rm. There is still considerable variation in the rate of the contributions among the funds, even in the same or nearby communities, but increasing uniformity is being attained as a result of deliberate measures being taken to this end by the Federal Office.

It should be clear that the establishment of contributions as a fixed per cent of wages means a fixed but not a uniform contribution. On the contrary, it means that each insured person is contributing according to "ability to pay" and that his employer is also contributing on a corresponding sliding scale. The reason for (and the significance of) this scale of contributions will appear after we have examined the benefits.

BENEFITS

The benefits provided in German sickness insurance are of two kinds, cash benefits and medical service. Of each kind, some benefits are required and others are optional with the funds. The required or statutory benefits are specified by federal law and their provision is obligatory upon the funds; the optional benefits may be established by the funds as additional to the statutory benefits when financial circumstances permit and the legal authorities approve. All benefits are administered by the officers of the funds.

CASH BENEFITS

Sickness Benefits. Under the law, the cash benefit for disability shall not be less than 50 per cent of the basic daily or representative wage, payable for the duration of disabling sickness from the fourth day to the end of twenty-six weeks after the beginning of sickness. This benefit may be increased by the sickness fund up to a maximum of 60 per cent of the basic wage and additional increments may be added in respect to dependents but the total may not exceed 75 per cent of the basic wage. The benefit is payable upon certification by a physician that the insured person is unable to work. There is no precise legal definition of "incapacity for work" and considerable latitude has been allowed physicians in their judgment. In the case of an unskilled laborer, incapacity is certified "when he cannot pursue the occupation previously exercised by him, if he has exercised it for a considerable period and if it has to some extent become his profession owing to the experience, skill and adaptation to its peculiar conditions gained by him."[7] It has also become the common practice to certify incapacity for work when the working capacity, though not yet completely gone, may be further reduced by continuance of work. Although this practice is grounded in a sound principle of prevention, clearly it is capable of abuse.

The intention of the cash benefit during disability is to provide a means of subsistence for the worker and his (or her) dependents, in the period when the wage-earner who has become disabled is without his ordinary income. Originally, it was also intended that this benefit should provide money for the purchase of such medical service as the illness required; but the provision of medical service as an insurance benefit simplified the dual objective of the cash benefit.

In fixing the size of the cash benefit, there is a difficult problem: if it is a small fraction of the ordinary wage, it is inadequate to provide subsistence; if it equals or even approximates the ordinary wage, it encourages an insured person to seek certification of disability on many pretexts. The statutory guarantee of 50 per cent of the basic wage represents a middle point between the horns of this dilemma. When the compromise figure was established, it was clearly recognized that 50 per cent might be insufficient. Hence, the law permits various extensions of the benefit, on the initiative of the insurance society and when their finances permit, on the assumption that the temptation of insured persons to seek excessive benefits will be most effectively controlled by the individual societies through the joint recognition of insured persons and their officers that insurance is a mutual undertaking and that contributions have to be increased above the minimum to furnish additional benefits.

It should be recognized that a cash benefit of 50 per cent is more substantial than may at first appear if account is taken of the deductions which ordinarily apply against the worker's wages. For example, the authorities estimate (September, 1935) that social insurance contributions, taxes, etc., ordinarily account for 25 per cent of wages and that the worker actually receives only 75 per cent of his ordinary wage. Hence, when he receives a cash sickness benefit of 50 per cent he is receiving a benefit actually equal to two-thirds of his usual cash income; and when he receives a benefit of 75 per cent he is receiving a benefit actually equal to his ordinary cash income. Thus, when insurance and tax deductions are large (as at present), the administration prefers to see cash sickness benefit fixed nearer 50 than 75 per cent.

Additional cash benefits, in excess of the statutory minimum, may take several forms:

1. Increase from 50 up to 75 per cent of the basic wage;
2. Bonuses for all insured persons who become incapacitated or for those in the lowest wage classes;
3. Graduation of the benefit (in excess of 50 per cent of the basic daily wage) according to the number of dependent children;
4. Elimination of the "waiting period," so that cash benefit becomes payable from the first, instead of from the fourth, day of incapacity;
5. Extension of the period of disability during which the benefit is payable, from 26 weeks up to 52 weeks; and
6. Provision of institutional treatment (in lieu of other cash and medical benefit) with cash allowance for dependents (so-called home benefit, which may range between 50 per cent and 100 per cent of the statutory cash benefit).

Thus, it becomes evident that the cash benefits constitute in effect a means of providing unemployment insurance when unemployment is due to sickness. It is therefore not surprising that the provision of cash benefits offers an especially potent incentive to malingering and to the exaggeration of acute or chronic illnesses, especially among seasonal workers. To them sickness benefits may serve to tide over periods of unemployment. Nor is it surprising that the demands for sick benefits increase vastly during periods of widespread unemployment. This was especially evident in 1925 and 1926 and particularly because the sickness insurance contributions are waived during a period of incapacity and the benefits exceed the unemployment doles. "When economic crises occur, sickness insurance bears the brunt of the first shock." Operating against this tendency there are others. When unemployment increases, many employed workers are fearful of becoming temporarily incapacitated; they conceal illnesses in order to avoid being known as less than first-class workers. Others fearing the approach of a period of unemployment stay at work to earn their maximum income. These and other trends are all confused in the statistics on incapacity. The actual experience of recent years may be illustrated by the following average percentages of persons (both sexes) sick and incapable of work among the insured members of local funds (*Ortskrankenkassen*):

1925	4.00
1926	3.42
1927	3.74
1928	4.22
1929	4.33
1930	3.60
1931	3.40
1932	2.86
1933	2.89
1934	2.67

The corresponding figures are higher for female than for male insured persons.

In the course of forty-five years of experience, the cost of cash sickness benefits steadily increased from 5.5 marks per member in 1885 to 23.0 marks per member in 1925, and to a peak value of 32.6 marks in 1929. This was the consequence of a rising wage level, voluntary increases in contributions, and an extension of the additional cash benefits. The insurance funds took advantage of the discretion given to them by the law to provide the sick with the means of supporting at least a minimum standard of decent living.

There need be no objection to the rising benefits *as such*, as long as the persons who receive the benefits are also those who pay all or most of the cost. And it must be kept in mind that the insured persons pay two-thirds of the contributions. The proper objections have been of two other kinds. First, there was the charge that the sickness funds became vast and powerful political organizations; it was alleged that the officers of the funds encouraged extravagances, both in contributions and expenditures, in the interest of building up political machines. Second, it has been alleged that the attractions of the cash benefits circumvent the effective operation of medical benefits, the prevention of disease and the maintenance of health and vitality. The first of these was the basis for the argument, commonly advanced, that, despite their usefulness as administrative agencies for the operation of sickness insurance, the societies were a political curse of the first magnitude. On this point there is obviously room for difference of opinion. (We shall note later how the funds are now controlled politically.) The second provides the ground for the contention that many of the failings of modern sickness insurance derive from the dual function of the physician: on the one hand, he must attempt to keep his patients well or cure them rapidly; on the other hand, he must be complacent and compliant in providing them with certificates of incapacity in order that they shall receive cash sickness (disability) benefit.

Our interest lies primarily in the economic problems of obtaining medical care and of furnishing security against the costs of sickness. The political attributes of insurance societies are therefore of secondary interest, except that Germany's experience with them warns us that they may be a mixed blessing. The rôle of cash benefits in interfering with medical benefits is, however, of the highest significance for an analysis, like the present one, designed to discover an effective, economic means of obtaining medical care.

Before leaving the subject of cash benefits, it is pertinent to emphasize a point mentioned only casually before. The basic daily wages have been rising and more and more commonly the societies have been providing the additional benefits with which they may legally supplement the fixed statutory benefits. Nevertheless, cash benefit (*Krankengeld*) has been consuming a decreasing proportion of the total budgets. This was true up to 1929, when cash benefit attained its maximum value, and has been true since then when cash benefits have been declining rapidly. Although cash sickness benefit formerly consumed nearly one-half the total insurance budget, it has come to consume less than one-fifth.

It has been remarked that the cash benefit during disability is essentially an unemployment benefit. There should be no mistaking the fact that even in this respect it may be considered as contributing to the public health in the sense that providing a means of subsistence, avoiding dependency, and preserving the unity of family life, are public health measures. But the desire for prolonged cash benefits undoubtedly also contributes to malingering, neglect of disease, exaggeration of morbidity, and to a complacent acceptance of dependency upon the insurance funds. Of the non-statutory or additional cash benefits, only one has been seriously alleged to have any direct value in encouraging good medical care, especially preventive care. This is the payment of benefit from the first, instead of from the fourth, day of incapacity.[8] It is said to encourage the earlier application of thorough treatment. Whether for this reason or merely because the societies have been in position to afford this additional benefit, in 1925, 82.3 per cent of the legal sickness funds dispensed with the waiting period.

Maternity Benefit. This is another statutory cash benefit. (It is supplemented by the statutory maternity medical-care benefit.) Each fund must pay to an insured woman a lump-sum maternity benefit of 10 Rm. and a daily benefit equal to cash sickness benefit (50 per cent of her wages), but not less than 0.50 Rm. per day, for four weeks before and six weeks after confinement. This daily benefit must be increased to three-fourths of her wages and be furnished for six weeks before confinement if she does no paid work during this period. In addition, the law prescribes a maternity nursing benefit equal to one-half the maternity benefit, but not less than 0.25 Rm. per day, for twelve weeks after confinement, provided the mother nurses her infant. These benefits are payable provided the insured woman has been insured for not less than ten months in the preceding two years and not less than six months in the last year before confinement.

The funds may voluntarily increase the maternity benefits; the lump-sum may be increased to 25 Rm. and the daily benefit to 75 per cent of the basic wage and up to a period of thirteen weeks. Nursing benefit may be increased to twenty-six weeks. Furthermore, the funds may extend maternity benefits to the uninsured wives or other dependents of insured persons, and practically all funds do so. As a result, approximately two-thirds of all maternity cases in Germany are assisted by maternity benefits. Total maternity benefits amounted in 1932 to 4.24 Rm. per insured person and to 170 Rm. per maternity case among insured persons and to 100 Rm. per dependent. These sums represent large increases over the corresponding figures for preceding years. In some of the large cities the maternity cash benefits paid by the stronger funds have been considerably larger than the general average. Although the total expenditures on maternity benefits have been declining in absolute amount (they fell to slightly less than 4 Rm. per insured person in 1933), they constitute a larger per cent of the total insurance budget than formerly. For example, they were only 4.4 per cent of the total in 1929, but 7.1 per cent in 1932.

Funeral Benefit. The federal law also provides another statutory cash benefit, the so-called funeral benefit. In the event of the death of an insured person, the insurance society must pay the family of the deceased a lump-sum of at least twenty times the basic daily wage of the deceased member. The societies are permitted to increase this benefit up to a maximum of forty times the basic wage, to fix a minimum sum up to 50 Rm., or to grant a funeral benefit upon the death of the husband or wife or child of an insured person.

MEDICAL BENEFITS

In addition to cash benefits, German sickness insurance laws require that the insurance societies shall provide for their sick members: (1) medical attendance; (2) prescribed medicines, spectacles, trusses and other minor medical or surgical appliances (subject to the requirement that the insured person shall pay a share of the cost); (3) hospital treatment when the nature of the illness or the circumstances require; (4) medical attendance for the members of the insured person's family; and (5) maternity care (obstetrical attendance and, if necessary, medical attendance and hospital treatment) for insured women and the wives and daughters of insured men.

Originally the medical benefits were granted for the duration of cash benefit, with a maximum period of thirteen weeks. Now, the statutory medical benefit, including specialist services, must be provided *without a waiting period* (i.e., from the first day of sickness) for as long as cash benefits continue. Where the duration of cash benefits has been increased beyond the statutory twenty-six weeks, medical benefit has also been extended.

Dental benefit was formerly restricted to treatment for acute toothache and the extraction of bad teeth or roots but has been extended to include prophylactic treatments, dental surgery, and financial contributions towards the cost of artificial teeth when the need for a denture involves the general health of the patient.

In addition to enlargement of the medical benefit by expanding the scope and quality of medical service for insured persons, there has been a general extension of medical benefit to the family dependents of insured persons. Additional benefits commonly provided by the societies include hospital and other institutional treatment for dependents, home nursing, convalescent care, special maternity care, artificial limbs, etc.

Although hospital and other institutional treatment is quite generally provided for insured persons, it is not yet so general for their dependents. Many funds which do not grant this benefit to dependents provide cash subsidies towards the cost of institutional treatment. When hospital or other institutional care is provided an insured person, the cash benefit is reduced, usually to one-half the statutory allowance. Reduction of the cash benefit renders many who are in need of hospital care loath to enter a hospital. Hence, the societies use their privilege of making additional grants by allowing a "home benefit" in the form of additional cash to assist in the support of dependents. In addition, many funds grant "pocket money"— small cash allowances to meet the incidental expenses of hospitalized insured members who have no dependents.

Home nursing includes, variously, graduate nurses, practical or attendant nurses, home help, etc. When this benefit is provided, cash benefit may be reduced by one-fourth the statutory allowance. Convalescent care, when provided, is limited to a maximum duration of one year after cessation of actual sickness benefits. Even beyond these, the societies generally furnish a variety of other medical benefits according to the patient's needs. These take the form of unusual specialist services, subsidies for invalid diets, X-ray, radium, physiotherapy and other treatments, provision of special orthopedic appliances or subsidies towards their costs, etc. In short, the basic medical benefits for insured persons have been expanded to embrace more or less complete medical service for them and their dependents.

Both the scope and quality of service vary widely, especially as between the large cities and the rural areas. Only qualified or licensed practitioners may be employed by the insurance societies; members of other healing professions may be utilized only on the request of responsible physicians.

REFERENCES AND NOTES

1. Frankel, Lee K. and Dawson, Miles M. (with L. I. Dublin): WORKINGMEN'S INSURANCE IN EUROPE. New York, Russell Sage Foundation, 1911, p. 228.

2. Except where otherwise specified, in this chapter and in the following two, the mark is taken at its former par value, 23.82 cents, the par value which obtained in the years to which the data apply, except during the period of post-war inflation.

3. In *guild* or *industrial* funds in which the employers contribute one-half the money, they have one-half the representatives in the delegates' meeting and in the managing committee.

4. Details cited here (and elsewhere in this chapter) have been taken from many and varied sources. For convenient reference in English, the following may be cited: Reference No. 1 above; HEALTH INSURANCE (1931) and SOCIAL INSURANCE LEGISLATION (1932), Monographs Three and Four. New York, Metropolitan Life Insurance Company, 1933, 1932; COMPULSORY SICKNESS INSURANCE, Series M (Social Insurance), No. 6. Geneva, International Labour Office, 1927, 810 pp.; BENEFITS OF THE GERMAN SICKNESS INSURANCE SYSTEM FROM THE POINT OF VIEW OF SOCIAL HYGIENE, by Franz Goldmann and Alfred Grotjahn. Geneva, The International Labour Office, 1928, 188 pp.; THE WAY OF HEALTH INSURANCE, by A. M. Simons and Nathan Sinai. Chicago, The University of Chicago Press, 1932, 250 pp. For an introduction to a more extensive bibliography on the controversial aspects of the subject, see the last reference cited here.

5. BENEFITS OF THE GERMAN SICKNESS INSURANCE SYSTEM FROM THE POINT OF VIEW OF SOCIAL HYGIENE, *op. cit.*, p. 10.

6. DIE ORTSKRANKENKASSE. June 1, 1935, p. 509; July 11, 1935, p. 677.

7. BENEFITS OF THE GERMAN SICKNESS INSURANCE SYSTEM FROM THE POINT OF VIEW OF SOCIAL HYGIENE, *op. cit.*, p. 53.

8. This additional benefit may be legally available in respect to diseases lasting longer than a week, having a fatal issue, caused by industrial accident, or in certain other specified cases.

CHAPTER VI

A STATISTICAL AND COST ANALYSIS OF SICKNESS INSURANCE IN GERMANY

THE COSTS OF INSURANCE BENEFITS

THE extension of benefits has, of course, meant an increase in the cost of insurance. The societies, free to fix contributions, have called for increasing sums. At one time, they began to approach the legal maximum of 6 to 7.5 per cent of earnings, but latterly the trend has been reversed, and contributions have, as has already been noted, declined to an average of approximately 5 per cent. The contributions are always divided between employee and employer in the proportion of two to one, respectively,* although the new (1934) law intends to divide them equally. Increasing costs have been more than balanced by increasing contributions, so that the societies have accumulated substantial reserves. The balance of income and expenditures is illustrated by the figures[1] in Table 2. Data for the years 1915–1923 are omitted because the normal financial operation of the insurance funds was made impossible by the war and the subsequent inflation of the currency; 1924 was the first year of normal operation following stabilization of the mark. It will be noted that income exceeded expenditures among the statutory funds in every year except 1931 and in every year without exception among the substitute funds (*Ersatzkassen*). Both income and expenditures attained peak values in 1929 and have been declining steadily since then. Preliminary figures for 1934 and the first half of 1935 show a continuation of the downward trend indicated in the table. As a result of the excess of income over expenditures, the funds have accumulated substantial reserves. For the legal sickness

*Except as recorded in note 3, p. 91.

TABLE 2

INCOME AND EXPENDITURE* PER INSURED PERSON IN GERMAN SICKNESS FUNDS
1913–1933

YEAR	STATUTORY FUNDS[a]		SUBSTITUTE FUNDS[b]	
	Income	Expenditure	Income	Expenditure
1913	$ 8.80	$ 8.54		
1914	9.30	7.90		
—	—	—		
1924	13.75	12.27		
1925	16.97	15.87		
1926	18.03	16.49		
1927	20.06	18.85	$25.71	$24.51
1928	22.51	21.51	29.16	27.48
1929	23.97	22.83	30.32	29.57
1930	22.50	21.07	29.84	28.69
1931	17.92	18.69	26.29	25.53
1932	15.04	14.85 .	22.64	22.17
1933	14.60	14.56	21.45	21.20

*Includes income from all sources and expenditures for all purposes.
a All legal sickness funds, including the seamen's fund.
b *Ersatzkassen* only.

funds, these reserves amounted at the close of 1933 to nearly
900,000,000 Rm., equivalent to approximately 50 Rm. per insured person or nearly one year's operating expenses. It is reported that the
funds are having some financial difficulties at present and that reserves may show some decline by the close of 1935. Whether or not
this will be so, in the face of economies now being attempted, remains to be seen.

It was noted in the preceding chapter that the cost of cash benefits
has been increasing in absolute amount during most of the past fifty
years. This is a consequence of (1) increase in the size of wages and
of contributions, and (2) greater liberality in the protection furnished
by the benefits of insurance. Both contributions and cash benefit are
measured as a percentage of wages. When wages increase, both contributions and benefits increase. Furthermore, we have seen that the
benefit period has been increased. It has been remarked, however,

that though cash benefits have increased in absolute amount, they have become smaller in relation to total contributions and to the total costs. These points are illustrated by the following figures:

Year	Annual Cost of Cash (Sickness) Benefit (Marks per insured person)	Per cent of Total Insurance Costs
1885	5.5	45.0
1900	7.2	40.0
1910	10.0	37.5
1925	23.0	35.0
1929	32.6	34.0
1930	25.0	28.2
1931	19.5	24.9
1932	12.9	20.7
1933	11.9	19.5

Sickness cash benefit increased sixfold in cost per insured person between 1885 and 1929 and even in 1933 was still more than twice what it had been in the early days of insurance. Yet, throughout this period, other benefits were increasing even more, so that the cost of this particular cash benefit declined from nearly one-half the total cost of insurance to less than one-fifth.

THE COSTS OF MEDICAL BENEFITS

The costs of medical benefits are illustrated by the figures in Table 3. The total cost of these benefits increased from less than 5 marks per member per year in 1885 to more than 50 in 1929, and then declined. Every type of medical benefit shared in these changes, the expenditure for each having risen more than six- to tenfold before the decline of the latest years set in.

It will repay us to examine in some detail the size and distribution of the total costs of sickness insurance, taking account not only of the medical benefits but also of the cash benefits and the costs of administration. The nature of the expenditures is illustrated in Table 4 from the data for the year 1933.

TABLE 3

The Costs of Medical Benefits for Insured Persons and Their Dependents,
Germany, 1885–1933

YEAR	EXPENDITURES OF ALL LEGAL SICKNESS FUNDS[a] (*Marks per Insured Person per Year*)				
	Physicians, Dentists, etc.[b]	Hospitals, etc.[c]	Medicines and Other Supplies[d]	Home Benefits, etc.[e]	All Medical Benefits[f]
1885	2.11	1.04	1.65	0.06	4.86
1900	3.60	2.06	2.73	0.16	8.55
1910	5.85	3.47	3.69	0.36	13.37
1925	15.92	8.24	7.32	1.09	32.57
1929	23.40	13.08	11.35	2.57	50.40
1930	23.45	13.77	10.14	2.47	49.83
1931	21.27	13.55	8.53	1.76	45.11
1932	18.94	10.67	6.75	0.93	37.29
1933	19.02	11.08	6.72	0.86	37.68

a Exclusive of expenditures for administration. See note f below.
b Includes all legal practitioners.
c Includes clinics, dispensaries, etc.
d Includes surgical supplies, spectacles, etc.
e Includes "home benefits and pocket money" (see page 90). Inasmuch as these benefits are provided in the form of *cash*, they are not strictly *medical* benefits. They are included here because they are extended by the societies in order to assist directly in the provision and in the effective utilization of hospital benefits.
f The cost of administration would add for the several years from 6.5 to 10 per cent to these figures to give the full cost of the medical benefits.

Medical benefits consume 61 per cent of all expenditures, all cash benefits 28 per cent, and administration 10 per cent. Of the total expenditures of $14.54 per insured person, $8.87 is consumed by the medical benefits. If it is assumed that 61 per cent of the costs of administration are chargeable to the medical benefits, the cost for these items is increased to $9.75 per insured person or approximately 67 per cent of the total specified costs of the insurance system. If we followed the practice noted on page 90 and used in Table 3, and considered "home benefits and pocket money" chargeable to the cost of medical benefit, the total cost of medical benefit would become $9.91 per insured person or 68.1 per cent of the total. Similarly, if we add a *pro rata* share of the miscellaneous expenditures (not specified) to the costs of medical benefit and a similar share of administration

TABLE 4

SICKNESS INSURANCE EXPENDITURES OF THE LEGAL (STATUTORY) SICKNESS FUNDS[a]
OF GERMANY, 1933*

EXPENDITURES	TOTAL	PER INSURED PERSON[b]	PER CENT
TOTAL	$244,800,000[c]	$14.54[d]	100.0
Medical services—Total	149,300,000	8.87	61.0
Physicians' fees	59,800,000	3.55	24.4
Hospital services	44,400,000	2.64	18.2
Drugs and appliances	26,900,000	1.60	11.0
Dental services	16,500,000	0.98	6.7
Public health	900,000	0.05	0.4
Other services[e]	800,000	0.05	0.3
Cash benefits—Total	68,600,000	4.08	28.0
Sickness (disablement)	50,600,000	3.01	20.7
Maternity	15,900,000	0.95	6.5
Death	2,100,000	0.12	0.8
Miscellaneous (not specified)	2,400,000	0.14	1.0
Administration	24,500,000	1.45	10.0

*Compiled and computed from *Amtliche Nachrichten für Reichsversicherung,* 1934, xii,
pp. 633–639.

a Including the seamen's fund; excluding the substitute funds.

b The average number of insured persons in 1933 was 16,827,000.

c Exclusive of capital changes ($253,000).

d The discrepancy between this figure and the corresponding figure in Table 2 is due
to the deduction mentioned in note c above.

e Services from other professional personnel; home services; convalescent care; and other
services for the sick, not specified.

f Including "home" and "pocket" money.

costs, the total for medical benefit finally becomes $10.03 per insured
person or 69 per cent of the total costs.

These figures lead to a very significant point. The insurance system
was originally and primarily designed to provide *cash* benefits to
replace wages lost through disabling sickness. Medical service, which
was first provided as a supplementary benefit, has become the principal benefit and accounts for more than two-thirds of the total
expenditures made from the insurance funds. *Restoration of the sick
person, rather than compensation of the disabled worker, has become
the chief objective of German sickness insurance.*

The per-capita cost data in Table 4 have an obvious value in indicating the amount of money which is used to pay for medical services. Inasmuch as the insured persons (and their employers) must pay these costs, it is sound to express the costs in terms of dollars per insured person. It will be recognized, however, that such figures may be misleading because they cover not merely services furnished to the insured persons but also services furnished to their dependents. If the same or similar services were uniformly available to insured persons and to their dependents, adjusted per-capita figures could readily be obtained by dividing the total costs shown in Table 4 by the total of insured persons and qualified dependents, or by dividing the costs per insured person in this table by the ratio of total persons receiving services to the number of insured persons. It will be recalled, however, that medical benefits are not furnished uniformly to insured persons and to their dependents; not all medical services which are furnished to insured persons are available to their dependents. It has therefore been necessary to arrive at the costs for insured persons and for dependents by recourse to the original data. Fortunately, most of the costs are available separately according to whether they apply to services rendered to the one or the other class of persons. In Table 5 appear the (direct or approximated) costs for these two classes of persons served by the insurance system.

It will be noted that the medical services furnished to insured persons (including the costs of administration) cost $6.96 per person, and the more limited services furnished to dependents cost $3.50 per person. As would be anticipated from the administrative arrangements under which these benefits are furnished, the composition of the total is quite different in the two cases.

In interpreting the data in Table 5 and in preceding tables it should be kept in mind that they apply to all of Germany and to the extremely diversified populations insured in cities, on the farms, in mines, etc. Costs (like contributions) are considerably higher in urban than in rural areas.

The expenditures for medical service provided through insurance

TABLE 5

THE COST OF MEDICAL SERVICE FOR INSURED PERSONS AND THEIR DEPENDENTS
Legal (Statutory) Sickness Funds of Germany, 1933*

SERVICE	EXPENDITURE PER PERSON[a]	
	Insured	Dependent
Physicians[b]	$1.94	$1.94
Hospital care[c]	2.17	0.56
Drugs and appliances[c]	1.34	0.32
Dental care[c]	0.75	0.28
All other[d]	0.06	0.05
SUB-TOTAL	$6.26	$3.15
Administration[e]	0.70	0.35
TOTAL	$6.96	$3.50

*Computed from *Die Krankenversicherung, Statistik des deutschen Reichs,* 1932, 1933; and from *Amtliche Nachrichten für Reichsversicherung,* 1934, xii.

a Based on 16,827,000 insured persons and 13,899,000 (estimated) dependents.

b Being equally available to both classes of persons, the total costs for this item were allocated proportionately.

c Data given separately in source volumes for the two classes of persons.

d All items except general public health are given separately; this specific item has been allocated proportionately between the two classes.

e Proportionate allocation of that fraction (67.8 per cent) of total administration costs which medical service costs are of total costs of all benefits.

take on additional significance when they are compared with the expenditures of similar economic groups in the United States. Among representative family groups studied in the years 1928–1931, it was found that the average annual expenditure for medical care among families with annual incomes of less than $1,200 was $8.12 per person, and among those with $1,200 to $2,000 a year, $12.16 per person. These figures include both the employed persons in these families and their dependents.[2] A special tabulation for the employed persons only gave $7.80 per person and $10.14 per person in these income classes, respectively. Thus, it is seen that the expenditures for medical service made by American families in the lower income brackets are substantially larger than are the expenditures made by the German sickness insurance funds. Unfortunately, there is no record of the private expenditures made by insured persons in Germany to supplement the insurance provisions. It is possible that if these were known, the differences noted above would largely or entirely disappear.

This comparison between the private expenditures of American families and the expenditures of German sickness insurance funds should not conceal a fundamental difference between them. Under the German insurance system, the costs of medical care are met by central administrative agencies from funds contributed in small, fixed, periodic payments by employed persons and their employers. Under our American system of private purchase, the costs are met by individual families out of their individual resources and according to the haphazard occurrence of illness. In the one case, the expenditure makes available medical service according to medical need (within the restrictions of the administrative arrangements); in the other, according to medical need and ability to pay the costs.

It is interesting to discover that the proportionate division of expenditures is substantially the same for the medical benefits of insured persons in Germany and for medical care purchased privately by families of the same income class in the United States.[3]

MEDICAL SERVICE	INSURED PERSONS IN GERMANY, 1933	FAMILIES WITH INCOMES OF LESS THAN $1,200 IN THE UNITED STATES, 1928–1931
ALL	100 per cent	100 per cent
Physicians	40	45
Hospitals (and nursing)	30	22
Drugs and appliances	18	21
Dental care	11	8
All other	1	4

The rising volume and costs of medical service, other than physicians' attendances, may be illustrated by a few examples. Consider dental care.

When German sickness insurance was first established no dental care was attempted beyond treatment for acute toothache and removal of damaged teeth or stumps. In those days modern dentistry had scarcely been born, and preventive and curative dentistry were all but unknown except to people of means. Then came the development of preventive and curative dentistry, recognition of the relation between dental diseases and general health and disease, the achievements of restorative dentistry, and increasing public demand for the service, and finally the discovery of vast opportunities to prevent dental disease and to improve health through comparatively simple dental care in childhood.[4] The insurance dental benefits were enlarged and the scope of the service was expanded. From almost nothing, dental benefit increased until, in 1926, 494 of the funds of the Central Union of German Sickness Funds (with nearly six million members) provided dental treatment *gratis* to members and their family dependents, and only 183 (with one and a quarter million members) continued to provide only dental cash benefits. In an effort to broaden the scope and reduce the costs of dental service, many of the large societies individually (and many in combinations) built and staffed their own dental clinics.[5] Expenditures for dental treatment by all legal sickness funds rose from almost nothing to about $0.24 per insured person in 1914, $0.56 in 1925, $0.90 in 1929, and $0.98 in 1933. The last figure, we have seen in Table 5, is equivalent to $0.75 per insured person and $0.28 per dependent for dental care.

The growth of dental service has been especially rapid in the large cities. In 1925, the General Local Sickness Fund of Hamburg, with an average membership of 340,000, provided dental treatment for 140,000 persons at a cost of $0.89 per member (or about $0.45 per eligible person, including insured persons and dependents); in Munich, with a membership of 219,000, the fund provided treatment for 98,000. The numbers continued to increase until the general declines in membership set in during 1930.

The expenditures made by insurance societies for dental treatments constitute an appreciable fraction of the total income of all dentists. The economic circumstances of dental practitioners are complicated and are not easily compared with those in the United States. In 1929, Germany had about 9,000 "dental physicians" (*Zahnaerzte*, perhaps comparable to American stomatologists), over 17,000 "dentists" (perhaps comparable to our dental surgeons or dentists), and many thousand "dental technicians" who engage not only in strictly mechanical pursuits but also in providing dental care. The bitter competition among these rival groups has added to the confusion of dental economics.

Three facts are prominent in the records of insurance dental service: (1) the number of people receiving treatment and the variety and importance of the treatments have been increasing; (2) the costs have been increasing; and (3) the benefits still provide only a small fraction of adequate dental care and the expenditures are still only 10 to 20 per cent of what would be needed to pay for adequate dentistry for an entire population. Yet these offer no particular indictment of German insurance dental benefit. Even in the United States, where dentistry has been more progressive than in almost any country of the world, and where it has been well publicized and its opportunity for service has become common knowledge, adequate dental service is still comparatively unknown among any but the people of moderate means and those who are wealthy. Everyone more than two years of age needs some dentistry each year;[6] yet in the years 1928–1931, among representative American families[7] only 10.1 per cent of the persons in families with incomes under $1,200 and only 15.5 per cent of those in families with incomes of $1,200 to $2,000 received *any* dental care during the period of a year. It is estimated that adequate dental care, even for the poor, would cost nearly $10 per person in the United States;[8] but the average annual charges (in 1928–1931) incurred for dental care among representative families[9] were vastly less, as appears in Table 6.

The cost of dental care is about the same ($0.90 per person) for the poor in the United States as for the insured persons in Germany in 1929. When allowance is made for the larger purchasing power of an equivalent sum of money in Germany than in the United States,

TABLE 6

ANNUAL DENTAL CHARGES PER PERSON AMONG GROUPS OF REPRESENTATIVE
FAMILIES IN THE UNITED STATES, 1928–1931

POPULATION OF COMMUNITY	FAMILY INCOME	
	Under $1,200	$1,200–$2,000
100,000 or more	$2.20	$2.65
5,000 to 100,000	0.37	2.02
Less than 5,000	0.82	1.61
ALL	$0.90	$2.00

it becomes evident that the poor in Germany fare not so badly with respect to dental service under insurance. These comparisons are valuable in reaching an understanding of German sickness insurance. Insurance medical benefit is too commonly evaluated only against a professional ideal of service; the comparison is too infrequently made with what the insured population might have without insurance or how well the insured fare by comparison with uninsured persons in other countries.

The expansion of hospital benefits has already received comment. It would be futile to attempt a closer analysis, for the subject is vast and complex and holds little promise of serving a useful purpose for our objectives because the German system of public hospitals is quite unlike anything common in the United States.

It will be recalled that drugs and medicines and other medical and surgical supplies are provided by the insurance societies. This type of benefit has been administered liberally—far too liberally is the consensus among nearly all observers. The cost per member increased from $0.39 in 1885 to $1.74 in 1925 and to $2.70 in 1929. An increasing liberality among the societies in providing needed supplies, a growing public demand cultivated by advertising and ballyhoo sponsored by manufacturers and commercial dealers, and an expanding custom among physicians to prescribe rather than to treat, have all contributed. However large a boon this has been to the pharmacies or to the manufacturing pharmacists, it indicates wasteful habits and practices. Yet lest the evil seem to be conditioned upon sickness insurance, it should be remembered that, without the aid of an insurance system, we in the United States spend, in a normal year, over $6 per person for similar medical supplies, and even the poor and those of modest income among us (those in families with incomes of less than $2,000 per year) ordinarily spend out of their own pockets $2 to $3 per person just for drug-store purchases and eye glasses.[10]

The efforts which have been made in recent years by the German sickness insurance authorities to curtail expenditures on medicines have been partially successful. Physicians have been pressed not to issue prescriptions unnecessarily and not to prescribe unnecessarily expensive medicines; insured persons have been advised not to request prescriptions and have been required to pay a share of the cost. Expenditures for medicines have shown the following decline:

Year	Rm. per Insured Person
1928	8.47
1929	9.26
1930	8.18
1931	7.09
1932	5.70
1933	5.62

THE COSTS OF ADMINISTRATION

Finally, before leaving the costs of German sickness insurance, a word may be said about the administration costs. It has long been customary for writers on this subject to refer to the low cost of administration in the German system. It may therefore have come as a surprise that the data in our tables show these costs amount to 10 per cent. This has not always been so; it is a result of the important decline which occurred in recent years in the number of insured persons and in the budgets for benefits without a proportionate decline in administration costs. The cost of administration expressed per insured person was only a little higher in 1933 than in 1928, but amounted to a considerably larger proportion of the total budget and of the contributions. The experience of recent years will be observed in the following figures for all legal (statutory) sickness funds:

Year	Insured Persons	Total Expenditures	Administration Costs		
			Total	Per Insured Person (Rm.)	Per Cent
1928	20,662,000	$444,400,000	$29,500,000	5.99	6.6
1929	20,956,000	478,400,000	31,000,000	6.21	6.5
1930	20,344,000	428,700,000	33,000,000	6.81	7.7
1931	18,998,000	355,000,000	32,100,000	7.09	9.0
1932	17,076,000	253,600,000	26,500,000	6.50	10.4
1933	16,827,000	244,800,000	24,500,000	6.11	10.0

At the present time serious efforts are being made to reduce the costs of administration to the customary level of about 6.5 per cent. These efforts are being assisted by the increases which are being recorded in the number of insured persons.

The personnel engaged in central and other administrative bureaus (for the legal sickness funds) has shown the following changes in the same years for which population and costs are cited above:

Personnel of Administrative Bureaus

Year	Total	Per 1,000 Insured Persons
1928	26,996	1.31
1929	27,996	1.34
1930	29,907	1.47
1931	29,346	1.54
1932	28,620	1.69
1933	28,100	1.67

The total number reached a maximum in 1930, directly after the peak was attained in membership, and then declined. The ratio of bureau personnel to insured persons runs closely parallel to the ratio of administration cost to total cost listed above.

SOME RELATIONS BETWEEN CONTRIBUTIONS, BENEFITS AND COSTS

It has already been noted that from the beginning German sickness insurance required that contributions should be a fixed percentage of the income (wages or salary) of the insured person. Inasmuch as the cash benefit furnished to the insured person when he was incapacitated by illness and was thereby deprived of income was also fixed as a percentage of income, the relation between contributions and this benefit was quantitative and direct. Although there were several alternative methods of defining the basic wage or wage class to which the contribution per cent was to be applied in fixing the absolute amount of contributions, the federal law prescribed that the same definition must be used by a fund in measuring the amount of the benefit. Thus, a 50-per-cent cash sickness benefit was (and is) computed from the same wage as a 5-per-cent contribution. Medical benefits, it will be recalled, were provided by German sickness insurance from the beginning. However, these benefits have always been furnished to the insured person according to his need, not according to the size of his contribution. Hence, the quantitative relation which always existed between the size of contributions and the size of *cash* benefit never obtained so far as medical benefits were concerned. This was not a matter of large concern when medical benefits consumed 10, 15 or 20 per cent of contributions and the insurance system was primarily a system of furnishing *cash* benefit.

The review of sickness insurance costs has shown that there has been a steady trend towards placing more and more emphasis (both absolute and relative) upon the *service* than upon the *cash* benefits. At the same time that the size of the contributions and the size of the benefits have been increasing, the proportion of the total expenditures devoted to the service benefits has also been increasing. We find that medical services now account for approximately 69 per cent of the total budget.* This means that more than two-thirds

---

*Service benefits, as distinguished from cash benefits, attained a peak value of 73 per cent in 1932.

of the benefits are now furnished to insured persons without regard to the size of the contributions they (and their employers) pay. During the past fifty years there has been a progressive and continuous departure in German sickness insurance from an elementary principle of *insurance* toward a basic principle of *social insurance*. The more completely the benefits of sickness insurance become those concerned with the prevention and cure of sickness, the more completely its finances come to be in accord with the principle upon which the physician has customarily given service—to each according to his need, from each according to his means. While this principle applies only in minor measure in other forms of social insurance—such as invalidity, accident, unemployment, old age, survivors', etc.—it is of notable importance in sickness insurance when contributions are a percentage of earnings (and not a fixed sum) and when emphasis is given to the service benefits.

Statistics on Incapacitating Sickness among Insured Persons

Having observed the course of sickness insurance in Germany and its steadily enlarging scope of benefits, it is not surprising to find that costs have been increasing. The mounting costs are in the first instance a reflection of the fact that benefits are larger, are paid for longer periods of time, and are allowed to more persons now than formerly. It is therefore a foregone conclusion that the *recorded* rates of incapacitating sickness among insured persons (i.e., the rates of illnesses which are reported to the insurance societies and for which benefits are received) will be found to be higher in recent than in former years.

It will be noted in Table 7 that the number of recorded cases of incapacitating illness showed practically no change between 1885 and 1913, increased after 1922, reached a peak in 1929, and declined to attain in 1932 the lowest level ever recorded. The average recorded days of incapacity per insured person (Table 8) have shown a similar trend, rising almost steadily to a maximum in 1929 and then declining to a new minimum in 1932. Both of these indices showed

TABLE 7

CASES OF ILLNESS ACCOMPANIED BY INCAPACITY FOR WORK RECORDED AMONG
INSURED MEMBERS OF THE LEGAL SICKNESS FUNDS,* 1885–1933

YEAR	AVERAGE NUMBER OF CASES PER INSURED PERSON		
	Insured Males	Insured Females	Both Sexes
1885	0.423	0.407	0.420
1900	0.402	0.334	0.386
1910	0.413	0.357	0.398
1913	0.441	0.375	0.421
No data available for years 1914–1921			
1922	0.479	0.472	0.477
1923	0.342	0.339	0.341
1924	0.455	0.394	0.432
1925	0.548	0.460	0.524
1926	0.494	0.404	0.461
1927	0.586	0.483	0.549
1928	0.602	0.493	0.562
1929	0.631	0.526	0.593
1930	0.443	0.396	0.426
1931	0.376	0.370	0.374
1932	0.309	0.322	0.314
1933	0.356	0.370	0.361

*Exclusive of the miner's funds in the years prior to 1929.

increases in 1933. The average recorded days of incapacity per illness
(Table 9) have, however, been showing a somewhat different trend;
they increased rather steadily until 1924, then declined somewhat up
to (and including) 1929—when the other indices were reaching their
peak values, increased between 1929 and 1932, and declined again in
1933. Thus, in recent years, this index has in general shown some
tendency toward an inverse trend from that shown by the preceding
ones.[11]

On the average, there is each year one case of incapacitating illness
recorded for each two insured persons. Statistically, this is equivalent
to saying that, on the average, of every two insured persons one is
incapacitated each year (Table 7). The recorded days of incapacity
per member mean that, on the average, the insured persons lost
about one week a year from work in 1885, about two weeks in 1929,

TABLE 8

RECORDED DAYS OF INCAPACITY AMONG INSURED MEMBERS OF THE LEGAL
SICKNESS FUNDS,* 1885–1933

YEAR	AVERAGE NUMBER OF RECORDED DAYS PER INSURED PERSON		
	Insured Males	Insured Females	Both Sexes
1885	5.93	5.71	5.89
1900	6.85	6.71	6.82
1910	7.81	8.53	8.01
1913	8.44	9.15	8.66
No data available for years 1914–1921			
1922	8.70	11.18	9.66
1923	6.35	7.94	6.96
1924	10.67	11.13	10.85
1925	12.31	12.89	12.53
1926	12.26	11.66	12.04
1927	12.99	12.77	12.91
1928	13.78	13.35	13.62
1929	14.32	13.57	14.04
1930	11.73	11.45	11.63
1931	10.57	11.02	10.73
1932	8.85	9.73	9.18
1933	8.64	10.35	9.27

*Exclusive of the miner's funds in the years prior to 1929.

and now lose about one and one-half weeks a year (Table 8.) The average duration of disabling illness increased from two weeks in 1885 to over four weeks in 1932 and is now about three and one-half weeks within the year (Table 9). Women show fewer cases of incapacitating sickness but more days of incapacity than men because their cases are in general of longer duration.

If the data recorded in Tables 7, 8, and 9 are taken at their apparent meaning they are very puzzling because there is no explanation in the general trends of health or sickness in the German population to explain them. We shall see directly that their interpretation requires an understanding of a number of factors. At this point it should be emphasized, however, that the figures which have been cited are not records of the true or complete occurrence or duration of sickness; they are only the count of cases of incapacitating sickness, or of days of

TABLE 9

RECORDED DURATION OF INCAPACITATING ILLNESS AMONG INSURED MEMBERS OF
THE LEGAL SICKNESS FUNDS,* 1885–1933

YEAR	AVERAGE NUMBER OF RECORDED DAYS PER RECORDED INCAPACITATING ILLNESS		
	Insured Males	Insured Females	Both Sexes
1885	14.1	14.1	14.1
1900	17.0	20.1	17.6
1910	18.9	23.9	20.1
1913	19.1	24.4	20.6
No data available for years 1914–1921			
1922	18.1	23.7	20.3
1923	18.6	23.4	20.4
1924	23.5	28.2	25.1
1925	22.5	28.0	24.4
1926	24.1	28.9	25.7
1927	21.5	26.4	23.2
1928	22.9	27.1	24.2
1929	22.7	25.8	23.7
1930	26.5	28.9	27.3
1931	28.1	29.8	28.7
1932	28.6	30.2	29.3
1933	24.2	28.0	25.6

*Exclusive of the miner's funds in the years prior to 1929.

such sickness, occurring among the insured persons and recorded in
respect to the receipt of benefits (medical services and cash).

SIGNIFICANCE OF THE RISE AND FALL IN THE INSURANCE SICKNESS RATES

It is a common practice among some writers on the subject of
national sickness insurance to give emphasis to the large increases
which have occurred under insurance in the demands for medical
care, in the annual number of days of incapacitating sickness per
member, and in the average costs per member. Such practice leads
to serious errors when it is based upon an uncritical comparison of
the statistics of one year with the statistics of another.

Insurance provision for medical benefit started with a very restricted scope and became increasingly more liberal as both contributions and reserves increased. It was therefore inevitable that the requests for medical care, the volume of medical service, and the costs should increase, entirely apart from any question concerning the actual amount of sickness, or the rise or fall of sickness. Judging by American experience (1928–1931) in a typical uninsured population of low income (family income of less than $1,200 per annum), on the average only a little more than 50 per cent of the individuals receive any medical care whatever during a normal year. Inasmuch as many of these people have minor—if not major—illnesses which go without professional attendance, it is no surprise that among insured persons the requests for care and the average number of recorded days of illness increase progressively with increasing opportunity to receive medical care without direct charge for service at the time it is secured. The published statistics on "cases of incapacitating illness" (as in Table 7) are more correctly "cases of incapacitating illness *attended* or *treated*"; the statistics on "days of incapacity" (as in Table 8) are more correctly "days of incapacity *attended and certified for cash benefits*"; and the statistics on "duration of incapacitating illness" (as in Table 9) are more correctly "duration of *cash benefit for incapacitating illness.*" When contributions and financial resources increase and benefits are made more liberal, all of these statistics show inevitable increases so long as the benefits still remain small, inadequate, or restricted.

The statistics of "increasing sickness" under sickness insurance have been widely quoted and have been taken at their face value by some writers on this subject. It is therefore pertinent to quote the following passage[12] from Professor Henry E. Sigerist of Johns Hopkins University:

It has repeatedly been pointed out that the average number of days of sickness has increased enormously since sickness insurance was introduced. While in 1888, one hundred insured were ill on an average of 547 days a year, the number increased in the following way: 1913, 856.6 days; 1924, 1,084.5 days; 1925, 1,250

days a year. This does not mean that the population is less
healthy, or that there is malingering. It is not that the days of
sickness have increased, but the days of treatment. Many illnesses that had gone untreated formerly, today are given medical
treatment in time, preventing fatal consequences. The general
health conditions have undoubtedly improved tremendously,
and this is illustrated by the fact that shortly after a lost war,
famine, revolution, inflation, and all the disturbances of a post-
war period, the German health conditions were just as good as
in the best situated, victorious countries. It is further illustrated
by the fact that the health conditions are better in the highly industrial centers than they are in the rural districts.

The official German statistics which show increasing sickness rates
also require other explanations. The statutory benefit period of 13
weeks (1883–1903) was extended to 26 weeks in 1903. Many funds
voluntarily extended the benefit period (for some benefits) to 39 and
to 52 weeks; other funds voluntarily reduced the waiting period before disability benefits become payable or eliminated this period
entirely. Other things being equal, it was absolutely inevitable that
the number of recorded days of incapacity for which cash sick
benefit was paid would increase, not because there was any more
sickness, but merely because cash benefit would be paid for a larger
part of the period of incapacity in illnesses of long duration. This
point will be explained later. Furthermore, in the same years in
which the cash and medical benefits have become more and more
generous, more severe "risks" have been brought within the scheme.
Women—who have higher sickness rates than men even among
non-insured populations—were added to the insured population in
increasing proportions and later medical benefits were extended to
dependents. In addition, the resources of sickness funds have had
unusually heavy drains in recent years for the care of those who
were injured or partially disabled in the World War and who found
industrial employment after the peace was negotiated. The post-war
collapse of the German currency and the wiping out of the savings
of the middle classes compelled many persons of moderate or

advanced ages to resume employment, and, by increasing the average age of insured persons, contributed to bring increasing loads upon the insurance funds. The declining birth rate has also appreciably increased the average age and the average need for medical care.

The influence of changes in the "benefit period" and in the "waiting period" upon sickness records may be illustrated quantitatively by means of a simple statistical experiment. There has been so much confusion of thought on this subject, especially in recent American writings on health insurance, that the illustration may be of value in clarifying the discussion and may contribute to a better understanding of the German insurance sickness statistics.

We have the records of all recognized illnesses which occurred among some 9,000 representative families in the United States during the years 1928–1931.[10] We proceed to separate the records of gainfully occupied persons from the records of their dependents and to further restrict the gainfully occupied by excluding housewives, farmers, farm laborers, professional persons, merchants, business men, etc., and all persons under 15 or over 64 years of age—leaving a group substantially like those who would be embraced by an industrial insurance fund (clerical workers; salesmen; skilled, semi-skilled and unskilled laborers— 15 to 64 years of age). We then tabulate only disabling (incapacitating) illnesses, taking account of the duration of each illness which caused incapacity for gainful employment.

First: in respect to the average incidence of disabling illness during a year, we obtain the following figures:

Annual Family Income	Disabling Illnesses per Person		
	Males	Females	Both Sexes
Under $1,200	0.35	0.42	0.36
$1,200– 2,000	0.36	0.46	0.37
2,000– 3,000	0.36	0.36	0.36

If these figures are compared with the figures for German sickness insurance in recent years, cited in Table 7, it will be found

that they agree reasonably well and show corresponding variations according to sex.

Second: in respect to the average amount of disability during
a year, we obtain the following:

Annual Family Income	Days of Disability per Person (Both Sexes)
Under $1,200	8.9
$1,200– 2,000	5.7
2,000– 3,000	5.0

If we compare these figures with the data for recent years in
Table 8, we find there is moderately close agreement for those
in families with the smallest incomes (under $1,200). This is
not surprising, because the population covered in Germany sickness insurance is, in general, in the lowest income brackets. In
any event, in our "experimental" American group the persons in
the lowest income bracket have an average *incidence* of disabling
illness and an average *amount* of such illness similar to that recorded in recent years for all insured persons in the legal sickness
funds of Germany.

Third: let us see what will be the effect upon our figures, for
this group of persons, of counting only the average days of disability which occurred during a year but within periods of 13
weeks, 26 weeks or 52 weeks, respectively, after the onset of illness. In other words, we are treating these disabling illnesses as
though they occurred among an insured (instead of among an
uninsured) population with, alternatively, a 13-, a 26-, or a 52-
weeks' benefit period.

"Benefit Period"	Days of Disability per Person (Both Sexes)
Within 13 weeks	6.4
" 26 "	7.4
" 52 "	8.9

Here we see, for our "experimental" group the effect of variations in the "benefit period" upon the average days of disability.
Now, let us carry this experiment a step further by counting only

the days of disabling illness occurring (within each of the three "benefit periods") after 0, 1, 2, 3, 4 or 5 days of disability have elapsed (i.e., allowing for various "waiting periods"). The averages then are as follows:

"Benefit Period"	Days of Disability per Person after the Following "Waiting Periods"					
	0	1	2	3	4	5 (Days)
Within 13 weeks	6.4	6.1	5.7	5.4	5.2	4.9
" 26 "	7.4	7.1	6.8	6.4	6.2	5.9
" 52 "	8.9	8.5	8.2	7.9	7.6	7.3

It will be seen, as was to be expected, that the "recorded" average number of days of disabling illness increases the longer the "benefit period" and the shorter the "waiting period," and *vice versa*. If these figures are compared with those in Table 8, it will also be noted that: (a) for a "benefit period" of 13 weeks and a "waiting period" of 3 days we have for our "experimental" group an annual disability rate of 5.4 days per person and that this is similar to the rates recorded for the German insured persons in the years 1883 to 1903 when the statutory cash benefit was payable from the fourth day and for 13 weeks; (b) for increasing "benefit periods" and decreasing "waiting periods," similar to the extensions which were made by statute or by the voluntary action of the insurance societies in Germany since 1903, the disability rates of the "experimental" group approach those of the insured population for the period 1903–1933.

What has been shown here from an "experimental" American population can also be shown from an actual American population. Since 1921, the United States Public Health Service has been accumulating records on the work of industrial sick-benefit associations through periodic reports furnished by the associations or company relief departments. These records contain data on disability with various combinations of waiting periods, benefit periods, size of benefits, etc. Without going into details, our immediate point may be illustrated by the figures showing the average calendar days of disability from sickness and non-industrial injuries in 1934 among the insured persons in sixteen sick-benefit associations. The figures are restricted to groups in which there is a 7-day waiting period but different benefit periods.[13]

Benefit Period	Days per Person	
	Males	Females
13 weeks	2.59	4.71
26 "	3.07	5.15
52 "	3.91	6.49

The long waiting period (7 days) explains the fact that these figures are lower than those cited above or in preceding tables. The effect of the benefit period is, however, quite evident.

These comparisons need not be pressed too far. They are intended only to illustrate the danger inherent in assuming that changing sickness rates reflect changes in the occurrence of sickness when they apply to years of changing benefit periods. The difference between a recorded and a true sickness rate should again be emphasized and caution urged upon those who have been interpreting the recorded rates of German sickness insurance experience without reference to the benefit periods. Otherwise, it is just as grievous an error to say that all of the increases in recorded sickness rates are to be ascribed to malingering as to say that "among the insured under practically every system the records show a constant increase of morbidity."[14]

It is not intended to deny that increasingly liberal cash benefits during sickness and a rising level of unemployment have contributed to increase the frequency and duration of recorded sickness. There is no question that this is true. Indeed, there appears to be no doubt that as unemployment increases, the incidence of disabling cases declines among insured persons. Inasmuch as this "voluntary" decline occurs principally among mild and short-term ("bagatelle") illnesses, the average recorded duration of illnesses increases. (See Tables 7, 8 and 9.)* But to argue or imply, as has been frequently

*The official summary on this point (*Die Krankenversicherung*, 1932, *Statistik des Deutschen Reichs*, p. 20) is pertinent: "Je grösser der Anteil der Arbeitslosen an der Gesamtzahl der Versicherten ist, desto niedriger ist demnach im allgemeinen die Zahl der Krankheitsfälle."

done, that an increase in the recorded cases of sickness indicates an actual increase in sickness and is therefore an indictment of insurance is absurd. Such argument ignores the real nature of the insurance statistics, the changes which have occurred in the population and in the benefits furnished by insurance, and the enormous incidence of sickness and disability which goes unrecognized or unattended among populations who must count the cost of each individual medical service. *Indeed, one of the most important objectives of an insurance scheme must be the increased recognition of illness and the increased provision of medical attendance. Except for malingering, exaggeration and fraud, substantial increase in the medical service which is furnished should be interpreted in favor of an insurance program, so long as the volume of service remains (as it still does) far below the level of adequate care.*

What needs clear recognition is that *exaggeration of the severity of sickness and of the duration of disability are primarily consequences of providing a cash benefit.* And this brings into sharp relief the issue whether cash and medical benefits should be provided conjointly in a single system of insurance. Or whether it is not wiser and more desirable to treat cash benefit as a feature of unemployment insurance and separate it as completely as possible from insurance for medical care.

In recent years the sickness insurance funds have attempted a partial solution of the difficult problems created by the joint administration of cash and medical benefits through the reorganization of their staffs of "confidential" physicians (*Vertrauensärzte*). Following the Acts of January 14, 1932 (*Verordnung über Kassenärtzliche Versorgung*) and of July 18, 1932 (*Bestimmungen über die Auswahl und das Dienstverhältnis der Vertrauensärzte*) and more recent regulations, these physicians are charged with the responsibilities of making diagnoses and of verifying the diagnoses of insurance doctors. Although verification of the alleged incapacity of an insured person is supposedly a secondary duty, it seems not improbable that this may become one of their main duties. To assure the independence of the confidential physician, he is a whole-time salaried officer, engaged under a contract which remains permanent and binding during his competency to work, and is assured a retirement annuity. He is forbidden to engage in private practice and is expected to work in collaboration with attending physicians. In the large cities he is supplied with special laboratory and institutional facilities to aid him in the observation and examination of patients. (In his present status, the *Vertrauensarzt* may be compared with the Regional Medical Officer in the British insurance system.)

Before turning to a consideration of the changes effected in the sickness insurance practice since the National Socialist revolution, certain broad problems and controversies which deserve attention will be considered. Recent changes are, with only one important exception, outgrowths of preceding trends and experiences.

References and Notes

1. HEALTH INSURANCE, Monograph Three (*revised edition*). New York, Metropolitan Life Insurance Company, 1933; DIE KRANKENVERSICHERUNG, STATISTIK DES DEUTSCHEN REICHS (annual issues); AMTLICHE NACHRICHTEN FÜR REICHSVERSICHERUNG, 1934, No. 12.

2. The figures given in the text ($8.12 and $12.16 per person) are the average charges incurred ($9.25 and $13.17) corrected for the average payment of charges (87.8 and 92.3 per cent, respectively). See THE INCIDENCE OF ILLNESS AND THE RECEIPT AND COSTS OF MEDICAL CARE AMONG REPRESENTATIVE FAMILY GROUPS, by I. S. Falk, Margaret C. Klem and Nathan Sinai. Chicago, The University of Chicago Press, 1933, pp. 146 and 203.

3. See reference cited in preceding note.

4. Simons, A. M. and Sinai, Nathan: THE WAY OF HEALTH INSURANCE. Chicago, The University of Chicago Press, 1932, p. 117.

5. Goldmann, Franz and Grotjahn, Alfred: BENEFITS OF THE GERMAN SICKNESS INSURANCE SYSTEM FROM THE POINT OF VIEW OF SOCIAL HYGIENE. Geneva, 1928, p. 30.

6. THE FUNDAMENTALS OF GOOD MEDICAL CARE, by R. I. Lee and L. W. Jones. Chicago, The University of Chicago Press, 1933, 310 pp.

7. THE INCIDENCE OF ILLNESS AND THE RECEIPT AND COSTS OF MEDICAL CARE AMONG REPRESENTATIVE FAMILY GROUPS, *op. cit.*, p. 101.

8. Falk, I. S., Rorem, C. Rufus and Ring, Martha D.: THE COSTS OF MEDICAL CARE. Chicago, The University of Chicago Press, 1933, p. 150.

9. THE INCIDENCE OF ILLNESS AND THE RECEIPT AND COSTS OF MEDICAL CARE AMONG REPRESENTATIVE FAMILY GROUPS, *op. cit.*, Tables 4 and B–32.

10. THE INCIDENCE OF ILLNESS AND THE RECEIPT AND COSTS OF MEDICAL CARE AMONG REPRESENTATIVE FAMILY GROUPS, *op. cit.*

11. The data shown in Tables 7, 8 and 9 are taken from more detailed tabulations compiled by Goldmann and Grotjahn, *op. cit.*, and from STATISTIK DES DEUTSCHEN REICHS for various years.

12. Sigerist, Henry E.: European Experience in Medical Organization. *Chapter in* THE MEDICAL PROFESSION AND THE PUBLIC. HISTORICAL DEVELOPMENTS. European Experience in Medical Organization. Philadelphia, American Academy of Political and Social Science, 1934, p. 37.

13. Brundage, Dean K.: Disabling Illness among Industrial Employees in 1934 as Compared with Earlier Years. *U. S. Public Health Reports,* November 1, 1935, 1, No. 44, pp. 1527–1539.

14. SICKNESS INSURANCE CATECHISM. Chicago, American Medical Association, 1934, p. 3.

CHAPTER VII

SOME GENERAL COMMENTS ON SICKNESS INSURANCE IN GERMANY

THIS brief description and analysis of Germany's sickness insurance would be incomplete without some comment on the course of administration and on the effectiveness of the system and its benefits. Yet one hesitates to touch upon these questions. Tradition seems almost to decree that whoever writes upon these phases of the subject shall assume the bitter tone of ardent partisanship and focus all attention on petty quarrels. If one doubts that the quarrels are petty—petty by comparison with the contribution of sickness insurance to social, economic, and medical security —let him try to find, in all the writings on the subject, proposals by any substantial group in Germany that sickness insurance be abolished.

Prince Bismarck first gave social insurance to the German people as an antidote to the rising power of the socialist movement. So well did it serve his opponents' as well as his own purposes that not many years later social insurance was embraced by the socialist parties whom it was designed to destroy and was lifted to the dignity of planks in their platforms. Yet from its earliest days the system has been attacked and maligned by those who do not distinguish between principle and practice, between the friction of remediable administrative process and the validity of the main objective. Neither the German State nor the German people have ever seriously contemplated withdrawing from the path of social insurance upon which they were started, perhaps rudely and brusquely, by the Iron Chancellor. By the standards of pragmatic judgment, one must therefore conclude that social insurance, and for our particular purposes, sickness insurance, works, at least to the satisfaction of the people and the state whom it serves. Let us hold fast to this conclusion and, examining some of the principal difficulties in insurance practice, consider them for what they may teach us in conceiving a happier way to security against sickness for the American people. We cannot give any substantial weight to the criticism which is sometimes advanced that German sickness insurance was established as either a "political panacea" or a "political palliative." If it cures or palliates social or economic deficiencies, that is its accomplishment, to be weighed as so much, neither more nor less.

Observers are in general agreement that the German sickness insurance laws and the central administration are very complex. For this there is a simple historical explanation and, perhaps one may say, justification. When first conceived, Bismarck contemplated a system which would absorb the existing insurance societies and provide for the formation of new ones. The State did not intend to contribute to the insurance benefits; the scheme was to be a mutual undertaking between employers and employees which the State was to supervise and regulate. In consequence, the benefits would be only those which the contributions from these two classes could finance.

The State wished to make benefits appear as attractive as possible; but it dared not promise more than the contributors could and would support. The laws were therefore framed on the principle of specifying the minimum benefits which must be furnished and the maximum contributions which may be required. The system had to be framed to cover widely differing conditions among urban and rural communities and to meet the needs of all industrial classes, from the most substantial down to the dependent poor. Flexibility was therefore essential, and *flexibility meant various, diverse, and complex legal provisions.* By retaining the existing insurance societies, by encouraging them to act as direct administrative agencies, and by empowering them to adjust both contributions and benefits to the means and the needs of their constituencies, flexibility and a semblance of autonomy were provided. This is of the essence in the German system. We have seen how these provisions have been utilized.

The central supervision of the insurance societies has been admittedly sound and conservative, if—as is charged—autocratic. During a period of unprecedented growth in membership and in spite of vast extensions of insurance benefits, the societies accumulated large financial reserves—to be sure, only to have them wiped out when the landslide of post-war inflation destroyed the currency and the capital value of fixed-interest investments. In the next decade the societies recovered their vanished reserves, again became solvent, and went forward with the task of administering sickness insurance. Whether or not the societies have been and are useful and necessary is difficult to determine. A long and bitter controversy rages on this question and it is difficult to disentangle *pro* and *con*.

On the one hand, it is alleged the societies have been wasteful and extravagant, have built palatial administration buildings from which to serve poor and needy beneficiaries, have developed a parasitic bureaucracy, and have squandered insurance funds in excessive expenditures for administration. That much of this is an obvious exaggeration is at once evident from the fact that the costs of administration have been limited by law and that the actual figures (cited in the preceding chapter) show the administration costs have generally been about 6.5 per cent and rose to about 10 per cent only in the recent years of severely reduced membership. We shall also see that administration costs are considerably higher in other countries where administrative inefficiency is rarely charged.

On the other hand, an impressive volume of critical writings assures us that the societies have been niggardly and penurious, hounding those who apply for benefits by checking and verifying the validity of claims, driving sharp and pauperizing bargains with physicians, dentists, and hospitals, in order that the annual audits may show impressive balance sheets and the treasuries may pile up surpluses.

Much of what is charged cannot possibly be true, because it is evidently contradicted by official records which have never been challenged and by much else which is also charged. Obviously the answer to the paradox is that criticisms directed against individual societies or particular features of administration have been incontinently exaggerated and generalized.

A vast body of evidence, published and expressed by word of mouth, testifies that some societies have been extravagant, others have been parsimonious, and still others have steered a middle course. Some societies have been efficiently administered, others have been indifferently managed, and still others have perhaps been incompetently directed in the functions with which they have been charged. It is for these (and other) reasons, we have seen, that many of the smaller, weaker, and poorly managed *Kassen* have been forced to accept absorption into the larger and more efficient. Be all this as it may, the *Kassen* are apparently appropriate to the German system, however undesirable they may be in a scheme conceived *de novo* elsewhere. This is evident, in a sense, from the fact that they survived the reorganization to which the entire system of social insurance was subjected in 1933–1934.

Inasmuch as our primary interest lies in the effective provision of medical service, it will repay us to examine briefly the operation of the system with respect to the medical benefits. The administration of these benefits has, from the beginning, been in the hands of the insurance societies. The medical professions were not particularly interested in social legislation and were scarcely consulted when the system was designed. The power to arrange for medical service was placed in the hands of the "lay" officials of the societies and, until 1934, remained with them. Everyone familiar with the attitude of professional people towards "lay control" will recognize that such an arrangement carries within itself the seeds of discord and bitter strife. The circumstances were made still more difficult by the fact that the medical schools did little or nothing to prepare future practitioners for the techniques of insurance practice. The insurance authorities had to assume the burden of educating new graduates in the special requirements of insurance service.

From the outset, the societies contracted with physicians to provide medical service and, of course, some of them sought individual physicians who would accept low rates. These were not always the best practitioners available to serve the insured population. Insurance medical practice was not of high grade and, in some places, fell into disgrace. Long and acrimonious wars have been fought among the societies, the professions, and the insured persons over the questions of "free choice of doctor," "professional freedom from lay control," "adequate professional income," "red tape," "certification for disability," etc., etc. The complete story is beyond the scope of this chapter;[1] but the essentials can be summarized by considering the problems from the points of view of the societies, the insured population, and the professions.

THE INSURANCE SOCIETIES

Subject to legal restraints, the societies have in the past had the sole power to enter into contracts to provide medical care; until 1934 the professions had no authoritative voice in designing the system of medical benefits. In consequence, many bad practices were established by lay administrators, despite the best intentions.

The societies wish to conserve their funds. They have tended to seek inexpensive contracts with physicians, dentists, specialists, hospitals, etc. and to expect large volumes of services from those with whom they made contracts. Thus, there have been opportunities for underpayment and overloading of the professional workers, recruiting of the cheapest rather than the best practitioners, and the provision of poor, hasty and superficial service.

Some of the societies, especially those operating in cities and with membership recruited chiefly from industrial workers, found that their task was simpler and their costs were less if they provided medical benefit through salaried physicians, dentists, nurses, etc., and through owned or contracted hospitals, than if they furnished the benefits through open contracts which permitted insured persons freedom in the choice of doctor and which required remuneration of the doctor on an attendance (fee-for-service) basis. Under open contracts, some societies found that the volume of service became "excessive," the cost exceeded "reasonable" bounds, supervision became "costly" and "difficult" and medical service was of highly variable and indifferent quality. Salaried practice was apparently highly desirable and acceptable to those practitioners who received the appointment; it was bitterly resented by other practitioners. And the war between the societies and the organized professional associations went apace with these practices.

Some societies found that practitioners who provided service under open contracts tended to curry favor with their patients through the liberal issuance of certificates of disability; that practitioners used insurance practice as a means of earning an assured basic income while they were engaged in building up a private practice among non-insured persons, rather than as a means of serving in their professions, and therefore substituted hasty and superficial consultations and the prescription of medicine for careful diagnosis and professional advice; that practitioners were unreasonably tardy or negligent in providing records and in submitting to the administrative supervision essential to orderly and responsible expenditure of society funds. Such societies therefore insisted upon checks and counterchecks upon independent practitioners engaged in insurance practice and, whenever they could, preferred to provide medical benefit through salaried practitioners and through society-owned or governmental institutions.

Many societies contended: that they are merely organizations of wage-earners who have joined together to pool their resources and the contributions of their employers against the contingencies of sickness; that neither the societies nor their constituents are responsible if the attractiveness of insurance medical practice (and the absolute guarantee of payment for service rendered to insured persons) resulted in a rush to the medical schools and an overcrowding

of the professions; that workingmen's societies are under no obligation to provide financial support to more practitioners than are
sufficient to serve the insured persons; and that the societies are
entitled and have the right to provide medical benefits through the
most economical contracts compatible with the delivery of good
medical care.

So runs the argument in the case for the societies in this conflict of
interests.

The Public

Insured persons wished to have their contributions held to a minimum; but having made their contributions, they sought maximum
benefits. All observers are agreed that most of the insured are reasonable in their practices and in their demands; but some make excessive requests for medical service and use all conceivable excuses and
artifices to receive cash benefits when disability, small 'earnings,
approaching unemployment, holidays, or other circumstances make
the cash benefits seem more attractive than the wages of labor. Millions have appreciated the mutual nature of insurance and abided by
the spirit as well as the letter of the insurance contract. But there
have been others, selfish, grasping and intractable, who have abused
their rights to medical benefit by unreasonable demands. Some of
these persons are psychopathic; almost joyfully they embrace the
martyrdom of real or imagined sickness. The existence of this class
in an insurance population calls not for abusive criticism, but for
psychiatric service. A far more vicious practice has taken the form
of using a covert threat of transfer to another physician as a means
of pressing the practitioner for a certificate of disability when the
physician doubts that disability exists or is certain that it does not.
Nevertheless, it must be remembered that those who have abused
the provisions of the insurance system have been but a small fraction of the insured population. On this point, observers are quite
generally agreed.

Employers contribute one-third of the insurance funds. Most of them have been and are convinced of the value of insurance and of the benefits which accrue to industry. Others, considering their insurance contributions as something forced from them by a timorous government to appease socialist movements, have used their influence and cast their votes in the managing committees of the societies for minimum contributions and minimum benefits.

To maintain a proper perspective in evaluating these comments, it should not be forgotten that, with entirely minor exceptions, neither workingmen nor employers would have sickness insurance repealed.

THE MEDICAL PROFESSIONS

The administration of both cash and medical benefits depends upon the medical professions, especially physicians—the one for certification of disability and the other for provision of service. The position of the professions in sickness insurance and their attitude toward its operation has therefore been of the greatest importance.

When sickness insurance was established, the professions had little or no interest in social insurance and took no active part in its design. They had no responsibility in planning the administrative arrangements. In consequence, many unwise provisions were written into the laws and many undesirable practices were established by the societies. Lay management of medical benefits and lay supervision of medical practitioners, designed primarily for financial reasons, are offensive to the professions and, at many points, have interfered with efficient and harmonious functioning of insurance medical practice. The professions have been waging vigorous warfare for belated recognition and to achieve a position of administrative responsibility. They sought the power of an authoritative voice in decisions affecting medical benefits and in controlling the system of medical practice. They have wanted to substitute professional for lay supervision of professional service. They would free the professions from red tape and all non-essential interferences with professional independence.

Physicians, dentists, and other professional groups have decried the tendency of the societies to underpay and pauperize the practitioners. Inadequate remuneration per patient or per service compels a physician to earn his livelihood by undertaking a large volume of work and leads to overwork, and to hasty, superficial, and unscientific practice. When some of the societies placed physicians on salaries, the profession objected that this limited insurance practice to a favored few led to development of a complacent attitude among salaried practitioners, and resulted in lowered standards of practice. The professions contended that the public interest required free competition among practitioners through open contracts under which all licensed members of the profession were equally eligible to insurance practice. They objected not only to salaried practice, but even to payment on a capitation basis (i.e., a fixed annual sum per person who receives care); they demanded payment according to "medical act" (per attendance or fee-for-service). They recognized that the societies have fixed annual sums with which to pay for all medical benefit and that payment according to "medical act" might lead to excessive service and to costs beyond the possibilities of payment. But they contended this was an unwarranted anticipation, in spite of experiences cited by the societies.

The physicians objected to their dual function of providing professional service and of certifying disability (and eligibility to cash benefit). They denounced most vigorously the invidious position which certification thrusts upon them; they decried the pressure toward unethical practices to which certification forces them; they stigmatized the administrative arrangement which prostitutes professional judgment for the financial gain of the patient. They said that the doctor finds himself "becoming more a judge as to fitness to work than a physician to treat and prevent illness."[2] Some representatives of the medical groups proposed that the physician who treats insured persons should not be responsible for certification of disability. They held to the view that the physician who treats a patient for his illness is best fitted to express an *opinion* on disability, but that the final judgment on the award of cash benefit should be certified by salaried officers of the society (lay and medical) and not by the practitioner. This view was not, however, held by all physicians nor even by all their leaders; many (whether more or less than a majority) remained convinced that the treating doctor is most competent to certify as to disability. Others, including Dr. Erwin Liek, one of the severe medical critics of German sickness insurance,[3] and one who is often quoted by opponents of sickness insurance systems, argued that all insurance doctors should be salaried state officials. Dr. Liek and his followers believed that remuneration through annual salaries would free physicians from that uncertainty of income which depends upon the incidence of sickness, from the pecuniary interest in the number of services they render a patient, and therefore from the pressure to issue certificates of disability in order to retain certain patients or to build up a large practice.

Before leaving these comments on professional attitudes, a few additional remarks may be pertinent to an understanding of this conflict of opinion. Germany has about 47,000 physicians, but only about 5 per cent of them engage solely in private practice. Some 15 per cent occupy salaried positions (with government authorities, insurance societies, hospitals, etc.). About 80 per cent or 38,000 to 39,000 physicians earn their incomes partly, largely, or entirely in insurance practice. Though insurance medical benefit is available to about two-thirds of the population, the insured population consists almost entirely of the poor and those of modest means. Despite the extension in income levels made in various successive laws, insurance practice has remained largely a "poor-man's practice" and the remuneration to the practitioners cannot exceed the resources of the insurance funds. The fact that employers contribute one-third of the insurance premiums does not alter the fact that the per-capita resources available for benefits are meager. It is therefore inevitable that a physician who serves only or chiefly insured persons cannot earn a large or even a substantial income unless he serves a very large number of patients.

The *Krankenkassen* have generally limited each insurance physician to 1,000 insured persons or to 1,350 insured persons and dependents. The total expenditure for physicians' services was $4.48 per member in 1929 and $3.55 per member in 1933 (see Table 4). These sums include expenditures for specialist's and similar services. If we assume that $3.00 per member is spent for the services of general practitioners, the *maximum* gross income from insurance practice is about $3,000 per general practitioner. The total expenditure of $98,600,000 in 1929 was actually equivalent to about $2,500 to $2,600 per physician engaged in insurance practice in that year, and the total of $59,800,000 in 1933 to about $1,700 per physician four years later. These figures must at once be qualified by noting again that the insurance practitioners are also private practitioners and earn additional income from their private practice. Although the insured persons and their dependents constitute nearly two-thirds of the total population, the remaining third—among whom the physicians practise on a private-fee basis—are the middle and upper income classes who spend considerably more, per capita, for medical care than those in the insurance levels.

As is the case in the United States, the physicians of Germany are located in excessive proportions in the large cities and in inadequate proportions in rural areas. And, as in the United States,[4] physicians do not all earn average incomes; most of them earn less than the average and the average is brought up by the larger earnings of the few. Recent evidence[5] indicates that with allowance for differences in the overhead costs of practice and in standards of living in the two countries, physicians' incomes are about the same in Germany as in the United States. And in the United States the incomes of a large proportion of all physicians are inadequate.

The inadequacy of professional income is even more discouraging in Germany than in the United States because it bears with unusual weight upon the insurance practitioners; whereas the less-than-average incomes of most physicians in the United States are "compensated" by the greater-than-average incomes of the others, in Germany the less-than-average incomes occur mainly among insurance practitioners whose clientele is largely among the poor, and the greater-than-average incomes occur chiefly among non-insurance practitioners who serve private patients in the higher income classes. In the United States, many physicians who practise chiefly among the poor augment their incomes, more or less, from practice among those who have larger means through a sliding scale of fees. In Germany, with nearly two-thirds of the entire population eligible to medical benefit, and more nearly 80 per cent in the large cities, the insurance practitioners have less opportunity to augment their insurance incomes by more remunerative private practice.

Much that is now insurance medical practice with an absolute guarantee of payment on an accepted schedule of fees was, before the days of insurance (as it still is in non-insurance countries), "free care" furnished by physicians to poor people. This seems often to be forgotten. The fixed periodic payment of insurance contributions enables the poor and those of modest means to spend more for medical care than they customarily spend under a system of private purchase, a fact which is quite generally overlooked.

There is wide difference of opinion on how large and how important a rôle the financial motive plays in the medical profession. None can deny, however, that each physician who is without independent means hopes to earn from his professional labors a decent livelihood, a competency for himself and his family, and to accumulate worldly goods sufficient to guarantee independence and maintenance in his declining years. Financial limitations which are inherent in poorly paid insurance practice for people of small or no means all but banish the physician's hope that he may be much more successful than his colleagues and earn an income larger than the average or several times the average. Insurance practice operated on a small per-capita budget has the levelling characteristics of salaried practice without the attributes of assured and stable income. The principal financial difficulty in earning a reasonable income in German insurance medical practice rests upon a fundamental characteristic of the system: it is a workingman's insurance and the remuneration of the physician is limited by the financial resources of the low income classes to whose means the contributions are adjusted.

SICKNESS INSURANCE VS. HEALTH INSURANCE

It is common practice to use the terms "sickness insurance" and "health insurance" more or less interchangeably. This is sometimes criticized, especially by those who would apply "health insurance" to activities concerned with the prevention rather than the cure of disease. With respect to medical benefits in kind, German sickness insurance operates primarily to provide diagnosis and cure; but these activities cannot be sharply separated from preventive care. All evidence indicates that the provision of medical service to all who are insured and to their dependents has led people to seek medical care early in the course of sickness—earlier than was the practice when medical care had to be purchased on a fee basis—and for lesser ailments. In this fashion "sickness insurance" is also "health insurance," because early diagnosis and the receipt of care for minor ailments are among the most important of preventive measures. The cash benefits also operate as health measures, by furnishing subsistence for the family during the disability of the wage-earner.

More particularly, sickness insurance has in recent years undertaken to an increasing extent the provision of benefits designed to improve both personal and community health; the societies turned their attention to the protection of healthy persons against disease. In the past, the laws specifically permitted the insurance societies to provide health benefits, as follows:[6]

1. Care of convalescents;
2. Measures for the prevention of disfigurement or deformity, with the object of restoring or maintaining capacity for work after treatment has ceased;
3. Measures for the individual protection of members of the sickness fund against disease; and
4. Utilization of the resources of such funds for the prevention of disease by special or general measures.

Especially under the third and fourth of these provisions, the insurance societies extended their activities in the field of health and prevention. Commonly, the benefits were provided through coöperative undertakings with the local officials responsible for public health services by bearing the costs for special care needed in individual cases, by making grants-in-aid to other service organizations, or by giving both financial and moral support to private and public welfare organizations. Special health benefits furnished by the societies have taken many forms: supplementary maternity benefits, infant and child health care, dental service for school children, periodical health examinations of "healthy" adolescents and adults, convalescent and sanatorium care, facilities and maintenance for tuberculous persons, venereal disease service, popular education in sex and in general hygiene, etc.

The extension of insurance benefits to include general health and welfare services is obviously commendable as a social measure and is, of course, sound economy. The principal criticism which might be directed against the societies in respect to health activities is that they have not spent enough in this field. When the sickness funds were able to show an excess of assets over liabilities amounting to $3.28 per member in 1924 and to $4.19 per member in 1925, they were spending only 5 to 6 cents per member towards general health promotion. In 1929, they spent 11 cents per member for public health services. In view of the recent changes in the law, in respect to the rôle of sickness funds in preventive work (see page 136), the following comment made nearly ten years ago by competent and critical authorities (Goldmann and Grotjahn)[7] seems especially pertinent concerning the past:

> It is fully recognized that the sickness funds must always have a cash reserve available to meet their liabilities and also for critical periods, and it may be granted that the sinking of capital in building property is both justifiable and useful, especially where the buildings are directly used for health purposes as in the case of convalescent homes or hydropathic institutions. Yet there is evidence, in these matters, of a somewhat exaggerated idea of the value of the institutional system, which is by no means confined to sickness insurance organizations, but prevails in many

quarters. Public welfare work makes far less demands on the financial resources of contributors, and is at the same time both effective and economical. It should therefore receive greater attention. Subsequent legislation will inevitably have to take this question into consideration; the sickness funds will in fact have to be compelled not to give precedence to the financing of health institutions, sanatoria and other special establishments, but to contribute towards the development and maintenance of efficient welfare centres in the various branches and to give adequate financial support to the organizations engaged in the work of health promotion.

Similar criticisms have been made by many other impartial students of German sickness insurance.[8] In spite of evidence of improvement in this respect, "sickness insurance" in Germany has not been as completely as it might be "health insurance."

RECENT CHANGES

The National Socialist revolution early in 1933 furnished an opportunity for the reorganization of social insurance in Germany. Indeed, the broad preëlection promises of the National Socialist leadership had committed the party to a reorganization on numerous counts. An occasion was thereby afforded to deal with a number of the conflicts and deficiencies to which attention has been directed in this brief review.

From the point of view of the government, there were two major reasons for a thorough reform of social insurance: (1) the economic depression had undermined the financial position of some of the social insurance institutions; and (2) the social-economic structure of the country had been altered in a fundamental way by the dissolution of the employers' and the workers' associations (leading toward the development of the so-called joint "Labor Front"). Reform had a double object: financial reconstruction and administrative reorganization.[9]

A series of laws issued during 1933 effected a number of essential changes. The general lines of administrative arrangement were covered by a number of acts decreed in 1933. The organization of professional personnel and relations to the *Krankenkassen*, the principles of health service administration, etc. were covered by another series of acts issued in the same year. (An Act of December 7, 1933, reformed the invalidity, old-age, and widows' and orphans' insurance.) As economic conditions in Germany then continued to show substantial improvement and unemployment declined, the membership of the social insurance systems increased rapidly and the financial position of the insurance institutions improved. These advances continued in the early part of 1934 and by the middle of the year the government was ready to inaugurate a far-reaching and all-inclusive reorganization of social insurance. This was finally instituted with the Act of July 5, 1934 (*Verordnung zum Aufbau der Sozialversicherung*) and parts have been carried into effect by eight decrees (to date). Many features of the Act are not directly concerned with sickness insurance and others are only of passing interest at this time because these have not yet been decreed in force. We may consider briefly a few which are significant for present purposes.[10]

Administration. 1. Social insurance institutions are integrated and declared to be elements of a single system. The sickness insurance funds are retained, but the substitute funds (*Ersatzkassen*—the hitherto private, mutual aid societies) are brought under the same supervision of government authorities as applies to other types of funds. Consolidation of funds is to continue. (For example, since January 1, 1934, the *Ortskrankenkasse* of Berlin includes what before then had been sixteen *Ortskrankenkassen*.)

2. The variations in contributions and cash benefits which had existed among the funds had been responsible for great confusion and for unnecessary inequalities in the strength of the funds. Segregation of risks had had the consequence that the membership of some funds was made up largely from classes of people with relatively low sickness rates, small numbers of dependents, and substantial salaries, and of other funds from classes with higher sickness

rates, more dependents and smaller wages. The result had been that many insured persons in greatest need of insurance protection and benefits were most feebly protected and received the smallest returns. The new Act provides for the establishment of a pool or equalization fund into which each sickness fund is to pay a fixed percentage of its income and from which it may receive assistance when in need (provided its need does not arise from its own actions).

3. Inasmuch as insurance against invalidity, old age and death for salaried workers and similar groups is centralized in Berlin, the sickness funds are made local agents for this type of insurance.

4. On the other hand, certain functions hitherto exercised by the local sickness funds are now transferred to the invalidity institutions. Chief among these duties from which the sickness funds are released are the ownership and administration of hospitals, sanatoria, convalescent homes and cure establishments and of preventive health and medical services generally. The result will be that instead of having three agencies in Germany operating in these fields: (a) the federal, provincial, and local governments; (b) the sickness insurance funds; and (c) the invalidity, old-age, etc. funds, there will be only two, and these will be closely coördinated. In addition, the contracts under which medical services will be arranged for the sickness funds, the administration and auditing of the reserves of the sickness funds and of the equalization fund are assigned to the invalidity institution. Thus, instead of diverse local, there will be central, negotiation and administration. Many scholars had long been urging these consolidations. (We shall see later that these arrangements are similar to practices which have long existed in Great Britain.)

5. In each sickness insurance fund three important changes are made in administration. (a) The *Leiter* or "leader" principle is applied to the funds; the powers hitherto exercised by the management committee of insured persons and employers are transferred to the "leader" who is to be appointed by the President, certain federal Ministers, provincial governments or others (specified in the Act), according to the type of fund. In each case, the "leader" will be a

permanent government officer, except in the case of the guild (trade) funds where he will be appointed by the guild or in the case of the industrial funds where he will be the head of the factory. (These changes have been only partly effected at this time.) (b) The management committee is replaced by an advisory board which will include equal numbers of insured persons and employers (not less than three nor more than five of each, depending upon the number of insured persons), a doctor and a local government officer. The first two classes of members are to be appointed by the supervising insurance office (not elected by their own colleagues); the doctor will be appointed by the "leader" of the local medical organization, and the local government representative by his office with the approval of the superior office. Thus, for the first time the medical profession is given a voice in the counsels of sickness fund administration. (c) The contract for medical service will no longer be made between each *Krankenkasse* and the individual doctor, but will be negotiated centrally between representatives of the insurance funds and representatives of the medical organization. Payment for services will actually be administered by the medical society. The substitution of uniform central for diverse local negotiation of service contracts is expected to put an end to the acrimonious disputes which have been waged for fifty years between the funds and the professions over the equity of rates of remuneration and will permit the establishment of fee schedules prepared by joint groups, with equal negotiating powers, and equipped with full and reliable knowledge of the financial position of each fund.

Finances and Benefits. In addition to points which have already been cited, the Act of July 5, 1934, and the subsequent decrees provide for two other important financial changes: (1) instead of contributions being charged two-thirds to the insured persons and one-third to their employers, the division is to be equal—one-half to each; and (2) the rate of contributions is, in effect, to be fixed by the higher supervising authorities instead of by the funds with the approval of the authorities. However, neither of these classes of provisions has as yet been decreed in effect. Benefits remain substantially unaltered.

Medical Care. The new law, the decrees, and the regulations have profoundly changed the arrangements under which medical services are furnished. Where hitherto the contract of service had been left to each fund to be negotiated with each doctor, it is now a central contract governed by law and regulation.

Between 1883 and 1911 (when the laws and regulations were codified), and between 1911 and 1933, the position of physicians, dentists and others had been determined by the outcome of numerous and bitter controversies.[1] The two leading professional organizations—the *Deutscher Aerztevereinsbund,* and the *Verband der Aerzte Deutschlands* (the latter better known after its founder as the *Hartmannbund*) — and the numerous smaller ones had fought largely losing battles along the lines of trade-union wars. These associations have been dissolved. Instead, exclusive legal status has been given to the *Krankenkassenaerztliche Vereinigung Deutschlands* (K.V.D.) which is placed under the supervision of the Minister of Labor (decree of August 2, 1933).

The K.V.D. is made responsible for medical services to the insured persons and to the population generally. The K.V.D. formulates regulations which, when approved by the government authorities, specify admission of doctors to membership and exclude from insurance practice those not admitted to membership in the association. The K.V.D. has the responsibility, on the one hand, for the furnishing of medical service, and, on the other hand, for the supervision, remuneration, geographical distribution, and punishment of its members. The insured person has free choice of doctor from among all in the local area who have been admitted to insurance practice. Each *Kasse* pays a lump-sum (according to an agreed percentage of its income or per-capita payment) quarterly to the K.V.D. or its divisional branch. Each physician is remunerated by the K.V.D. according to an agreed fee schedule (in terms of *points*) if the total point-earnings of physicians do not exceed the sum available for distribution among the physicians serving the *Kasse*. If the total earnings exceed the sum available, those physicians whose insurance patients have received the average or less than the average services per case of sickness are paid in full the average remuneration available per point of service rendered; the others are paid *pro rata* according to the ratio between the total point-services rendered by such physicians and the remaining money available.

Membership in the K.V.D. is restricted to physicians who are German citizens with full status; "non-Aryans" are excluded from the membership lists of the K.V.D. Admissions to the register of insurance physicians are limited to a maximum of one physician per 600 insured persons, not counting dependents (equivalent in 1934–1935 to a maximum of approximately one physician per 1,100 persons).[10c]

By a decree of December 13, 1935 (*Reichsärzteordnung*, effective April 1, 1936), the K.V.D. becomes an adjunct of the *Reichsärztekammer* (State Physicians' Chamber). This decree also lays down rules concerning who may practise medicine, relations with sickness insurance, etc.

Thus, except for the introduction of the "leader" in the administration of both the funds and the medical societies, the principal changes made in administration of sickness insurance may be said to have been foreshadowed by preceding events and to be outgrowths of trends and necessities more or less clearly defined before January 30, 1933, when the National Socialists came into power. The operation of the new arrangements will be watched with great interest.

Only a brief review of German sickness insurance has been attempted here. Some phases of the subject have been presented in greater detail than will appear in succeeding chapters dealing with the systems practised in other countries. This procedure has been followed only out of reasons of priority. Much that has been set down in this and in the preceding chapters on objectives, intentions, arguments for and against specific procedures, etc. would apply, in greater or lesser measure, in the succeeding pages devoted to insurance in other countries. In the interest of brevity, these details will not be repeated. Instead, emphasis will be laid upon those characteristics of other systems which are peculiar or unique to them.

REFERENCES AND NOTES

1. A review may be found in THE WAY OF HEALTH INSURANCE, by A. M. Simons and Nathan Sinai. Chicago, The University of Chicago Press, 1932, 250 pp.

2. MEDICAL EDUCATION AND RELATED PROBLEMS IN EUROPE. New Haven, Commission on Medical Education, 1930, 200 pp.

3. Liek, Erwin: DIE SCHADEN DER SOZIALEN VERSICHERUNG UND WEGE ZUR BESSERUNG. Munich, 1928.

4. Falk, I. S., Rorem, C. Rufus and Ring, Martha D.: THE COSTS OF MEDICAL CARE. Chicago, The University of Chicago Press, 1933, 648 pp.

5. THE WAY OF HEALTH INSURANCE, op. cit., p. 83 et seq.

6. Goldmann, Franz and Grotjahn, Alfred: BENEFITS OF THE GERMAN SICKNESS INSURANCE SYSTEM FROM THE POINT OF VIEW OF SOCIAL HYGIENE. Geneva, 1928, p. 67.

7. BENEFITS OF THE GERMAN SICKNESS INSURANCE SYSTEM FROM THE POINT OF VIEW OF SOCIAL HYGIENE, op. cit., p. 161.

8. Newsholme, Sir Arthur: INTERNATIONAL STUDIES ON THE RELATION BETWEEN THE PRIVATE AND OFFICIAL PRACTICE OF MEDICINE, op. cit., Volume I, Chapter V (see page 70).

9. SOCIAL INSURANCE IN 1934 (Year-Book, 1934–1935). Geneva, International Labour Office, 1935, p. 225.

10. A brief review appears in the paper, Recent Changes in German Health Insurance under the Hitler Government, by Michael M. Davis and Gertrud Kroeger. New England Journal of Medicine, May 30, 1935, ccxii, pp. 1037–1042.
    A concise summary is available in German, complete to the middle of 1935: GRUNDRISS DER REICHSVERSICHERUNG, by Lutz Richter. Berlin, 1935, 100 pp.; or, more briefly, in Die Neuordnung der deutschen Sozialversicherung (three papers), by Karl Haedenkamp. Münchener medizinische Wochenschrift, 1935, pp. 100, 341 and 824. For more detailed information, the following may be cited:
    a. DAS NEUE DEUTSCHE SOZIALVERSICHERUNGSRECHT, by Alexander Grünewald and Wilhelm Kilian (loose-leaf, up-to-date). Berlin, 1935.
    b. DIE GESETZGEBUNG ÜBER DEN SOZIALVERSICHERUNG, by Krohn, Zschimmer, Eckert, Knoll, Sauerborn and Dobbernack (loose-leaf, up-to-date). Berlin, 1935.
    c. DAS NEUE KASSENARZTRECHT, by Wilhelm Sonnenberg, Leipzig, 1933, 1935 (2nd ed.), 356 pp.
    d. Zulassungsordnung vom 17. Mai 1934, Kassenärztliche Vereinigung Deutschlands.

CHAPTER VIII

A DESCRIPTION OF COMPULSORY HEALTH
INSURANCE IN GREAT BRITAIN*

The Insured Population

THE British system of health insurance came into being through the National Insurance Act, 1911, which became effective in 1912. The original Act applied to workers employed under a contract of service, covering all manual workers and those non-manual workers who earn not more than £160 ($779)[14] a year. The system applies to both male and female workers of the ages sixteen and over. Such persons are employed contributors. The income limit for non-manual workers has since been extended to £250 ($1,217) to allow for the diminished purchasing power of the currency which occurred during the war and the post-war years.†

The number of insured persons in Great Britain was approximately 14,000,000 in the early years after establishment of the system. At the beginning of 1935, more than twenty years later, the numbers were as follows:

	Men	Women	Both
England	10,267,000	5,254,000	15,521,000
Wales	723,600	213,400	937,000
Scotland	1,264,300	637,900	1,902,200
TOTAL	12,254,900	6,105,300	18,360,200

The insured persons constitute about 40 per cent of the entire population and about 80 per cent of the gainfully occupied persons. The range of occupations covered by the scheme is very nearly the same now as it was at the beginning; the insurance system covers

*For more detailed analyses than space permits here, the first thirteen references cited at the end of this chapter should be consulted.

†When the income limit was raised, the rates of contributions and of cash benefits and the physician's capitation fees (see page 156) were also increased.

all occupations in which there is a contract of service or apprentice-ship, except those covered by special insurance schemes (e.g., civil servants and railway clerks) and except the non-manual workers earning more than £250 a year; it embraces those engaged in in-dustrial occupations, transport, agriculture, and domestic service—both wage-earners and salaried workers. Any person who has been an employed contributor for two years or more and who ceases to be one (by reason of employment in an excepted or an exempted occu-pation, or for certain other reasons) may continue in insurance as a voluntary contributor. This class of insured persons has never become large; there were 565,000 voluntary contributors at the end of 1934. Voluntary insurance remains an insignificant aspect of the national system, although there has been some increase in recent years in the number who are voluntarily insured as a consequence of the attrac-tive pensions scheme established by an Act of 1925, and because pensions and health insurance are coëxtensive.

In the following pages, for reasons of convenience, description and analysis are confined largely to England and Wales. National health insurance in Scotland differs only in minor details except for the special provisions which apply under the Highlands and Islands (Medical Service) Fund and which are coördinated with the health insurance agreements in these areas. In England and Wales the cen-tral authority resides with the Ministry of Health; in Scotland, with the Department of Health for Scotland.

CONTRIBUTIONS

The Act of 1924 fixed the weekly contributions as follows:

Contributor	Insured Male	Insured Female
Employer	9 cents	9 cents
Employee	9 cents	8 cents
Government	(a) 1/7th of the cost of benefits and of local adminis-tration	1/5th of the cost of benefits and of local administra-tion
	(b) The entire cost of central administration	

Apart from certain negligible exceptions in respect to persons earning very low wages, the contributions of insured persons and their employers do not vary with wages, are independent of the age of the insured and, as will be noted, differ only little according to sex. No contributions are required for any week in which the insured person is incapable of work by reason of disability. None is payable by the employed or voluntary contributor after he attains the age of 65 years, for at this age he ceases to be entitled to sickness and disablement (cash) benefits and becomes eligible to his old-age (contributory) pension. He remains an insured person, however, entitled to receive medical benefit until he dies. If he remains employed, his employer must pay the employer's usual contributions. Whether or not he continues in employment, the regular allotment is made by the central authorities for his medical care to the fund from which physicians and pharmacists are remunerated.*

The employer is responsible for the payment of contributions, both his own and the employee's, being empowered under the law to deduct the employee's contribution from his wages.[15] The employer makes the contribution by purchasing special stamps from the Post Office and affixing them to the insurance card of the employee. At the end of each six months, the employee delivers the card to his Approved Society, whence it is sent to the Ministry of Health. There,

---

*By the recently passed Act of 1935, an important extension of benefits is made for insured persons in arrears on account of unemployment. "On ceasing to be insurably employed all insured persons are to have a free insurance period on an average of 21 months. During this period insured persons are to be protected for all pensions purposes and entitled to all health insurance benefits—medical, sickness and disablement, maternity, and additional benefits. If at the end of the free period an insured person who has been continuously insured for ten years, up to the date when he ceased work, proves that throughout the period he (or she) has been unable to obtain insurable work his insurance will be extended so long as unemployment continues to be proved year by year. . . . He will not be entitled to sickness and disablement benefit, but he can regain title to these benefits at the full rates if he again obtains insurable employment, although of course not immediately.

". . . Insurance doctors, especially those in the depressed areas, will thus have restored to their lists many of the insured persons removed under the 1932 axe. As from July, 1934, all arrears due to proved unemployment are to be excused in full; half the cost will be met by a levy on each contribution paid by members of approved societies and the other half by an annual Exchequer grant." (*Lancet*, August 17, 1935, p. 397.)

the number of stamps is counted and appropriate credits are assigned to each Approved Society according to the contributions received for its members. The Post Office periodically transfers to the national insurance fund the total sums received from the sale of stamps. Employers make no contributions for voluntarily insured persons; these persons pay the contributions usually paid by both employers and employees.

BENEFITS

Benefits are of two kinds: (a) cash, and (b) medical care, including prescribed medicines and certain appliances.

Cash *sickness* benefits become payable only if disability lasts more than three days. Beginning with the fourth day of disability,* this benefit amounts to 15s. ($3.65) per week for men, 12s. ($2.92) per week for unmarried women, and 10s. ($2.43) per week for married women, for a period not exceeding twenty-six weeks. If disability continues for a longer period, the insured person becomes eligible to a weekly *disablement* benefit equal to one-half of the sickness benefit.[16] The disablement benefit continues until the insured person recovers capacity to work, or dies, or (attaining the age 65) becomes eligible for an old-age pension. The insured person is not eligible to receive cash benefit until he has paid contributions for at least six months and he is entitled only to a reduced benefit in the succeeding eighteen months; he is not eligible to receive the cash disablement benefit until he has made contributions for two years. Cash benefits may be reduced if the contributions of the insured person are in arrears.† (We shall see later that the Approved Societies furnish small additional sums to augment these statutory benefit sums.) *Maternity* cash benefit is payable after forty-two weeks of membership, and amounts to a lump-sum of 80s. ($19.47) if both husband and wife or if the wife alone is an employed contributor, and to

---

*The three-day waiting period applies only to a first illness; there is no waiting period for a subsequent illness occurring within twelve months of recovery from the preceding illness.

†See the footnote on page 143.

40s. ($9.73) if the husband alone is insured or the woman is insured but unmarried.

Medical benefit which is guaranteed to all insured persons includes all necessary care such as can be provided by the average general practitioner, in his office and in the patient's home, and such drugs and appliances (the latter specified in a list approved by the Ministry of Health) as the physician considers necessary. There is no waiting period and no time limitation for medical benefit; the insured person is eligible to receive care when needed from the first until the last day of insurance. The services of specialists are not provided as statutory benefits. The provision of such medical service as is ordinarily considered to be beyond the attainments of the general practitioner remains a matter of private arrangement between the physician and his patient. To clarify the distinction between general and specialist service, we may quote a few of the regulations:[17]

> 1. The treatment which a practitioner is required to give to his patients comprises all proper and necessary medical services other than those involving the application of special skill and experience of a degree or kind which general practitioners as a class cannot reasonably be expected to possess . . .
> 2. In the case of emergency the practitioner is required to render whatever services are, having regard to the circumstances, in the best interest of the patient.
> 3. . . . the treatment which a practitioner is required to give does not include treatment in respect of a confinement.*
> 4. In determining whether a particular service is a service involving the application of such special skill and experience as aforesaid, regard is to be had to the question whether services of the kind are or are not usually undertaken by general practitioners practicing in the area in which the question arose.
> 5. When the service has been rendered by the practitioner it shall be deemed to be a service not involving the application of special skill and experience as aforesaid, unless he proves either,

---

*"Treatment in respect of a confinement" is defined in the regulations as "attendance in labour resulting in the issue of a living child, or attendance after twenty-eight weeks of pregnancy resulting in the issue of a child whether alive or dead, or attendance within ten days after labour in respect of any condition resulting therefrom."

a. That he has held hospital or other appointments affording special opportunities for acquiring special skill and experience of the kind required for the performance of the service rendered, and has had actual recent practice in performing the service rendered or services of a similar character, or

b. That he has had special academic or postgraduate study of a subject which comprises the service rendered, and has had actual recent practice as aforesaid, or

c. That he is generally recognized by other practitioners in the area as having special proficiency and experience in a subject which comprises the service rendered.

The general intent of the provision is clear, though obviously there is room for differences of opinion in the application of the principles to specific cases. The regulations further prescribe procedures whereby the physician advises the patient on the need for special services and the circumstances under which the services are provided through a private fee agreement with the general practitioner or by reference to another physician or a hospital.

Medical benefit is furnished to all employed contributors and to all voluntary contributors except those who earn more than £250 ($1,217) a year. (The contributions of voluntary contributors who are not eligible to medical benefit are therefore reduced by six cents a week.)

The provision of additional medical benefits is restricted by statute. For a time, the regulations permitted the extension of medical benefits to members of the insured person's family; but this privilege was never utilized and the legal permission has been revoked. When financial circumstances permit, certain "additional benefits" may be supplied to insured persons. These additional benefits commonly take the form of increased cash (sickness and disablement) benefits, of dental and ophthalmic treatment (cash) benefits, and sometimes of special grants of funds to meet the cost of hospital or other institutional treatment.

General Plan of Administration

Before examining in more detail the administration of the benefits, we may consider briefly the general arrangements under which the British insurance system operates.

The administrative machinery of the British system is in many respects unique. This arises out of the fact that when the plan was first adopted in 1911, approximately one-third of the working population was enrolled in the "friendly societies," the "benefit associations" of trade unions, and various insurance agencies which provided sickness, funeral, and other benefits for industrial workers. These associations played an important part in the inception of the National Insurance System by establishing subsidiary organizations which, when approved by the Government, became "Approved Societies." Among the conditions of approval were the requirements that the society should not be operated for profit, and that its constitution should leave complete control of the affairs of the society in the hands of its insured members. An unexpected development was the fact that the large commercial insurance companies organized Approved Societies which presumably met these requirements.

There are about 800 Approved Societies with some 6,000 branches or administrative units in England and Wales. Their memberships range from less than 100 to over 2,000,000. To these Approved Societies is entrusted, subject to the supervision of the Minister of Health, the task of enrolling members and the duty of administering the statutory cash benefits and such additional benefits as the financial position of the societies permits them to give. In these respects the Approved Societies are analogous to the *Krankenkassen* of German sickness insurance. They are unlike the German insurance societies in several important respects: they are not organized on a territorial or regional basis (as are the principal *Krankenkassen*); they do not administer the medical benefits; they are not controlled jointly by employers and insured contributors, but by the latter only; and persons who are required by law to insure are not compelled in England, as they are in Germany, to become members of a society.

The difference between the rôle of the *Krankenkasse* in Germany and of the Approved Society in England in the administration of medical benefit is especially important. Medical benefit in England is controlled not by the Approved Societies but by Insurance Committees, one in each county or county borough. A majority of the members in each Insurance Committee are elected representatives of the insured persons; minorities include representatives of the local doctors and members appointed by the Local County Council and the Ministry of Health. One of the members appointed by the county council must be a doctor and, unless the Committee has less than twenty-five members, one of those appointed by the Minister of Health must be a doctor. Thus, while German insurance physicians were given formal representation on the advisory committees of the *Krankenkassen* for the first time in 1934, the British insurance physicians have been represented on the committees which manage medical benefit since the inauguration of the British system.

The Insurance Committee of London, for example, consists of forty members, as follows:

24 (three-fifths) being representatives of the insured persons, appointed by the Approved Societies;

8 (one-fifth) being representatives of the Local County Council (these may be physicians);

8 (one-fifth) being appointed as follows: five by the Minister of Health (at least one must be a physician); two (medical practitioners) by the local Panel Committee; and one (a medical practitioner) by the Local County Council.

The Panel Committee is elected by the local insurance practitioners; the members are all physicians. The Pharmaceutical Committee is the corresponding body elected by and representing the local insurance chemists (pharmacists). These two committees are statutory bodies, and are independent of the Insurance Committee, serving in local negotiations and adjudications. (The Local Medical Committee is an optional body, and—if set up—represents *all* the physicians, whether insurance practitioners or not, who reside in the local area. In nearly all insurance areas the Minister of Health has recognized the local Panel Committee as the Local Medical Committee.)

An Insurance Committee must, under the Regulations, create a Finance Sub-Committee, a Medical Service Sub-Committee and a Pharmaceutical Sub-Committee. In addition, it may create such other sub-committees as are desirable. The London Insurance Committee, for example, has in addition to the Finance and General Purpose Committee and the Medical Benefits Committee, a Medical Service Sub-Committee (consisting of equal numbers of physicians and lay-men, with a neutral chairman) to hear complaints from patients against physicians, a corresponding committee for pharmacists and laymen, committees to hear both physicians and pharmacists, etc.

The separation of function between the Approved Societies and the Insurance Committees was not part of the original insurance plan proposed to Parliament by Lloyd George. It came in response to the demand of the medical profession that medical benefit should not be administered by the Approved Societies. The Insurance Committees, on which the physicians are represented, were created *ad hoc*. It was intended, when they were created, that these Committees should administer insurance medical benefit and should perform additional functions, that they should carry on an effective propaganda of health education among the insured persons and constantly stimulate the local public health authorities to vigorous programs in preventive medicine. In practice, however, the Insurance Committees have not been granted funds by the Ministry of Health for preventive purposes and have done practically nothing except administer their routine insurance functions. (We shall see later that the Royal Commission on National Health Insurance recommended that the Insurance Committees be abolished and their functions transferred to the local public health authorities.)

Inasmuch as the British system did not intend to compel insured persons to become members of Approved Societies or to compel

Approved Societies to accept all applicants, a third administrative unit was organized, the Deposit Contributor's Fund, operating on a savings bank principle. Insured persons who are not affiliated with Approved Societies and their employers make contributions to this Fund. (The number of deposit contributors has always been small; in 1934–1935 there were 244,000 in England and Wales.)

Finally, there is a central administrative authority, the Minister of Health, who supervises the operation of the entire organization in England and Wales. (This function is served in Scotland by the Department of Health for Scotland.) In addition to the central offices and authorities, the Ministry of Health operates the Regional Medical Staff whose services are of the highest importance in the supervision of both cash and medical benefits. The Staff was created in 1920 (one year after the Ministry of Health was constituted by the union of the National Health Insurance Commission of England and the Local Government Board). The Regional Medical Officers are whole-time, salaried physicians, all of whom have had considerable experience in the general practice of medicine as insurance and non-insurance practitioners. There are now about eighty officers, operating from regional offices. The Regional Medical Officer is available to examine an insured person who has received a certificate of incapacity from his insurance physician and whose incapacity is questioned or doubted by the Approved Society (these are known as "incapacity references"). The Regional Medical Officer is also available to examine an insured person, the termination of whose incapacitating illness the Approved Society considers may be hastened by a second medical opinion on diagnosis and treatment to supplement that of the patient's insurance doctor (these are known as "consultation references"). In addition, references to the Regional Medical Officer may—and, to a larger extent than formerly, do—initiate with the treating physicians who desire the benefit of consultations on questions of incapacity or treatment.*

*Consultation references originating with the treating physicians are apparently more common in Scotland than in England. It is reported by authorities in Scot-

(Continued on page 151)

When a case is referred to the Regional Medical Officer by an Approved Society, both the treating physician and the patient are advised of the time and place of the examination and both are invited to attend. The Regional Medical Officer has available an abstract of the patient's history, furnished by the physician. The findings from the examination are reported to both the Approved Society and the physician.

In addition to these responsibilities, the Regional Medical Officers periodically visit all insurance practitioners and inspect the records which they are required to keep concerning their insurance patients,* and also are charged with keeping the records and making inquiries concerning the frequency with which individual practitioners prescribe medicines or specify expensive medicines in the prescriptions which they issue.

Thus, in effect, the salaried doctors of the Regional Medical Staff are an intermediate administrative agency between the insurance practitioners and the Ministry of Health, the Approved Societies and the Insurance Committees. Broadly considered, their duties are of two kinds: to check abuses (unjustified issuance of certificates of incapacity, and excessive prescribing), and to supervise and improve the quality of medical care furnished the insured persons. Both official records and personal inquiries give ample evidence that the Regional Medical Officers serve both functions tactfully and effectively. In no small measure is the efficiency of the insurance medical service due to the work of this staff. (In Chapter X will appear some data concerning the work of the staff.) The success of the Regional Medical Officer has led to the creation of the Regional Dental Staff serving corresponding functions in respect to dental care.

The administrative and financial complexity of the British system arises out of peculiar circumstances. *First,* there was the admission

land, where the relations between the Regional Medical Officers and the insurance doctors are perhaps more intimate than in England, that such references occur in about 5 per cent of all incapacitating illnesses among the insured persons of Scotland.

*These records are kept on standard forms furnished by the Insurance Committee. When the patient changes his doctor or moves to another area, these records are transferred to the new doctor.

into the scheme of the Approved Societies, created largely from the existing and influential "friendly societies," trade unions, and collective societies. *Second,* there was the necessity of creating the independent Insurance Committees to administer the medical benefits. This led to the establishment of two sets of administrative bodies— one (the Insurance Committees) being organized on a territorial basis and the other (the Approved Societies) operating without regard to specific geographical relations. As a result, the insured persons are subject to a multiple system of registration. In fact, there are four registrations: one maintained by each Society in respect to members; two maintained by each Insurance Committee—one in Approved Society order and another in doctor order; and the Central Index Register of the Ministry of Health, primarily designed to prevent undue inflation of the local registers. *Third,* provision had to be made for the transfer of reserve values from one Society to another when an insured person changes his membership. *Fourth,* independence and flexibility were retained through the creation of the Deposit Contributor's Fund. *Fifth,* actuarial complexity was added by the organization of part of the system on the principle of "capitalization" (accumulation of funds) instead of "distribution of costs" (assessment). A few words will explain the last point.

In a system of insurance based on the simple "distribution of costs," the "account" of each individual or, more particularly, of the entire group of insured individuals is nominally opened at the beginning and is closed at the end of the fiscal year, when there should be neither credit nor debit balances. If the insured risks change, the premiums (i.e., the contributions) are changed for the next fiscal year; if surplus accumulates in one year, premiums can be reduced or additional benefits added the next; if a deficit remains in one year, premiums can be increased or benefits reduced the next. There is no capital unless a surplus accumulates and there is no reserve except that which is accumulated to reduce such fluctuations in contributions as would be required to meet the consequences of epidemics or other unusual changes in the insured risk. The estimate of the insured risk (the incidence of sickness, disability, etc.) is adjustable from one fiscal period to the next and the contributions can be varied to balance the cost of the benefits.

In a system based on "capitalization," the "account" is opened for the insured individual or for the insured group when the institution begins to operate and, though periodically audited, is never closed. Deposits are interest-bearing and premiums are fixed. If the insured risk is less in the early years of life than in the later years (as is the case with sickness and disability insurance just as with life insurance), the fixed premium is first in excess of disbursements and later is deficient. Hence, at the end of each year there are credit balances carried forward to the next year as actuarial reserves from the ages of low risk to the ages of high risk.[18] Under the "capitalization" system, the insurance premium for each contributor was computed on the assumption that he becomes insured at age sixteen. The cash reserves, accumulated by his premiums in the early years of his insurance against the greater risk of the later years, are then transferable from one Approved Society to another if the insured person changes his membership. This is the specific reason for the adoption of the "capitalization" system in British Health Insurance.*

Great Britain adopted the "capitalization" principle because the national health insurance program took over the system under which the "friendly societies" and other insurance carriers had long practised. In consequence, there has developed a complex and cumbersome financial structure. Procedure has, however, become sufficiently standardized so that in practice the system is not nearly so complex as in concept. Fortunately, it is possible to separate the costs of the medical benefits from the other items in the balance sheets because the cost of medical benefit is a first charge on the insurance funds and its finances are administered on the "distribution" plan, despite the fact that benefits are "capitalized." Each year the central admin-

---

*The reserves which had to be established when the insurance system was created were set up as credits by Parliamentary grant. This indebtedness is being gradually liquidated out of current budgets. Hence, it should later be possible for the contributions to support larger benefits than at present after this liquidation is completed.

istration sets up certain "funds" from which the costs of medical benefit are to be defrayed in the succeeding year. Except for certain contingency items and for occasions when the bases of the computations are changed, these "funds" constitute the actual amounts to be distributed among those who furnish medical service. For example, the "doctors' fund" equals a fixed per-capita fee to be paid to the doctors multiplied by the estimated total number of insured persons. Inasmuch as the per-capita fee is not changed from year to year, the physician's remuneration varies only with the number of persons whom he serves. And having a first call on the funds of the insurance system, he is not financially concerned with the fluctuations which occur in the income or expenditures of the system.

ADMINISTRATION OF THE MEDICAL BENEFITS

The organization of the insurance medical administration is peculiar to Great Britain. The law provides that every licensed practitioner who elects to do so may practise under the system by having his name entered on the list of physicians (the panel) who agree to give medical service to insured persons under the regulations. Correspondingly, the patient has a free choice of physician from among those on the local list or panel. The physician may refuse to accept any patient or may withdraw from the panel after due notice; and the patient may change his physician. The insurance doctors of each area are collectively responsible for the treatment of all insured persons in the area. Although these provisions in British health insurance were not contained in the original program of the government, they were introduced into the system at the outset *upon the insistence of the medical profession.*

It is an unusually serious reflection upon the reliability of American writings on this subject, particularly in professional journals, that the "panel" system is often cited as illustrative of procedures which were forced upon the British physicians. Yet, in point of fact, observers are generally agreed that it is probably owing to these very elements in the scheme, introduced to meet the insistent demands of the profession, that insurance medical benefit has been furnished with less friction in Great Britain than in any other equally large insurance scheme and that the satisfaction of doctors with insurance practice is probably greater in Great Britain than in any other large insurance country.[19]

Insurance medical practice is conducted under regulations formulated by the Ministry of Health after consultation with representatives of the medical profession. The regulations apply uniformly to all of England and Wales.

Inasmuch as medical benefit is administered by the local Insurance Committees, the insurance practitioners receive their remuneration from these Committees, not from the Approved Societies. *The insurance practitioners have no direct relations with the Approved Societies.* The law leaves wide latitude to the physicians in the choice of the method of their remuneration. The Central Practitioners' Fund, representing the total amount of money available for the payment of doctors, is allocated each year to the various counties and county boroughs, *pro rata* according to the number of insured persons. In each area the insurance doctors may, with the concurrence of the local Insurance Committee, choose how the money allocated to them shall be distributed. The medical benefit regulations[20] give them the following choice:

"(a) A capitation system, that is to say, payment by reference to the number of insured persons included in the practitioner's list.

"(b) An attendance system, that is to say, payment by reference to the attendances given and services rendered by a practitioner to insured persons.

"(c) A combined system, that is to say, payment by capitation except in respect of special classes of service for which payment is made by reference to the services actually rendered.

"(d) Such other combination or modification of the above-mentioned systems, or any of them, as the Minister may approve."

It is highly significant that, with this choice available to them, the insurance doctors have elected remuneration on a capitation basis [system (a) above]; of the areas which chose the attendance basis [system (b) above] only two retained this choice until 1927 and these discarded it in favor of capitation. It was found that remuneration at a fixed annual fee per person under the doctor's care involved the least "red tape" and operated most equably among the insurance doctors. The capitation fee was fixed in 1923 at 9s. ($2.19) and this remained unaltered until October, 1931, when insurance doctors, in common with many persons paid from public funds, voluntarily accepted a temporary 10 per cent reduction in the interests of national economy during a period of emergency. In 1934, when the national budget showed a substantial surplus, one-half of the reduction was restored (as from July 1, 1934); now the remaining half has been restored (as from July 1, 1935).

It may be emphasized that the "panel" system is merely a system of arranging a local list or "panel" of doctors upon which every legally qualified doctor is entitled to have his name placed; the capitation method of paying doctors is (as explained above) merely one of several procedures which may be combined with the "panel" system and is no necessary part of the "panel" system. This point is emphasized because there appears to be some misunderstanding on these relations.

The Central Mileage Fund is allocated to insurance doctors, according to proportionate local needs, by the Medical Distribution Committee which consists of representatives of insurance doctors, Insurance Committees, and the Ministry of Health. Certain subsidiary funds are used for special grants to physicians whose practice involves unusual expenses or to defray the cost of desirable postgraduate study. Physicians who practise in rural areas where no pharmacist is available receive an additional annual fee of 2s. 3d. ($0.55) per person to defray the costs of medicines and appliances which they furnish their patients; other physicians receive 1s. 3d. ($0.30) per 100 persons for medicines used in the course of ordinary practice. Special payments are made for unusually expensive materials (sera, vaccines, etc.) required for the effective treatment of patients.

A practitioner working alone may not accept more than 2,500 insured persons, but if he employs a permanent assistant he is permitted to accept up to 4,000. In 1931, 15,760 physicians in England and Wales (45 per cent of all licensed practitioners) were insurance practitioners. This number increased to 16,430 on April 1, 1935. In 1930 the average number of insured persons on a physician's list was 979; in 1932 it was 954; in 1933 it was almost exactly 1,000, and in the fiscal year 1934–1935 it was 968. The average income *from insurance practice* was £458 ($2,230) per insurance doctor in 1930; in 1933 it was almost exactly 10 per cent less—the amount of the economy reduction; in 1934 it was £424 ($2,065). This average is, however, somewhat misleading because it embraces physicians whose practice is largely insurance practice and others whose insurance practice is only a small fraction of their total practice. There are no physicians who do only insurance practice; apart from non-insured patients, every insurance physician serves dependents of his insured patients. The physician with a panel of 2,000 potential insurance patients received, when the emergency deduction of 10 per cent was in effect, $3,937 in capitation fees, and the physician with the legal maximum of 2,500 on his panel, $4,921. Now, with the full capitation fee in effect again, a panel of 2,500 guarantees an income of $5,474. In addition, the insurance physician earns, on the average, as much or more from private general or specialist practice as from insurance practice.

In the London area, there were in 1934, on the average, about 1,880,000 insured persons on the index register entitled to medical benefit. Of these, about 1,780,000, on the average, were on the lists of insurance practitioners of whom there were, in the several quarters of the year, about 2,185. The average number of insured persons per insurance doctor's list was about 810, or, excluding assistants to insurance doctors, about 925 per list.* The size of doctor's lists varied considerably. For the quarter ending December 31, 1934, the distribution was as follows:

Insured Persons on a List	Number of Lists
Less than 500	939
501 — 1,000	364
1,001 — 1,500	283
1,501 — 2,000	206
2,001 — 3,000	218
More than 3,000	36
ALL	2,046

The variation depends not only upon the practitioner's popularity among insured persons, but upon the density of the insured population residing in the area in which he practises, the extent to which he devotes himself to insurance or to other practice, whether he practises alone or with an assistant physician, whether his practice is primarily in the Insurance Committee area or in an adjacent area but with a clientele which overlaps,† his skill in caring for a relatively large number of patients, etc. *Inasmuch as there is no direct financial relation between the insured persons and the physician of their choice, the size of a practitioner's list does not depend upon the size of his fees.*

The law provides that those insured persons who prefer to make independent arrangements for medical care may do so if they secure the permission of their local Insurance Committee; they pay their own medical fees and receive partial remuneration from the insurance authorities. (These persons are commonly known as "own arrangers.") But the practice is not common; about 15,000 persons (0.1 per cent of all insured persons) make their own arrangements for insurance medical care. In addition, insured persons may secure

---

*Assistant physicians do not have lists in their own names.

†A physician can require the local Insurance Committees to place his name on more than one list; if he lives in a place where, for example, the boundaries of three insurance areas are close together, he may have his name entered on all three lists.

their medical benefit (including medicines) from Approved Institutions of which there are about thirty. The total expenditures in England during 1934 on behalf of persons who exercised their option to claim treatment from Approved Institutions and on behalf of persons who were required, or allowed, to make their own arrangements for medical benefit were £71,750 ($349,136).

The provision in the law which enables insured persons to make their own arrangements for medical care is utilized in the town of Swindon in a manner which deserves special mention. The headquarters and factories of the Great Western Railway are located in Swindon. Employment is steady and the population is moderately prosperous. The G.W.R. Medical Fund Society was established in 1847 and has had a continuous and prosperous career. Its membership includes practically all single and married employees of the G.W.R. and their dependents. The Society furnishes no financial benefits, but does furnish, to members and their dependents under age sixteen, extensive medical care, including the services of general practitioners and specialists, dental and hospital care. The medical services are furnished through an organized, salaried staff and a wholly owned hospital and clinic. Members' contributions are collected by voluntary weekly deductions from wages. The local Insurance Committee accepts the G.W.R. Medical Fund Society provisions. Being thereby relieved of the necessity of furnishing the statutory insurance medical benefits (general practitioner care, medicines and appliances), the Insurance Committee remits to the Society a sum equivalent to that fraction of the compulsory contributions which is paid by the insured persons for the statutory medical benefits. The arrangement is, in effect, one in which the provision of medical benefits in National Health Insurance is carried out by organized group medical service rather than by individual practitioners. The insured persons covered by such a local scheme are known as "collective own arrangers." The economy of group provision apparently operates to extend the scope of medical benefits which may be furnished for a specified sum. Although the arrangements in effect in Swindon are probably unique in Great Britain, somewhat similar arrangements are found in mining (and other) districts, especially in Wales.[21]

It will be recalled that insurance medical benefit includes, in addition to the services of a general practitioner, such medicines and appliances as the patient needs.* This provision of the law also operates under the local Insurance Committees. Medicines and appliances are supplied by the physician or by pharmacists on the written prescription of the physician. In each local area, all qualified pharmacists may have their names entered on the local pharmaceutical list maintained by the Insurance Committee. The insured person has free choice of pharmacist from the list; he takes his prescription to his pharmacist and receives the medicine or appliance prescribed. (He may patronize a single pharmacist or different pharmacists.) The pharmacist sends the prescription to the Insurance Committee and is remunerated by the Committee according to a Drug Tariff mutually agreed by the Minister of Health and the central organization of pharmacists. In a typical year, there are somewhat more than 10,000 insurance pharmacies and they dispense between 55,000,000 and 60,000,000 prescriptions or about 5,400 per pharmacy. The total annual expenditure for medicines and appliances is about £2,300,000. Of this sum, about £2,000,000 (approximately $10,000,000) is paid to pharmacists, equivalent to about $1,000 per pharmacy and 18.4 cents per prescription. The average cost of this benefit per insured person is about 2s. 9d. ($0.67).

In the London area, with about 1,780,000 persons on physicians' lists and eligible to pharmaceutical benefit, there are about 1,035 chemists and institutions on the Chemists' Register of the Insurance Committee. They dispensed 8,483,000 insurance prescriptions during 1934, or 4.75 per insured person, having a total value of $1,340,300. The average cost per prescription (ingredients and dispensing fee) was 15.6 cents, and the average cost per insured person was 74 cents.

---

*The appliances which a physician may prescribe are, however, restricted to those included in a list approved by the Ministry of Health.

To an American reader it will appear that the average price of "prescriptions" is very low. The reason is that, under insurance, the category "prescriptions" includes simple home remedies and inexpensive sick-room supplies as well as the more complex and more expensive medicaments ordinarily furnished on prescription. Thus, the average price reflects the inclusion of expensive items such as are customarily purchased in the United States only on a doctor's prescription and also the inexpensive items such as are usually purchased on the doctor's orders or on the patient's initiative without such a prescription.

THE VOLUME OF MEDICAL SERVICES

We might wish it were possible to measure the adequacy of the *volume* of medical service received by the insured persons in Great Britain. Unfortunately the data required for this purpose do not exist. It will be of some interest, however, to consider the following comparison. It was found in July, 1923, that during a typical year the insurance medical practitioners of England and Wales made on the average 3.5 attendances per insured person (equivalent in a year of 300 working days to 12 per working day for each physician), and of these, on the average, two-thirds were office services and one-third home visits. Thus, the average annual rates of service were 2.3 office calls and 1.2 home visits per insured person.* There being no direct fee relations between doctor and patient, most of the calls made by patients are not first calls in an illness and many are trivial and require only brief attention. The doctors' average insurance load is not very heavy. In the United States, a survey of representative families[22] yields the figures shown in Table 10 for services rendered by physicians to all members of these families.

It will be recalled that insured persons in Great Britain are essentially limited to those who earn less than $1,200 a year.† Allow-

---

*There were indications that the volume of insurance services in 1935 was about four—or slightly more—(instead of 3.5) attendances per insured person.

†Although the income limit of £250 applies only to non-manual workers, there are comparatively very few manual workers who earn more than this sum.

TABLE 10

ANNUAL SERVICES FURNISHED BY PHYSICIANS TO THE MEMBERS OF REPRESENTATIVE
AMERICAN FAMILIES, 1928–1931

FAMILY INCOME	PHYSICIANS' SERVICES PER PERSON				
	Office	Home	Office and Home	Clinic	Total
Under $1,200	0.8	0.9	1.7	0.5	2.2
$1,200–2,000	1.1	0.8	1.9	0.3	2.2
2,000–3,000	1.3	1.0	2.3	0.2	2.5
3,000–5,000	1.5	1.3	2.8	0.2	3.0
5,000–10,000	2.5	1.3	3.8	0.2	4.0
10,000 and over	2.9	2.4	5.3	0.0[a]	5.3
ALL INCOMES (weighted)	1.3	1.0	2.3	0.3	2.6

a Less than 0.1; actually 0.04.

ing for the fact that some families have more than one wage-earner,
the insured persons are in general members of families with annual
incomes of less than $2,000; most of them are members of families
with incomes *much* less than $2,000. It will be observed in Table 10,
however, that to find American families with an average volume of
service equal to that received by the British insured (2.3 office calls
and 1.2 home visits per person) we must turn to families whose incomes exceed $3,000 or $5,000 per annum. Among the families with
incomes of less than $1,200 the combined total of office and home
visits is only 1.7 per person and among those with incomes of
$1,200–$2,000 the total is only 1.9 per person. Nor will the addition
of clinic services bring these totals up to the level of the British
insurance service. The comparison in volume of services is even more
in favor of the British figures than appears, because the American
data contain—and the British do not contain—the volume of services
rendered in maternity cases and by specialists. The British insurance
medical benefit does not embrace these two classes of service.

It is often alleged that without health insurance America's poor
receive medical care which is as good as or better than that received
by the poor in other countries with insurance. The limited com-

parison in terms of *volume* of service fails to substantiate this assertion in respect to British health insurance practice. The British insurance expenditure for medical benefit may be small by American standards, but the volume of service is large. There are no substantial grounds on which one could predict the results of a similar comparison in terms of *quality* of the service furnished. The only fact available is that insured persons in England and Wales receive more than one and one-half times as many services from physicians as are received by the members of representative American families in substantially the same income classes.

The Scope and Administration of Additional Benefits

In addition to the cash and medical benefits which are guaranteed by statute, an insured person may become eligible to additional cash or treatment benefits if the Approved Society of which he is a member has a disposable surplus of funds. The financial position of each Society is determined by periodic valuation. Formerly, the valuations were conducted at five-year intervals. Recently, for the purposes of the fourth valuation now in progress, the Societies were divided into four groups to be valued as at the end of the years 1931 to 1934, respectively. This valuation is not yet completed. However, the status of additional benefit schemes in force (in England only) January 1, 1935, is shown in Table 11.

TABLE 11

ADDITIONAL BENEFIT SCHEMES IN OPERATION IN ENGLAND, JANUARY 1, 1935

ADDITIONAL BENEFIT	NUMBER OF SCHEMES	MEMBERSHIP COVERED[a]
Cash only	62	36,000
Treatment only	320	2,822,000
Cash and treatment	4,869	9,896,000
TOTAL	5,251	12,754,000

a Total membership covered by the fourth valuation, 14,000,000; total number of insured persons in England, 15,521,000.

Not all of the members of Approved Societies with sanctioned schemes for additional benefits are at once entitled to these benefits. The right matures for cash additional benefits at the beginning of the fifth year and for treatment benefits at the beginning of the third year after admission to membership.

The amount of additional cash benefit varies considerably. Nearly 7,000,000 members are covered by schemes which give additional sickness benefit at the rate of 1s. to 5s. per week. Among the Approved Societies already covered by the fourth valuation, the average additional benefits are: 4s. per week for sickness benefit; 2s. per week for disablement benefit; and 8s. for maternity benefit. In the case of 210 of these sanctioned schemes, embracing 320,000 members, the additional sickness benefit takes the form of making payments from the first (instead of as normally from the fourth) day of incapacity.

Among the additional treatment benefits furnished by the British insurance system, dental and eye care are the most important. And of these two, dental care is the more popular and more extensive. Indeed, in 1925, the Royal Commission, engaged in a revaluation of the insurance system, was urged by dentists, Approved Societies, government officials, and insured persons to recommend that dental care be made a statutory benefit. The Commission did not adopt this course of action but did recommend liberal administration of dental care as an additional benefit. Inasmuch as the additional benefits must be financed from the surplus funds of the Approved Societies, their administration and provision are entirely under the Societies, subject to the control of the Minister of Health.

There are in England some 5,000 administrative units of Approved Societies, with 9,800,000 members, furnishing dental (cash) treatment benefit.[23] The annual sum allocated for this additional benefit (as of January 1, 1935) is $10,300,000. The Dental Benefit Regulations (1930) provide that the Committee of Management of every Society which administers dental benefit shall fix a proportion of the cost of treatment to be paid by the Society and may vary the proportion from time to time, but in no case may the proportion be less than one-half the cost of treatment. If the cost is less than 10 shillings ($2.43), the Society must pay the entire cost. In practice it is found that the Societies which furnish dental benefit pay about 50 per cent of the cost of dentures and about 75 per cent of the cost of treatments; the remainder is in each case paid by the insured person.

The administrative practice for dental benefit is comparatively simple. An insured person who seeks dental care applies to his Society and receives a "dental letter." He may present this to any licensed dentist.[24] If the patient is accepted by the dentist, a program of treatment is prepared by the practitioner and, if accepted by the Society,[25] the treatment is furnished by the dentist and he is remunerated jointly by the Society and the patient according to a scale of fees prescribed by the Dental Benefit Regulations and the rules of the Society. All private bargaining between dentist and patient is forbidden.

The administration of dental benefit by the Approved Societies is subject to the general supervision of the Dental Benefit Council, established in accordance with the Act of 1924. In addition, there is a staff of Regional Dental Officers appointed by the Minister of Health to advise on questions arising in connection with applications for dental benefit. The Council is responsible for the arrangements under which disputes and professional problems are adjudicated. In 1933 the costs of the central administration of dental benefit for all of Great Britain were as follows:

Regional Dental Officers	$138,500
Dental Benefit Council	29,500
TOTAL	$168,000

These administrative costs constituted 1.91 per cent of the total sum spent on dental benefits.

The scope of dental benefit varies widely among the Approved Societies.[26] The total expenditures (of insurance funds only) on dental benefit in England and Wales were £2,106,000 ($10,248,000) in 1931, equivalent to $1.05 per person eligible to receive this benefit. Inasmuch as the insured person pays part (about 40 per cent) of the cost of dental care, these figures understate the total expenditure for dental care furnished to these insured persons. From limited data,[27] it may be estimated that the total cost of insurance dental service is about $17,000,000 or about $1.75 per insured person eligible to receive the benefit.

Ophthalmic benefit includes examination and treatment of the eyes and the provision of glasses. The insured person obtains the benefit by applying to his Approved Society for an "ophthalmic letter" and follows the same procedure as in the case of dental benefit. There is no register of opticians; the insured person takes the letter to his physician for approval, and then may take it to any qualified optician who accepts the agreed schedule of fees. In 1931 about 9,000,000 members were included in the English societies which furnished ophthalmic benefit. These Societies had about 1s. ($0.24) per member available for eye care and spent, in the aggregate, £413,564 ($2,012,000). Inasmuch as the average payment per case was somewhat under £1, it may be inferred that nearly 500,000 insured persons received eye care during the year.[28]

In 1934 the expenditures for ophthalmic benefit amounted to £343,000 ($1,670,000). On January 1, 1935, there were 9,953,000 members covered by approved schemes furnishing ophthalmic benefit and $2,360,000 per year had been allocated for this purpose. These sums represent only the proportion of the cost borne by the Approved Societies; the insured persons pay the balance of the cost, their share varying with the nature of the services, the cost of the spectacle frames selected, etc.

The following quotation from the Thirteenth Annual Report of the Ministry of Health reflects the general conditions which have prevailed:

.. There are several alternative methods by which the (ophthalmic) benefit may be obtained; thus, insured persons may make use of the services of ophthalmic specialists, ophthalmic hospitals, combined arrangements for ophthalmic examination and the necessary appliances, and the provision of glasses by opticians. Certain bodies of practitioners have made organized arrangements which particular Societies may recognize in accordance with the Regulations. These are largely competing bodies and the Department does not seek to influence a Society's choice of its normal arrangements, but insists that, in accordance with the Regulations, the individual member must be free to go outside those arrangements if he so desires.

A result of these conditions is that the benefit does not work in as smooth and certain a manner as dental benefit, for which a central control over the service has been set up. Nevertheless, there is reason to believe that the needs of insured persons who suffer from defective eyesight are on the whole being adequately met. The difficulties that exist relate rather to the administrative machinery for providing the benefit, and to the variety of prices charged, and uncertainty as to the necessity for Societies meeting the cost of various types of lenses and frames, which may be the vagaries of fashion or individual taste.[28]

Since this was written (1932), progress has been made in placing ophthalmic benefit upon a better administrative basis. The (unofficial) Ophthalmic Benefit Joint Committee, representing various groups of Approved Societies and of organizations of opticians, has recommended standards for the optical letter, for quality and prices of appliances, for the qualifications of opticians and the establishment of a register of qualified opticians, and for the creation of an agency equivalent to the Dental Benefit Joint Committee—the precursor of the Dental Benefit Council. These recommendations (reported in the Fifteenth and Sixteenth Annual Reports of the Ministry, 1933–1934 and 1934–1935) are apparently receiving careful consideration.

THE HIGHLANDS AND ISLANDS MEDICAL SERVICE OF SCOTLAND

Before closing a description of national health insurance in Great Britain attention may be briefly directed to the special arrangements which supplement the Insurance Act in respect to certain sparsely settled parts in Scotland. These, it must be understood, supplement insurance provisions which in all important respects are identical for Scotland with those described in preceding pages for England and Wales.

In an area which is about 400 miles by 150 miles in extent and which represents more than half the land surface of Scotland, there was prior to 1914 such a scarcity of physicians and other medical personnel and of institutions for the care of the sick as to present one of the serious deficiencies in the medical services of Great Britain. The population is very sparse, including only about one-seventeenth of the population of Scotland, and for the most part the people are extremely poor. As long ago as 1850 the Royal College of Physicians called attention to the dearth of personnel to care for the most elementary needs of this population and concluded that the conditions could not be greatly improved unless financial support were provided from outside the area itself. The report of the Commission on the Poor Laws in 1909 corroborated the findings of this earlier inquiry and showed that "in the Highlands and Islands medical treatment and nursing were on the whole luxuries beyond the reach of the normal highland family."

No substantial improvement in the situation was made until Parliament created the *Highlands and Islands (Medical Service) Fund* in 1913, following the recommendations of the report presented by the Dewar Committee. By this Act of 1913, Parliament adopted the policy of voting annually a sum of money which would be spent in accordance with approved schemes "for the purpose of improving medical service, including nursing, in the Highlands and Islands of Scotland and otherwise providing and improving means for the prevention of treatment and alleviation of illness and suffering therein." The Fund applies to "crofters, cotters, dependents of insured persons and others in like circumstances on whom the doctor's usual fee would be an undue burden."

The Department of Health for Scotland administers the Fund and pays subsidies to the general practitioners practising in the affected areas. In return for these subventions the practitioners, who in all cases live somewhere within the areas, agree to attend the specified classes of people at modified fees. The regulations which came into effect July 1, 1926, included the following fee schedule:

"I. In ordinary cases the Fee shall not exceed 5s. for the first visit and 3s. 6d. for each subsequent visit in the same illness.

"II. In midwifery cases the maximum Fee chargeable shall be £2. 2s., including any subsequent visits that may be necessary.

"III. Fees as specified below may be charged for certain special services, namely:—

Service	Fee Not to Exceed
(a) Operation requiring general anaesthetic or major operation performed under spinal or extensive local anaesthesia	£2. 2s.
(b) Fee to anaesthetist if one is employed	£1. 1s.
(c) Minor operation requiring simple local anaesthesia	£1. 1s.
(d) Abortion or miscarriage ..... £2. 2s. or £1. 1s. (according as general anaesthetic is, or is not, required)	
(e) Setting of fracture	£1. 1s.
(f) Reduction of dislocation	£1. 1s.

"In all cases under Head III, except (b), the Fee is intended to cover two subsequent visits."

It is of special significance to note that the Highlands and Islands Fund, unlike national health insurance, does not restrict medical benefit to the services of the general practitioner. In addition to subventions to the physicians (based upon individually negotiated contracts between the medical practitioner and the Department of Health for Scotland, including general grants to assist the physician to earn a reasonable income, a mileage allowance in respect to insured and non-insured persons, subventions towards his operation of an automobile and towards the construction and maintenance of his house and professional facilities), the Fund also provides for nursing, hospital and ambulance, specialist, and other services.

Among the results attained by the scheme may be mentioned increases in the number of physicians who practise in the area, improvement in their condition of living and practice, and elevation of the standards of service. Formerly it was very difficult, if not impossible, to find physicians who would settle in some parts of the Highlands and Islands; but now the administrators report that it is difficult in many cases to make selection from the large number of well-qualified physicians who apply for appointments under the Act. In 1931 the Fund served a population of 327,500 persons and the number of doctors practising among these people was 178, or approximately one for each 1,840 persons. The Fund now spends annually nearly £80,000[29] of which £47,000 is spent for medical services, some £18,000 for nursing service, and more than £5,000 for hospital and ambulance service.

It should be emphasized that the Fund does not provide the whole income of physicians practising in the highland areas; it supplements the incomes earned by these physicians from (1) services rendered to insured persons; (2) medical attendance on the sick-poor under arrangements made by the Local County Council; and (3) medical attendance on those able to pay the ordinary fees for service.

The subventions available from the Fund have not only brought important improvements in the availability and quality of the physicians' services but have also transformed the nursing service. There has been built up, through grants to individual nurses and to nursing associations, a staff of nearly two hundred trained nurses who now serve in these areas. In addition, the Fund is used to maintain hospitals, build houses for doctors and nurses, extend telegraph and telephone lines, help with laboratories, clinics, dentistry and ophthalmology, to assist in the maintenance of an ambulance service, and to provide holiday relief and opportunities for postgraduate education at medical centers for physicians.

Although not primarily an insurance scheme, the Highlands and

Islands Fund is an interesting example of how a special governmental arrangement has been devised to meet the exigencies arising from the poverty and the special circumstances prevailing in a sparsely settled area, and to supplement the limited benefits furnished under the general insurance plan.[30]

The Highlands and Islands plan has certain obvious implications for the problems presented by many areas in the United States. It is therefore of interest that both lay and professional testimony in Scotland and in England support the official views on the large measure of success with which this plan has been operated.

REFERENCES AND NOTES

1. Harris, Henry J.: NATIONAL HEALTH INSURANCE IN GREAT BRITAIN, 1911 TO 1921. Washington, U. S. Bureau of Labor Statistics, Bulletin No. 312, 1923, 104 pp.

2. NATIONAL HEALTH INSURANCE ACT, 1924. London, His Majesty's Stationery Office, 1924, 158 pp.

3. COMPULSORY SICKNESS INSURANCE, Series M (Social Insurance) No. 6. Geneva, International Labour Office, 1927, 810 pp.

4. REPORT OF THE ROYAL COMMISSION ON NATIONAL HEALTH INSURANCE. London, His Majesty's Stationery Office, 1928, 408 pp.

5. NATIONAL HEALTH INSURANCE. MEDICAL BENEFIT CONSOLIDATED REGULATIONS, 1928 (No. 965). London, His Majesty's Stationery Office, 1933, 80 pp.

6. NATIONAL HEALTH INSURANCE. DENTAL BENEFIT REGULATIONS, 1930 (No. 1060). London, His Majesty's Stationery Office, 1931, 26 pp.

7. Newsholme, Sir Arthur: INTERNATIONAL STUDIES ON THE RELATION BETWEEN THE PRIVATE AND OFFICIAL PRACTICE OF MEDICINE, op. cit., Volume III (see page 70).

8. THIRTEENTH ANNUAL REPORT OF THE MINISTRY OF HEALTH, 1931–1932. London, His Majesty's Stationery Office, 1932.

9. Newsholme, Sir Arthur: MEDICINE AND THE STATE. London, George Allen & Unwin, Ltd., and Baltimore, Williams & Wilkins Co., 1932, 320 pp.

10. FOURTH ANNUAL REPORT OF THE DEPARTMENT OF HEALTH FOR SCOTLAND, 1932. Edinburgh, His Majesty's Stationery Office, 1933.

11. Newman, Sir George: On the State of the Public Health. In ANNUAL REPORT OF THE CHIEF MEDICAL OFFICER OF THE MINISTRY OF HEALTH FOR THE YEAR 1932. London, His Majesty's Stationery Office, 1933.

12. Simons, A. M. and Sinai, Nathan: THE WAY OF HEALTH INSURANCE. Chicago, The University of Chicago Press, 1932, 250 pp.

13. McCleary, George F.: NATIONAL HEALTH INSURANCE. London, H. K. Lewis & Co., Ltd., 1932, 195 pp.

14. In this chapter the pound sterling is taken at par, $4.866.

15. Each person who is required to be insured under the National Health Insurance Scheme is also required to be insured under the Widows', Orphans' and Old Age Contributory Pensions Scheme. Inasmuch as both employer and employee also contribute towards the latter, the employer purchases the stamps for both types of insurance. In the aggregate, the weekly contributions are 1s. 6d. (36 cents) for men and 1s. 1d. (26 cents) for women.

16. Prior to January 1, 1933, the cash sickness benefit was 12s. for both married and unmarried women, and the disablement benefit was uniform for all men and women. Actuarial revaluation of the financial position of the insurance societies and of the central funds led to revision of the benefits.

17. NATIONAL HEALTH INSURANCE. MEDICAL BENEFIT CONSOLIDATED REGULATIONS, 1928, op. cit., First Schedule, Part I, Section 8.

18. For a more detailed analysis and for applications to health insurance, see COMPULSORY SICKNESS INSURANCE, op. cit., p. 433 et seq.

19. For a lucid description of the doctor's rôle in insurance practice, see NATIONAL HEALTH INSURANCE, op. cit.

20. NATIONAL HEALTH INSURANCE. MEDICAL BENEFIT CONSOLIDATED REGULATIONS, 1928, op. cit., First Schedule, Part II, Section 1.

21. See reference No. 7 above, Chapter XVII, etc.

22. Falk, I. S., Klem, Margaret C. and Sinai, Nathan: THE INCIDENCE OF ILLNESS AND THE RECEIPT AND COSTS OF MEDICAL CARE AMONG REPRESENTATIVE FAMILY GROUPS. Chicago, The University of Chicago Press, 1933, p. 283.

23. The number of Societies and the insured population receiving dental benefit declined to these numbers from some 6,000 with 12,350,000 members in 1930. This was a consequence of the third valuation of resources of the Societies which showed a decline in surpluses.

24. There is complete freedom in the choice of dentist by the insured person; there is no dental "panel," local or regional, despite common statements to the contrary. The only limitation on the insured person is that he is restricted to dentists who have agreed to accept the insurance fee schedule and the rules of procedure.

25. Approval by the Society is not necessary if the estimated cost is less than 10s. ($2.43).

26. Cf. THE WAY OF HEALTH INSURANCE (reference 12 above) for further analysis of the administration of dental benefit.

27. The computation has been made from the experience of a representative Society cited by the Ministry of Health (THIRTEENTH ANNUAL REPORT, 1931–1932, p. 224). The average cost of approved dental estimates for men was $21.73 and for women $17.69. Of these sums the Society paid $13.31 and $10.46, respectively, "leaving the member to find" $8.42 in the case of men and $7.23 of women. The Society's average contribution was 61 per cent in the former and 59 per cent in the latter cases. It may be noted that the Dental Benefit Council, in its annual report for the year ended December 31, 1933 (FIFTEENTH ANNUAL REPORT OF THE MINISTRY OF HEALTH, 1933–1934, p. 365) uses an allocation nearer 50 per cent for Great Britain.

28. THIRTEENTH ANNUAL REPORT OF THE MINISTRY OF HEALTH, 1931–1932, *op. cit.,*
    p. 226.

29. SIXTH ANNUAL REPORT OF THE DEPARTMENT OF HEALTH FOR SCOTLAND: 1934.
    Edinburgh, His Majesty's Stationery Office, 1935, p. 106.

30. "Highlands and Islands (Medical Service) Fund," Department of Health for Scot-
    land; "Highlands and Islands Medical Service" leaflets 1, 2, 3/1930, *ibid.* In
    addition, special reports by Dr. A. Shearer have been consulted.

CHAPTER IX

THE COSTS OF HEALTH INSURANCE
IN GREAT BRITAIN

INCOME AND EXPENDITURES

AS the insurance system has grown to include more and more persons, the number receiving benefit, the frequency of receipt of benefits and the costs have all been increasing. Average receipts per insured person increased from $7.91 in 1916 to $13.06 in 1921; average expenditures per insured person increased from $5.09 to $9.59 in the same period.[1] The figures for more recent years are shown in Table 12, where the expenditures have been apportioned according to the purposes for which they are made.

In each year since 1912, receipts have exceeded expenditures, except in 1927 and 1929. Between 1922 and 1933 receipts declined from $12.28 to $9.97 per person, while expenditures increased from $9.56 to $9.88 (with a maximum of $11.12 in 1930). Benefits consumed $7.99 to $9.50 per person; the remaining $1.49 to $1.62 per person paid for the costs of administration. Among the several benefits, sickness (cash) allowances and medical services are the most expensive; each consumes approximately $3 per person.

A DETAILED ANALYSIS OF COSTS

For a closer inspection of the costs of British health insurance, the experience of England in 1934–1935 has been analyzed in more detail (Table 13) and the costs have been expressed in dollars *per person eligible* to various benefits rather than in dollars *per person*. In this recent year, the total cost of health insurance was $9.51 or $11.38 per person, according as the costs are computed on the basis of all insured persons or of those entitled to the several benefits. Of the

174

TABLE 12

RECEIPTS AND EXPENDITURES PER PERSON ENTITLED TO BENEFITS, ENGLAND
AND WALES, 1922–1933*

RECEIPTS OR EXPENDITURES	1922	1925	1930	1931	1933
TOTAL RECEIPTS	$12.28	$13.08	$11.35	$11.38	$9.97
TOTAL EXPENDITURES[a]	9.56	10.01	11.12	10.97	9.88
Administration	1.57	1.51	1.62	1.61	1.49
All Benefits	7.99	8.50	9.50	9.36	8.39
Sickness	2.98	3.22	3.23	3.16	3.01
Disablement	1.21	1.57	1.82	1.73	1.60
Maternity	0.59	0.51	0.51	0.49	0.41
Medical	3.08	2.92	2.96	3.04	2.69
Other	0.13	0.28	0.98	0.94	0.68

*Compiled and computed from Appendices XXXI and XLIII of the FIFTEENTH ANNUAL
REPORT OF THE MINISTRY OF HEALTH, 1933–1934.
a Per-capita expenditures have been computed in this table by dividing expenditures by
the total number of insured persons.

total sum, medical services consumed slightly more than one-third,
cash benefits nearly one-half, and administration a little over one-
seventh.

If the administration costs are charged against the various benefits,[2]
the general division of expenditures becomes:

All medical benefits	38.2 per cent
Statutory	30.3
Additional	7.9
Total cash benefits	61.8 per cent
ALL BENEFITS	100.0 per cent

Thus, cash benefits and the cost of providing them account for 62
per cent of the total expenditures; benefits in kind and the cost of
providing them are responsible for the remaining 38 per cent. These
proportions are the reverse of those which obtain in German insurance practice (see page 96). British "health" insurance, more than
German "sickness" insurance, is a system of providing cash rather

TABLE 13

HEALTH INSURANCE EXPENDITURES IN ENGLAND, 1934–1935*

EXPENDITURES	TOTAL[a]	PER PERSON[b] ELIGIBLE	PER CENT[c] OF TOTAL
TOTAL	$147,581,000	$11.38[d]	100.0
MEDICAL SERVICES[e]—TOTAL	52,232,000	3.96	35.4
Statutory[f]	41,638,000	2.78	28.2
Additional	10,594,000	1.18	7.2
Physicians' fees, etc.[g]	32,372,000	2.16	21.9
Dental services	7,280,000	0.74	4.9
Drugs and appliances[h]	9,455,000	0.64	6.4
Eye care	1,669,000	0.17	1.1
Hospital services	428,000	0.11	0.3
Convalescent homes, etc.	491,000	0.05	0.3
Other services	537,000	0.09	0.5
CASH BENEFITS—TOTAL	72,518,000	5.83	49.1
Sickness	40,417,000	3.06	27.4
Disablement	25,722,000	2.23	17.4
Maternity	6,379,000	0.54	4.3
ADMINISTRATION—TOTAL	22,831,000	1.59	15.5
Central Departments	4,180,000	0.27	2.8
Insurance Committees	1,713,000	0.11	1.2
Approved Societies	16,938,000	1.21	11.5

*Compiled and computed from the SIXTEENTH ANNUAL REPORT OF THE MINISTRY OF HEALTH, 1934–1935.

a Computed on the basis £1 = $4.866.

b The costs divided by the appropriate numbers of persons eligible to the several benefits. The total number of insured persons was 15,521,000. The statutory medical benefits were available to 14,990,000; additional treatment benefits were available to from 3,743,000 for hospital care up to 10,041,000 for convalescent homes and treatment. The populations used in respect of the cash benefits make allowance for statutory eligibility, age restrictions, new entrants, qualification (waiting periods), etc. The eligible populations were as follows: for sickness benefit, 13,200,000; for disablement benefit, 11,400,000; for maternity benefit, 11,900,000. Administration costs were allocated among the following populations: Central Departments, 15,521,000; Insurance Committees, 14,990,000; Approved Societies, 13,887,000.

c Computed from total expenditures; slightly different results are obtained when computed from the *per-capita* costs because of the effect upon the latter of variations in the eligible population.

d The total cost divided by the total population, without regard to eligibility to each benefit, equals $9.51 *per capita*.

e The statutory benefits are furnished in the form of services through the local Insurance Committees; the additional treatment benefits are furnished through the Approved Societies from disposable surpluses.

f Medical care furnished by general practitioners, and prescribed medicines and appliances.

g Payments to physicians, including capitation fees, mileage allowances, remuneration for medicines used in practice, payments to non-insurance practitioners for services rendered to insured persons allowed to make their own arrangements, and subventions for postgraduate study.

h Statutory and additional benefits combined.

than medical care. The financial emphasis in Britain is still primarily on *compensation* of the insured person for income lost on account of incapacity to work rather than on *restoration* of his health.

When the expenditures for the several medical services shown in Table 13 are in turn adjusted by the addition of proportionate shares of the administration costs, the costs of the medical benefits are found to be divided as follows:

ALL MEDICAL BENEFITS	100.0 per cent
Physicians' services	61.4
Drugs and appliances	18.7
Dental services	14.2
Eye care	3.4
Convalescent services	0.8
Hospital services	0.7
Other services	0.8

This method of dividing the expenditures for medical benefit again emphasizes that the British system furnishes the services of doctors and dentists and supplies drugs and medicines; other medical services consume but negligible fractions of the funds. The figures demonstrate that hospital care is not furnished to any substantial extent by the insurance scheme, despite the fact that extensive discussions in Great Britain on the administration of institutional benefit would appear to lead to a contrary conclusion.

If to the appropriate figures for England and Wales we add the corresponding data for Scotland, the expenditures on medical benefit for Great Britain (1931) become as follows:

Statutory medical benefits	$52,010,000
Additional medical benefits	16,072,000
ALL MEDICAL BENEFITS	$68,082,000

If a share of the costs of administration is added *pro rata*, the grand total for medical benefit in Great Britain (1931) becomes $75,750,000. The costs are somewhat lower for 1934.

It will be recalled that the weekly sickness benefit amounts to $3.65 if the disabled person is a man, $2.92 if an unmarried woman and $2.43 if a married woman. In addition to these statutory sums, the Approved Societies pay, on the average, about 4s. ($1.00) more out of their disposable surpluses.* That these sums are inadequate to support a disabled worker (and his or her dependents) is obvious. A significant, though small, proportion of insured workers who receive sickness benefit apply for poor relief to assist in the maintenance of dependents. Sickness insurance provides only partial compensation for loss in wages and is, in this respect, inadequate. Employed persons who earn small wages cannot use sickness insurance as a substitute for thrift. Many insured persons—particularly those in families with more than one member gainfully employed—carry voluntary, in addition to the required, insurance. Approximately one-third of those who are compulsorily insured are voluntarily insured with the friendly societies for extra sickness benefits. But those whose earnings are insufficient to provide more than the bare necessities of life—those for whom thrift has no practical significance—are forced to rely upon poor relief or other assistance when they are disabled by sickness, despite the benefits of sickness insurance.

In 1934 and 1935 the expenditure for statutory medical benefits (the service of a general practitioner and the supply of medicines and appliances) was $2.78 per person and for all insurance medical benefits, $3.96 per person. With a maximum allowance for differences in purchasing power of money and recognizing that these costs have been somewhat higher in prior years, it is still important for a resident of the United States to realize that the statutory medical benefits are meager.

To make the point clearer, consider a few comparisons. There are no substantial American data with which the British figures can be compared, but there is a sample. Among some 9,000 families which were surveyed in the United States in the years 1928–1931, there were

---

*Attention may be directed to the fact that when the "reserve values" of the insurance system have been redeemed in the future, the contributions will support larger cash benefits.

884 wage-earners and salaried workers (ages 15–64 years, inclusive) in those families with incomes of less than $1,200 per year, and 2,471 in those families with $1,200 to $2,000 per year. The numbers are small, but they comprise carefully selected representative groups.[3] In Table 14 we have arranged a few comparisons of expenditures for medical care. The data are not strictly comparable. The expenditures of the American worker cover all medical care for himself for which he pays; the British insurance expenditures cover only the benefits provided by the system and do not include the private expenditures of insured persons for specialists, dentistry, hospital care, etc. In spite of this discrepancy,* several interesting points appear from the figures:

1. Despite the fact that the insured British worker pays only one-half the contributions (and his employer the other half) and despite subventions from Parliament, expenditures for insurance medical benefit are less than the private expenditures of (economically) similar workers in the United States.

2. The American workman spends more for the services of physicians (general practitioners and specialists) than national health

TABLE 14

EXPENDITURES FOR MEDICAL CARE

MEDICAL SERVICE	ENGLAND AND WALES, 1931, EXPENDITURE PER INSURED PERSON	U. S. SAMPLE FAMILIES, 1928–1931, EXPENDITURE PER WORKER IN FAMILIES WITH INCOMES OF:	
		Less than $1,200	$1,200–$2,000
ALL SERVICES	$3.96	$7.80	$10.14
Physicians	2.16	3.63	4.19
Drugs and appliances	0.64	0.83	0.81
Dentistry	0.74	0.90	2.57
Hospitals	0.11	1.72	1.26
All other	0.31	0.72	1.31

*The discrepancy is not as great as American readers may expect, because traditionally the British wage-earner is accustomed to receive his hospital care largely or entirely without direct payment of costs.

insurance spends for general practitioners serving insured workers in England and Wales. Of course, this is not surprising, since the fees of specialists are far higher than those of general practitioners. The proportion of specialists to general practitioners is higher in the United States than in Great Britain.

3. The American workman in the lowest income class spends more for physicians and medicines than British health insurance spends for all medical benefits; the American workman in the next higher income class spends considerably more.

4. Dental benefit is non-statutory (i.e., "additional") in England and Wales. The insurance expenditures for this service compare favorably with private expenditures made by the very poor in the United States, but are only 29 per cent of those made by workers in American families with incomes of $1,200–$2,000. It will be recalled (see page 166) that the aggregate expenditure for dental care (insurance expenditure plus the private expenditures of insured persons) was about $1.75 per insured person eligible to this service. This sum is nearly double what the poorest American workmen spend and is nearly 70 per cent of what is spent by American workmen in families with annual incomes of $1,200–$2,000.

These observations are not in themselves significant; but they fortify the general inference that, judged by American standards, British insurance expenditures for medical benefit are not very liberal for furnishing medical care even of the kinds prescribed by law.

We know from American experience that if expenditures are insufficient to purchase adequate medical care, physicians' incomes will, in general, be small. It is commonly accepted in the United States that a competent physician can provide the ordinary services required by 1,000–1,200 persons living in urban or semi-urban areas. An insurance practitioner who accepted 1,000 insured persons on his list (not 1,000 actual patients) would now earn in Great Britain $2,187 in capitation fees; if he accepted 2,500 persons, the legal maximum, he could earn $5,474. In short, health insurance in Great Britain provides only a limited medical benefit and sets up what in the United States would generally be regarded as a "poor-man's" practice of medicine for insurance doctors. If it succeeds nevertheless in making a substantial contribution to the problems of medical need, despite the financial consequences of being limited to those who are manual workers and those non-manual workers who earn less than £250 a year, it is the more to be congratulated. The effectiveness of insurance medical benefit must be evaluated against conditions of medical service in years preceding insurance or against the provision of medical service for a similar economic population in a non-insurance country, not against concepts of good medical care nor against the practice of medicine among people of sufficient means.

Comparisons like these are dangerous unless qualified. It should be kept in mind that the British insurance practice obtains among people with very small earnings. In non-insurance practice among the industrial population of urban areas, the general practitioner ordinarily earns rather small fees. In ordinary circumstances, his nominal fee is 2s. 6d. (about $0.60) and he actually collects, on the average, about 1s. 6d. (about $0.36) per attendance. In addition, in private practice the physician ordinarily dispenses medicine (this is much more generally true in England than in Scotland) and thus still further reduces his net earnings. Hence the insurance capitation fee, amounting to about 2s. 6d. per attendance, is better remuneration than would ordinarily be earned without insurance by the same doctors serving the same class of patients. Furthermore, any direct comparison of remuneration in terms of fee-per-attendance must take account of the fact that in private practice the physician makes fewer calls than in insurance practice. Finally, it must be remembered that the insurance practitioner always has his private practice, much of which he acquires through his contacts with insured persons.

It is also of interest that insurance general practitioners must give identical treatment to insured persons and to private patients. A substantial body of evidence indicates that in fact this is quite generally the current practice in Great Britain. The limitation in the range of insurance medical benefit is, in a small measure, rectified by the fact that the insurance practitioner is required, in cases in which specialist or institutional treatment is necessary, to indicate the need to the patient and to advise him on the steps he should take in order to obtain it through private or public facilities.

SOLVENCY OF NATIONAL HEALTH INSURANCE

In the United States, it is sometimes thought that the solvency of health insurance systems has been threatened by the economic crisis of recent years. To be sure, all large scale insurance systems—like so many private undertakings—have faced serious problems. Yet it is difficult to understand how health insurance can become insolvent if it has been administered with reasonable operating reserves. The "risk" in health insurance is not capitalized over any long period of time; in principle, the income of a fiscal period must merely balance the expenditures of that period. If any substantial surplus or deficit develops, contributions or benefits must be (and can readily be) adjusted as may be necessary. A small operating reserve renders frequent changes unnecessary.

The solvency of the British system may be seen from the fact that for many years the accumulated funds (as of January 1st of each year) have been practically constant and have amounted to approximately £114,000,000 or about $570,000,000. This reserve is equal, on the average, to the operating expenses for three and one-third years. Decreases in the number of employed and insured persons have required economies of administration and of payments for services rendered to insured persons. The operating balance has, however, been maintained with no very large change in the contributions of Parliament and with no change in the scale of contributions which must be paid by insured persons and their employers. The economy reductions in professional fees (which were applied to civil servants generally) have—as has been noted before—been restored.

One often reads, in the United States, that health insurance has required increasing support from tax funds. We have already seen that, as a matter of fact, the government contributions which used to be made in Germany have been abolished. The facts as to England and Wales are summarized in the following figures which are the total Parliamentary votes and grants to health insurance in the last ten years:

1925	£7,228,100
1926	6,254,900
1927	6,842,600
1928	6,389,900
1929	6,873,300
1930	6,605,900
1931	6,356,300
1932	5,515,100
1933	5,395,700
1934	5,562,900

Tax support, it will be noted, has declined. Solvency has been maintained despite reduced Parliamentary grants.

References and Notes

1. social insurance legislation, Monograph Four. New York, Metropolitan Life Insurance Company, 1932, p. 13.

2. The allocation of administrative costs was made as follows: expenditures for Insurance Committees were assigned to the costs of statutory medical benefits; expenditures for Approved Societies were divided between cash benefits and non-statutory medical benefits by deducting 5 per cent of the cost of additional treatment benefits (the statutory allowance) and applying this sum to these benefits, and applying the remainder of this class of administrative cost to the cash benefits; expenditures for central departments were divided pro rata among all benefits.

3. The American data cited here are based on special tabulations for wage-earners and salaried workers (ages 15–64 inclusive) in the 9,000 families described in THE INCIDENCE OF ILLNESS AND THE RECEIPT AND COSTS OF MEDICAL CARE AMONG REPRESENTATIVE FAMILY GROUPS, by I. S. Falk, Margaret C. Klem and Nathan Sinai. Chicago, The University of Chicago Press, 1933, 327 pp. Due correction has been made in the data for the difference between charges incurred and expenditures made.

CHAPTER X

THE PRESENT POSITION OF HEALTH INSURANCE IN GREAT BRITAIN

THE health insurance law guarantees medical care to some sixteen and a half million persons in England and Wales and to nearly two millions more in Scotland, and the privilege of engaging in insurance medicine to every licensed physician. Obviously, the administration of these provisions involves large and complex problems. Many of the difficulties have been solved through arrangements which are characteristic of the British system.

The range of medical service which comes under the statutory guarantee was left vague and indefinite in the law. It has, however, been the subject of careful and coöperative interpretation by the medical profession and the central authorities. This element in the law is now administered without much friction, especially because in this matter, as in others, the medical regulations established by the Ministry of Health are developed with the close coöperation of the medical profession.

Each year there arise a few situations which are not easily solved by the local authorities (the Insurance Committee and the Local Medical Committee, the latter elected entirely by the practitioners of an area); and there are occasional disputes in particular cases as to whether a physician is entitled to a specialist's fee on the ground that a service is beyond the competence of a general practitioner. Decisions of local authorities are occasionally reviewed by the appeal tribunal which consists of a lawyer and two doctors.[1] The number of such cases occurring each year is, however, small. Indeed, in the course of a year there are in England, Wales and Scotland only about 200 appeals which involve only practitioners, and less than 1,000 cases in which insurance practitioners proposed to charge fees for services they considered outside the scope of general practice.

It will be recalled that medical benefit includes the provision of proper and sufficient medicines and appliances. "Experience has shown that the great majority of insurance practitioners treat their patients properly without squandering public money in an unnecessary use of drugs,"[2] but this is not always the case. A supervising procedure has been developed which seems to place reasonable and effective checks upon over-prescribing, without interfering with the proper freedom of physicians in prescribing.

Prescriptions are priced and tabulated by the local Insurance Committees for each physician. Where there is evidence of excessive prescribing or of excessive use of expensive medicines, the matter is considered by the physician concerned and the Regional Medical Officer. If a practitioner is repeatedly extravagant, the matter is referred to the Ministry of Health and the case may be submitted to the Panel (or the Local Medical) Committee of the local area. If the Committee, consisting of the physician's own colleagues, finds against the physician, he may appeal to the Minister of Health who then appoints an independent tribunal of Referees. Of these, at least one in three must be a physician; usually all are physicians. If the decision remains against the physician, the Minister may withhold from the physician's remuneration a sum proportionate to his offense. The administration of this procedure of control is acceptable to physicians and officials, and is effective.

In 1934, the salaried Regional Medical Officers paid 928 visits to physicians in reference to evidence of excessive prescribing; in ten cases referred to the Minister of Health, the matter was dropped; only four cases were referred to Panel Committees; in all four of these the Committees found against the physicians and in none was there an appeal against the medical judgment of excessive prescribing.[3] These facts are cited in detail because they are significant in indicating the infrequency of serious offenses.

In Britain, as was seen to be the case in Germany (Chapter VII), the greatest difficulty in the administration of insurance benefits arises over the medical certification of incapacity for work.* The difficulties inherent in this function have already been noted in the discussion of German sickness insurance and it is unnecessary to repeat the story, for it is essentially the same in Great Britain *despite the fact that the physicians have no direct relations with the Approved Societies.*

The English system of controlling over-certification operates (since 1920) primarily through the whole-time salaried Regional Medical Officers. There are some eighty of these officers and all have had extensive experience as general practitioners. When an insured person is certified to be incapacitated, the Approved Society may, if it doubts the medical judgment, refer the patient to the Regional Medical Staff for examination and a second opinion on the reported incapacity. A reference may also initiate with the physician. (Formerly, a reference in respect to persons insured under the Navy, Army and Air Force Fund could originate with an Insurance Committee. This function is now exercised by the central administration.) The Regional Medical Officer arranges for an examination of the patient, notifies the physician and invites him to attend. The result of the examination is reported to the Society and to the physician. In 1934,[4] there were in England 468,476 references for advice as to incapacity for work (466,172 from Approved Societies and 2,304 from insurance doctors). Of these, 246,088 were examined; 134,678 were reported to have received a final certificate before the date fixed for examination; and 86,628 failed to attend for other reasons. Of those examined, incapacity for work was confirmed in 179,010 cases; absence of incapacity was reported in 67,078.

Additional checks on certification include the use of uniform pro-

*A number of administrative problems concerned with certification of disability have been recently subjected to careful, objective inquiry in Scotland. These studies appear in the "Report on Sickness Statistics for the Insured Population of Scotland for the Year from 1st July 1930 to 30th June 1931" (Edinburgh, 1932), the first of four interesting reports published to date upon the morbidity of insured persons in Scotland.

cedures, a system of home visits by representatives of the Approved Societies, and statistical comparisons of the frequency with which various doctors issue certificates of incapacity. Finally, there is the additional check that a dissatisfied patient cannot make an immediate transfer from one physician who has refused a certificate to another physician; he can make the transfer only at the end of each quarter and then only after giving a month's notice to the Insurance Committee.*

There is some reason to believe the "disciplinary" functions suffer from the fact that penalties are not sufficiently flexible. There are no penalties for doctors between (a) fines of a few pounds and (b) refusing them the right to enter their names on the local panel. On the whole, fines are of little service to control the doctor who is deliberately lax in issuing certificates of incapacity or who is repeatedly guilty of over-prescribing; and refusing a doctor admission to the panel is practically equivalent to depriving him of his livelihood. Penalties of intermediate grade seem to be needed.

From all appearances, the difficulties over certification are not nearly so acute and the abuse of the practice is not so common in Great Britain as in Germany. Yet, though there are important arrangements separating the physician's responsibility for treating his patient and for certifying disability for cash benefits, the dual function is still there. The societies which have the responsibility of guarding the treasuries expect reasonable conservatism in certification of disability; the physician who refuses a certificate is fearful of losing from his practice the insured patient, his family, relatives, or friends. Despite a variety of supervisory and disciplinary devices, over-certification is apparently common. The comparatively small number of reversals of judgment on certificates noted above indicates that, in general, insurance doctors use reasonable care and discretion in the issuance. But one must consider that millions of certificates are issued

---

*The transfer can be made at any time from one doctor to another if both doctors consent; but the alternative procedure cited above is much more commonly used.

each year in order to appreciate the frequency and the extent of the burden which certification places upon the physician. Skill in the design of administrative arrangements, checks and counterchecks may reduce to a minimum the difficulties inherent in a system which gives the physician the dual function of treating patients and of certifying disability; but though these may ameliorate they do not solve the doctor's dilemma.

The analysis of British health insurance in the preceding chapters emphasized the limited range of the medical benefits and showed presumptively from the financial data that insurance medical service is still probably inadequate medical service. Nevertheless, all disinterested observers are agreed it represents a vast improvement over the medical service which was furnished to the laboring population before the days of insurance. Millions who formerly received little or no medical care now enjoy at least the elementary benefit of medicine; millions of others receive more and better care than they received formerly or than they would receive now were it not for insurance. More than sixteen millions of people in the lowest economic circumstances have been freed from the fear that in time of sickness their poverty might compel them to forgo the ministrations of the physicians or that the burden of medical costs might weigh them down.

That the public served by insurance continues to favor medical benefit and continually asks for enlargement of the benefit, is not surprising. But that the medical profession, which at first was bitter about many provisions in National Health Insurance, has come to support it and now recommends extension of medical benefit, is a more significant endorsement. The British Medical Association, which had formerly inveighed against contract practice, in 1926 expressed its official position before the Royal Commission on National Health Insurance[5] as follows:

> The evidence as to the incidence of sickness benefit does point to the fact that the Scheme has almost certainly reduced national sickness, and we are quite sure that if the immense gain

to national health includes immense gain to the comfort of the individual in knowing that he can have medical attention whenever he needs it, the gain is most marked; . . .

The Royal Commissioners expressed a similar opinion:[6]

We can, however, say at once that we are satisfied that the scheme of National Health Insurance has fully justified itself and has, on the whole, been successful in operation.

The British Medical Association gave as their reasons for endorsing the continuance of medical benefit, the following:[7]

a. Large numbers, indeed whole classes of persons are now receiving a real medical attention which they formerly did not receive at all.

b. The number of practitioners in proportion to the population in densely populated areas has increased.

c. The amount and character of the medical attention given is superior to that formerly given in the best of the old clubs, and immensely superior to that given in the great majority of the clubs which were far from the best.

d. Illness is now coming under skilled observation and treatment at an earlier stage than was formerly the case.

e. Speaking generally, the work of practitioners has been given a bias towards prevention which was formerly not so marked.

f. Clinical records have been or are provided which may be made of great service in relation to medical research and public health.

g. Coöperation among practitioners is being encouraged to an increasing degree.

h. There is now a more marked recognition than formerly of the collective responsibility of the profession to the community in respect of all health matters.

The Association adds that "all these are immense gains, and though it is possible that some of them may not be wholly due to the establishment of the National Health Insurance Scheme, they have certainly been hastened and intensified by that system."

There are many evidences, especially according to recent writings, of hasty and superficial medical care in insurance practice. But it seems to be forgotten by many that those who receive insurance medical benefit would have the same service or none at all if it were purchased privately. No doubt there is much insurance medical service which is contract practice of inferior quality. Yet all competent observers agree that this criticism does not apply to the bulk of insurance medical practice. The large majority of insurance doctors give honest and competent service and this is attested by all careful surveys.[8]

Of the highest significance are the results of a thorough reinvestigation of the entire subject by the British Medical Association. In a recent report,[9] which is apparently little known to the medical profession in the United States, this body representing the physicians of the British Empire expresses itself in favor of a large extension in the scope of insurance medical benefit and builds its proposals on the following eight principles:

> I. That a satisfactory system of medical service must be directed to the prevention of disease no less than to the relief of individual sufferers.
>
> II. That the medical service of the community must be based on the provision for every individual of a general practitioner or family doctor.
>
> III. That a consultant service and all necessary specialist and auxiliary forms of diagnosis and treatment should be available for the individual patient, normally through the agency of the family doctor.
>
> IV. That the interposition of any third party between the doctor and the patient, so far as actual medical attendance is concerned, shall be as limited as possible.
>
> V. That as regards the control of the purely professional side of the service, the guaranteeing of the quality of the service, and the discipline of the doctors taking part in it, as much responsibility as possible should be placed on the organized medical profession.
>
> VI. That in any arrangements made for communal or sub-

sidized or insurance medical service, the organized medical profession should be freely consulted from the outset on all professional matters by those responsible for the financial and administrative control of that service.

VII. That medical benefits of the present National Health Insurance Acts should be extended so as to include the dependents of all persons insured thereunder and entitled to medical benefit.

VIII. That every effort should be made to provide medical and nursing service facilities in institutions (Home Hospitals) where the family doctor may treat those of his own patients who need such provision and who can thus remain under his care.

The British Medical Association envisages as an answer to many existing defects in medical practice:

1. Enlarging the scope of medical benefit to include specialist treatment, dental service, institutional care, etc.;
2. Enlarging the scope of the insured population to embrace the dependents of insured persons; and
3. Consolidating the administration of insurance medicine with other medical bodies (public health, poor law, hospital services, etc.).

It would still retain the contributory nature of insurance and would continue to restrict it to people of small means by limiting voluntary contributors (and their dependents) to those whose incomes do not exceed £250 ($1,217) per year.

These proposals of the British Medical Association are broad and far-reaching, but yet are more conservative than the proposals of others.[10] Miscellaneous proposals to extend the scope of insurance medical benefit brought to the attention of the Royal Commission on National Health Insurance "the extremely important problem of coördination of health services generally." The Commissioners were impressed by the large number and variety of medical and public health agencies operating independently of insurance medicine. The need for a unified medical service was urged from many quarters, proposing the merger of all *public* medical services—including insurance medicine—"into one National Medical Service, thereby creating one unified organization for the prevention and cure of disease. Under this system, the service would be provided for all persons below a given income limit."[11] The Commission was led to the conclusion that "whatever may be the changes which are made in the Insurance scheme in the near future, the trend of the development will be towards a unified health service."

The Commission recognized that enlarging the scope of medical benefit increased the difficulty of retaining the insurance principle and maintaining support jointly from contributions and public funds. "The ultimate solution will lie, we think, in the direction of divorcing the medical service entirely from the insurance system and recognizing it along with all the other public health activities as a service to be supported from the general public funds."

When the Royal Commission on National Health Insurance undertook revaluation of the system more than a decade of experience had been accumulated. Yet when the Commission investigated the validity of various administrative elements in the scheme, there were few unambiguous judgments. The Approved Societies were under considerable fire. It was argued on many grounds[12] that the Societies had outlived their usefulness and should be abolished; that their administration is expensive, their non-territorial organization interferes with the efficiency of administering medical benefits (which must, of necessity, be organized on a geographical basis), their devices for selecting membership lead to segregation of risks and to unequal benefits among members who make the same contributions, their administration is autocratic and, in reality, is not in the control of insured persons, their funds are not always utilized in the best interests of insured persons, etc., etc. Yet, all considered, the majority of the Commissioners recommended:

> That the Approved Society system as a means for the administration of the cash benefits of National Health Insurance should be retained, but that this question might have to be re-

considered in the event of fundamental changes being made in the system of social insurance.

That the administration of additional benefits of the nature of treatment should remain in the hands of the Approved Societies in so far as the consideration of claims for benefit is concerned.

But they also recommended:

That where a treatment benefit has been so widely adopted as an additional benefit as to be available for a large proportion of the total insured population, the negotiations as to terms and conditions of service with the profession by whom the service is provided should be undertaken by the Central Departments, and that the organization and supervision of the service should rest with those Departments either directly or through the agency of the local bodies responsible for the administration of medical benefit.

On the other hand, the Minority of the Commission reviewed the same evidence and came to the conclusions:[13]

That the intentions of Parliament as to the control of Approved Societies by their members have not been realized.

That the Approved Society system is a hindrance to the development of a complete public health policy.

That it is undesirable to retain Approved Societies any longer as the agencies for the distribution of cash benefits to insured persons.

That local authorities could and should take the place of Approved Societies as the bodies through whom sickness and disablement benefits should be administered.

The entire Commission was in agreement that the development of a procedure of national negotiation on questions of professional relations and remuneration had left only routine tasks to the Insurance Committees and that these bodies were therefore no longer necessary. The Commission recommended:

That Insurance Committees be abolished and their powers and duties transferred to committees of the appropriate local authorities.

The Minority also recommended "That medical benefit should be extended to include attendance at confinement and dental and ophthalmic advice and treatment" and "that medical benefit should be provided for the dependents of insured persons." The majority of the commissioners did not concur in these recommendations; they were entirely sympathetic with the intent and with the evidence on the need, but were influenced contrariwise by other considerations of which the financial were the most weighty.

Since 1926, when the Commission was taking evidence, a large step was taken in the predicted direction by the Local Government Act of 1929 which consolidated all local medical and public health activities, *excepting only insurance medical service*, under the County and County Borough Councils. The further course of events is anticipated by Dr. McCleary in the following words with which he closes his book on British NATIONAL HEALTH INSURANCE:

> But the Act of 1929 did not touch the insurance medical service. It remains a thing apart—practically without coördination with the health work of the local authorities. It needs no gift of prophecy to foresee that a state of things so opposed to the spirit of unification that is now everywhere at work in the health services of this country cannot long continue, and that the medical treatment provisions of the insurance scheme will develop not as part of the scheme, but as part of a great unified system of national health service.

Thus, in Great Britain the march of events has been from voluntary insurance to compulsory insurance, and this has been accompanied by extension of the benefits—especially of the treatment (cash) benefits. At the present time the outlook is such that when general economic conditions improve, specialist service will be made if not a statutory at least an additional benefit for insured persons, and that medical benefit will probably be extended to the dependents of insured persons. The need for a readjustment in respect to specialist service is all the more acute because most of the service of this type is furnished to the poor and those with small incomes in Great Britain by unpaid members of the staffs of hospital out-patient departments. It also seems possible that there will be an increasing tendency to adjust the administration of medical benefits so that they will cease to be furnished in the present way (through independent practitioners serving under Insurance Committees created especially for this purpose) and will be absorbed into a national health service either through private practitioners operating under contract with the local (public health) authorities or through practitioners employed by these authorities or both. It seems at this time that of these two alternative procedures for medical benefit the former (contract service under the local government authorities) is the more probable development for the near future. Under such arrangements medical benefit would be further divorced from cash benefits, and insurance medical service would become part of a unified system of public health service embracing all medical and health agencies. It seems, further, that the financial difficulties in the way of extending medical benefits to the dependents of insured persons are greater than the corresponding difficulties in respect to making specialist services a statutory or additional benefit for insured persons. The latter is apparently the more likely next development because it would not require a general Parliamentary measure and because all but a few (and small) Approved Societies have surpluses which will be sufficient to furnish specialist care if the cost of such service is made the second charge on insurance funds. (Medical benefit is now the first charge on these funds.)

It is, of course, conceivable that the apparent course of events does not correctly anticipate what will happen. Yet, in serving our purpose in a search for the lessons which foreign experience holds for us in the United States, we must venture the judgment which the evidence compels.

Whatever the future course of events may be in Great Britain, judgment on the past and the present should be clear. There has never been any doubt among American students of health insurance that the British system has been highly esteemed by the British public and by the British government. In spite of the formal approval which the system has been accorded on numerous occasions by the British Medical Association, it has nevertheless been repeatedly alleged or implied in some American medical journals that the system does not have the approval of the British medical profession and that it does not operate successfully from the professional point of view. Upon inquiry in Great Britain among responsible representatives of the medical profession, one is told that the general view is correctly expressed by the colloquialism: "You couldn't blast the doctors off insurance practice with dynamite." In Edinburgh as well as in London one hears over and over again that not one physician in ten or one in twenty engaged in insurance practice would give it up. It is pertinent to quote at some length from a recent statement by Sir Henry B. Brackenbury, Chairman of the Council of the British Medical Association. His article was written for American periodicals[14] with the intent of dissipating any misunderstanding which may exist in the United States concerning the attitude of British physicians towards their own system of health insurance:

> On the whole, and leaving out of account for the moment those features of the British system which are not directly concerned with the provision of medical attendance and treatment, the results are beneficial to both [insured persons and physicians]: and when the expression "on the whole" is used it is not intended to imply that the benefit is just on the right side after nicely balanced consideration, but merely that there are some points of disadvantage which may be set over against an overwhelming preponderance of advantage. That this is so may be judged from the official resolution passed by the Representative Body of the British Medical Association almost without dissent: "The measure of success which has attended the experiment of providing medical benefit under the National Health Insurance Acts system has been sufficient to justify the profession in uniting to secure the continuance and improvement of an insurance system." It is some eight years ago that this resolution was passed, but since then it has been endorsed, further resolutions have been adopted pressing for an extension of the system

to bodies of persons who are not at present included in it, and by a growing conviction, born of intimate experience, it is acknowledged that any suggestion of the abolition of the scheme would be received by an overwhelming and emphatic protest from the profession and insured population alike.

It is important to emphasize the official and definite character of these and the following expressions of opinion of the medical profession of Great Britain in view of the different and incorrect impressions which have been conveyed to American physicians in certain British "correspondence."

. . . the fact that the provision of cash benefits payable during incapacitating sickness has led to increased claims cannot be taken as indicating any actual deterioration in the general health. It must be borne in mind that the insurance scheme applies to not much more than one-third of the population, that the effects of prolonged unemployment and the aftermath of war are still with us, that the propaganda in favor of securing early medical attention and of realizing the importance of minor illness must at first tend to swell the periods of sickness, and that the recent actual prolongation of life almost necessarily increases the total of such periods. These and other purely medical considerations fully account for an increase in sickness claims. Whatever be its actual effects on the public health there is no doubt at all that the insurance scheme has brought to large numbers of persons the advantage and comfort of having a family physician or private medical adviser in whom they have confidence.

The results to the medical profession itself have also been, in general, advantageous. The system has, in almost all areas and in the case of a large proportion of individual practitioners, increased the feeling that we are colleagues rather than rivals, and has brought about a more conscious relationship between family practice and various aspects of public health service. These are considerable gains. Financially, too, the effects have been beneficial. The aggregate income of members of the profession practicing under the scheme has been largely augmented. There are probably thousands of general medical practitioners today who, without the insurance scheme, would not have been able to earn by the exercise of their profession a sufficient income on which to live. It must not be understood that any money is coming to them through these state insurance arrangements which they have not fully earned. It is the greatly increased amount of work which the scheme provides for a guaranteed reasonable (though some think not a fully adequate) payment that has led to this improvement. In addition, a large number of physicians find it a relief and comfort that they can now give a fuller attention to many of their poorer patients without the thought that those patients will be afterwards distressed by the presentation of a bill. There is not evidence that the general quality of professional work has in any way deteriorated. No doubt, as in other branches of medical work, there are some who are less skillful and less conscientious than others; but comparing like with like, the best with the best, or the average with the average, it is safe to say that the quality of the service rendered is at least as high among insurance doctors as it is, say, in private practice or in hospital out-patient departments.

Sir Henry Brackenbury adds to his comments on the experience of British physicians some pointed advice which seems highly significant for American students of health insurance and which is pertinent here:

> In conclusion, if, as the result of the British experience, one were to offer any advice to members of the profession or other persons interested in public health elsewhere, one would feel inclined to say with a good deal of emphasis, that, whatever variation there might be in many details of any proposed insurance health service, certain conditions should be regarded as essential for smooth working and success.
>
> First the three unusual features of the English scheme . . . should be regarded as absolutely fundamental—the right of all doctors to be members of the service, the absence of interference between doctor and patient as such when once this relationship has been brought about; the close and appropriate association of the profession itself with the administration.
>
> Secondly, the scheme for provision of medical benefit (i.e., medical advice and treatment) should be separated as completely as possible, both financially and administratively, from any insurance provision for cash payments of any kind.
>
> Thirdly, the scheme should, from the beginning, make provision for a full medical service, not merely for general prac-

titioner attention but also for consultant, specialist, and other ancillary services, and, where circumstances allow, for institutional treatment also. Because of historic reasons which govern the provision and maintenance of the institutional care of the sick in Great Britain, it is found impossible in this country to incorporate hospital provision as an integral part of an insurance scheme, but practicable, however, to secure such provision in direct and intimate association therewith.

Fourthly, the scheme should be administered as simply as possible in topographical areas, and not through a multiplicity of "approved societies." In Great Britain, owing to the vested interests which have already been established, it is recognized that Approved Societies may require to be represented on whatever local committees administer the scheme. Most of the difficulties and complications that have from time to time arisen under the existing English scheme have been due to the fact that these last three conditions have not been fulfilled; and the British Medical Association in the spring of 1930 issued "Proposals for a General Medical Service for the Nation," incorporating the above stated general principles and urging the extension of the sickness insurance law to cover not only the insured employees themselves but also the members of their families, to provide the services of specialists as well as of general practitioners, and to arrange for hospital care, as measures for increasing the provision which the present law furnishes for attending to the health of the people by securing full medical attention for them. Financial stringency has prevented any attempt to establish such provision during the past three years, but the scheme has been very favorably received in general, and it is under discussion by societies and authorities interested in the public health.

Finally, attention should be called to the fact that at least one of the inadequacies of British National Health Insurance has been in part corrected through the development of an important movement for voluntary hospital insurance. It has been repeatedly emphasized in the preceding pages that the British system applies only to the low income classes, covers only about 40 per cent of the population, and guarantees only the services of the general practitioner and the medicines and appliances which he prescribes. Sixty per cent of the population does not fall within the scope of the law; neither the middle nor upper income classes are embraced nor the families of the insured persons. Nor is maternity care, specialist or hospital service provided.

In ordinary circumstances, the services of the general practitioner are responsible for only a fraction of medical costs. The services of the specialist and of the hospital account for large portions of the costs and for even larger portions of those costs which come unexpectedly, in large sums and in a burdensome manner. It is therefore not surprising that insurance against one or both of these types of medical costs, especially against hospital costs, has been developed on a voluntary basis to supplement the benefits of compulsory insurance. The rapidity with which contributory schemes of voluntary hospital insurance have grown may be seen from the following figures applying to the Hospital Saving Association (London):

Year	Number of Contributors
1924	62,390
1927	351,875
1930	810,144
1933	1,156,888

The following paragraphs, quoted from a recent review[15] by Dr. Michael M. Davis, give some pertinent facts concerning the development in respect to hospital insurance:[16]

The hospitals in Great Britain include about 170,000 beds, of which about 120,000 (more than two thirds) are tax-supported. The remaining 50,000 beds are in the voluntary hospitals, which confine their work to acute cases. The government hospitals provide for practically all chronic cases and are taking an increasing proportion of acute conditions. These hospitals collect payments from patients who are able to pay, up to the cost of care. Their medical staffs are mostly salaried.

Voluntary hospital insurance has grown extensively during the last ten years, under the name of "contributory schemes." The members of these schemes include wage earners, and others of economic groups similar to persons insured under the national health-insurance act. A part of the costs of the hospital care of these persons and their dependents is thus met. Twelve million persons or more are now covered by these schemes, and the membership is mounting steadily. In some British communities, the schemes now pay enough to cover three fourths or more of the hospital costs. In other places only half the costs are met, but the proportion is tending to increase. Physicians' services have by tradition been given free in the voluntary hospitals of Britain but the principle that payment should be made to physicians by the contributory schemes is becoming recognized and will gradually be extended in practice. Contributory schemes for middle-class people, at much higher rates and including professional fees, are also beginning.

Taking the British system as a whole, and including both the compulsory and the voluntary insurance systems, it is apparent that only a part of the total cost of medical care is paid for by insurance, even for insured persons, and very little for the members of their families. The scope of medical care under British compulsory insurance has thus far been scaled down to a cost that could be met by the lower-paid wage earners and their employers, with some aid from the state.

Whether hospital insurance will continue to grow as an independent and voluntary form of contributory insurance, or whether it will be absorbed into an enlarged and unified program of national health insurance, remains to be seen.

The evidence is clear that the British public, the professions and the government authorities are united in seeking a path to broaden the scope of insurance medical benefits and to enlarge the size of the insured population. The development of municipal (county) general hospitals under the powers delegated to local authorities by the Local Government Act, 1929, is now beginning to have far-reaching consequences for the whole question of hospital care and medical services generally. The municipal hospitals are open to the public at large and the duty is laid upon the authorities to recover fees from all patients able to pay (except in Scotland where the authorities *may* collect fees). The visiting and consultant staffs, as well as the resident staffs, of the municipal hospitals are paid for the services they render; the staffs (except the resident staffs) of the voluntary hospitals are unpaid. These (and other) paradoxical conditions have created a large hiatus in British hospital services, especially because a large proportion of hospital medical service is furnished by salaried staffs in Great Britain.

Although voluntary, contributory, hospital insurance has given a new element of financial strength to the voluntary hospitals, it remains to be seen to what extent it will serve as an effective alternative to the growing movement for the provision of hospital service through the public purse. The outcome of the present developments will have important effects, not only upon hospital care but also upon all medical services, including those furnished under National Health Insurance. This is evident when it is recalled that "hospital care" is coming to mean not merely bed, board and nursing in the hospital but also general and specialist medical care, consultant services and general medical care for the ambulatory sick in the clinics and out-patient departments. Public demand, technical need and economy of cost combine to place more and more emphasis upon the hospital as the place where the coördinated services demanded by modern medical arts and sciences may be made available.

As against those currents which seem to be carrying Great Britain towards the development of a comprehensive public medical service, the British Medical Association has published carefully devised plans for the provision of services to supplement those furnished under National Health Insurance.[17] These apply particularly to: (a) medical service by private practitioners for those persons who are dependent upon public support, for ante-natal and natal care, and for school medical services; (b) private consultant and specialist services for people of small means; and (c) paid medical-staff services in the voluntary hospitals. Interesting developments may be expected in the next few years.

REFERENCES AND NOTES

1. For reviews of the disciplinary machinery, the interested reader is referred to MEDICAL INSURANCE PRACTICE (*3rd ed.*), by R. W. Harris and L. S. Sack. London, British Medical Association, 1929, 384 pp.; to the ANNUAL REPORTS OF THE MINISTRY OF HEALTH; and to the ANNUAL REPORTS OF THE CHIEF MEDICAL OFFICER OF THE MINISTRY OF HEALTH. London, His Majesty's Stationery Office.

2. McCleary, George F.: NATIONAL HEALTH INSURANCE. London, H. K. Lewis & Co., Ltd., 1932, p. 127.

3. SIXTEENTH ANNUAL REPORT OF THE MINISTRY OF HEALTH, 1934–1935. London, His Majesty's Stationery Office, 1936, p. 255.

4. *Ibid*, p. 242; *see also* p. 264 for the corresponding data for Wales.

5. REPORT OF THE ROYAL COMMISSION ON NATIONAL HEALTH INSURANCE. London, His Majesty's Stationery Office, 1928, p. 13.

6. *Ibid*, p. 16.

7. *Ibid*, p. 34.

8. For an extensive review of this subject, *see* INTERNATIONAL STUDIES ON THE RELATION BETWEEN THE PRIVATE AND OFFICIAL PRACTICE OF MEDICINE, by Sir Arthur Newsholme, *op. cit.*, Volume III (see page 70).

9. THE BRITISH MEDICAL ASSOCIATION'S PROPOSALS FOR A GENERAL MEDICAL SERVICE FOR THE NATION. London, Office of the Association, August, 1930, 48 pp.

10. For a discussion, *see* NATIONAL HEALTH INSURANCE, *op. cit.*, p. 166 *et seq.* and the REPORT OF THE ROYAL COMMISSION ON NATIONAL HEALTH INSURANCE, *op. cit.*, 408 pp.

11. REPORT OF THE ROYAL COMMISSION ON NATIONAL HEALTH INSURANCE, *op. cit.*, p. 58.

12. *Ibid*, pp. 95–122.

13. *Ibid*, p. 327.

14. Brackenbury, Sir Henry B.: Health Insurance in England. *New England Journal of Medicine*, April 12, 1934, ccx, No. 15; *also* The Milbank Memorial Fund *Quarterly*, July, 1934, xii, No. 3, pp. 194–202.

15. Davis, Michael M.: How Europeans Pay Sickness Bills. *Survey Graphic*, December 1, 1934, xxiii, No. 12, pp. 617–619.

16. For a comprehensive discussion of the hospital situation, *see* Recent Tendencies in the Development of General Hospitals in England, by M. D. Mackenzie. *Quarterly Bulletin of the Health Organisation*, League of Nations, June, 1934, iii, No. 2; and concerning hospital insurance, British Hospitals Finance with Special Reference to Hospitals Contributory Funds, by Sydney Lamb. Address at American Hospital Association Convention, Philadelphia, September 27, 1934, 32 pp.

17. *See,* for example, the summary in The Future of Medical Practice, by G. C. Anderson, Supplement to the *British Medical Journal,* June 29, 1935, i, p. 301; *also* Free Choice of Doctor for Rate-Aided Persons, Supplement to the *British Medical Journal,* January 6 and 13, 1934; Domiciliary Public Assistance Medical Service Schemes, *ibid,* May 4, 1935; *also* B.M.A.'s Proposals for the Provision of a Public Assistance Medical Service. London, British Medical Association.

CHAPTER XI

COMPULSORY SICKNESS INSURANCE IN FRANCE

INTRODUCTORY

AFTER nearly ten years of parliamentary discussion, France finally adopted on April 30, 1930, a comprehensive law on social insurance, furnishing protection against the hazards of sickness, maternity, invalidity, old age, and death. About eight and three-quarter million employed workers were at that time brought into a plan which provides cash and medical benefits during illness.

It is too soon to attempt more than a preliminary evaluation of the operation of the French health insurance system, especially in respect to the medical provisions. Nevertheless, the system is of great interest because medical benefit is provided through arrangements which are in many respects unique and which are particularly significant because many fundamental elements in their design were dictated by the medical professions.

France has had long experience with voluntary insurance against sickness.[1] Such insurance received legal status by the law of July 15, 1850, and the organic decree of March 26, 1852. In 1853 there were already 2,695 mutual insurance societies; in 1880 there were 6,777 societies with over 1,000,000 members; in 1920 these had increased to 19,651 societies and 4,061,000 members, and in 1930 to 22,470 societies and 6,595,000 members.[2] Although they had functioned through a period of approximately eighty years and had fostered the idea of insurance, these associations had been of limited usefulness, principally because the fees paid by their members were so small that they provided inadequate payments to physicians and were incapable of supporting extensive or satisfactory medical service. After the World War, the need for more comprehensive insurance was made acute by the existence in Alsace and Lorraine of the insurance system formerly established by Germany. France had to choose between establishing a system of similar scope in the other provinces and discontinuing the existing and well-supported system in Alsace and Lorraine. Successive governments decided in favor of the former. A movement for the extension of sickness insurance was also stimulated by the general need for an expansion of social insurance to deal with the underlying causes of social and political unrest throughout the country and to attempt a reduction in the alarmingly high death rate of France. Social insurance was formulated as an answer to economic and social insecurity.

The original social insurance bill of 1921 experienced many vicissitudes during its nine years of debate and discussion in the legislature.[3] Finally, a thoroughly revised draft was passed by the Senate in July, 1927, by a vote of 269 to 2, was passed by the Chamber of Deputies in the following March, and became a law as the Act of April 5, 1928. After subsequent revisions (especially on August 5, 1929, and April 30, 1930), the final text came into effect July 1, 1930, although benefits did not become payable until October 1, 1930, thus providing a three-months' period during which operating reserves accumulated. Although the law provides insurance against sickness, maternity, invalidity, old age, and death, we shall review only the provisions against sickness and maternity and shall consider only briefly insurance against invalidity.[4]

Before the scope and substance of the present law can be profitably considered, certain explanatory remarks are necessary to outline the general framework of social insurance in France. Otherwise the description will seem confusing and contradictory.

While it is true that the law of April 5, 1928, *coördinated* the several measures designed to give social and economic security to the citizens, it did not *integrate* them; various measures are brought under coördinated supervision in the central government bureaus and there are coördinating relationships in the local administrative agencies, but a number of these measures remain otherwise separate and discrete. Sickness insurance must be visualized as one element in a broad program whose composition reflects its historical background and which consists of the following:[5]

    I. *General System of Social Insurance*
        Scope: Sickness, maternity, invalidity, old age, and death
        A. System applying to workers in industry and commerce, and to domestic servants
        B. System applying to agricultural workers
    II. *Workmen's Compensation and Occupational Disease Insurance*
    III. *Miners' Insurance*
        A. Sickness insurance
        B. Invalidity, old-age, and widows' and orphans' insurance
    IV. *Seamen's Insurance*
        Scope: Accident, sickness, invalidity, old age, and death
        A. Insurance against occupational risks with Seamen's Provident Fund
        B. Invalidity, old-age, and widows' and orphans' insurance
    V. *Railwaymen's Insurance*
    VI. *Postal Workers' Insurance*
    VII. *Government Manual Workers' Insurance*
    VIII. *Social Insurance in Alsace and Lorraine*
        A. Workmen's compensation
        B. Sickness insurance
        C. Workers' invalidity, old-age, and widows' and orphans' insurance
        D. Salaried employees' invalidity, old-age, and widows' and orphans' insurance
        E. Miners' invalidity, old-age, and widows' and orphans' insurance
    IX. *Voluntary Unemployment Insurance*
    X. *Voluntary Social Insurance*

In addition, there is the system of *Social Assistance* which includes:

    1. Assistance for the aged, infirm and incurable
    2. Unemployment relief

3. Shipowners' liability toward sick and injured seamen
4. Welfare offices
5. Free medical and hospital assistance for indigents
6. Tuberculosis service
7. Lunacy service
8. Assistance for large families
9. National scheme to encourage large families
10. Birth bonuses
11. Maternity assistance
12. Assistance for destitute children

Review of the entire program is beyond the scope of this chapter. Our interest lies with the first element, the *General System of Social Insurance*, but it must be kept in mind that this is part of the larger program and that its limitations are in part explained by the provision of other measures of social insurance or social assistance. In addition, it must be remembered that there are other public health and welfare provisions of the national government and of the *départements, cantons* and *communes*.

For the purposes of this chapter, attention will be concentrated upon sickness insurance of class I–A in the foregoing outline, dealing with the largest system of sickness insurance and embracing workers in industry and commerce and domestic servants. When reference is made to sickness insurance for agricultural workers (or for other groups), this will be specified.

SCOPE AND CONTRIBUTIONS

The present law applies to all employed workers of both sexes who are between the ages of thirteen and sixty and who earn less than a specified income. The limit is placed, in general, at 15,000 francs (about $600 when the franc was worth about 4 cents and now about $1,000)[6] for those who live in the country or have no children. In large cities, the limit is set at 18,000 francs. It increases 2,000 francs for each of the first two dependent children; the maximum for larger families is fixed at 25,000 francs. Children who work for their own parents without pay, temporary or occasional workers, and those employed less than 90 days in a year and those earning less than 1,500 francs a year are excluded from obligatory insurance. Those employed persons who are already covered by similar insurance (civil servants, employees of railways, coal mines, etc.) are also excluded temporarily until the insurance systems can be amalgamated. Furthermore, this law does not apply to Alsace and Lorraine (Haut-Rhin, Bas-Rhin and Moselle) where the special local scheme remains in force.

In commerce and industry, the contributions are divided equally between employers and employees and vary according to the size of the wages earned by the insured persons. The insured persons are grouped in five wage classes. As a rule, the payment of contributions is effected by affixing stamps to a card or a sheet bearing the name of the insured person, the system being similar to that in vogue in Great Britain. The employer is responsible for paying the joint contribution, and the worker's share is deducted from his wage. Some classes of workers, for example those working for several employers within a short space of time, are responsible for paying the contributions themselves.

When the insurance scheme was put into force the total contribution required to cover all the different risks was fixed at 8 per cent of the basic wage. The Act of 1930, however, provided that in order to cover the risk of invalidity, which according to the actuarial estimates required a contribution of 2 per cent of the wages, the contribution rate should be increased by one-eighth on April 1, 1934, and again by one-eighth on April 1, 1940. The original rate of 8 per cent would thus have been increased in two stages to 10 per cent. Article 37 of the Finance Act of February 28, 1934, amended these provisions. It provided that until January 1, 1937, the expenditures on account of invalidity should continue to be met by a central fund and out of the general resources of that fund without any increase of contributions. On January 1, 1937, a special law shall determine the method by which invalidity expenditures shall be met. At the present time, the nominal contribution of 8 per cent of the basic wage is divided into two parts, one of which is allotted to sickness and maternity, and death insurance, and the other to invalidity and old-age insurance.

In the insurance scheme for agricultural workers, the contributions for invalidity and old-age insurance were formerly proportional to the basic wage, being fixed at 4 per cent; the contributions for sickness, maternity and death insurance were fixed by the rules of each fund, but could not be less than 10 francs per month, shared equally by the employer and the insured person. The decree-law of October 30, 1935, substitutes the following contributions covering all risks in agriculture:

Class	Annual Contributions (francs)		
	Insured	Employer	Total
1. Children under 16 years	72	72	144
2. Women	96	96	192
3. Men	120	120	240

These contributions are allocated between the risks of sickness-maternity and old age as follows:

Class	Sickness-Maternity	Old Age
1.	10/12ths	2/12ths
2.	10/16ths	6/16ths
3.	10/20ths	10/20ths

The fraction of the contribution pertaining to sickness-maternity is in turn divided to cover these risks, invalidity and death.

As a supplement to the contributions of employers and employees, the government contributes certain subventions for insured persons engaged in agriculture and agrees to turn over to the insurance system: (a) such sums as are due on account of the arrangement whereby the new insurance system relieved the government of established pension and old-age obligations (540 million francs a year); and (b) all the savings which may be effected in the expenditures of the central government for charitable purposes and one-half of the savings of local governments.

The combined contributions of employers and employees have in practice amounted to only 6.4 per cent of wages actually paid out. Various provisions of the law and difficulties of practice have operated to produce this net effect. Surpluses accumulated in the first periods of insurance practice have permitted the scheme to remain solvent despite the receipt of contributions at a lower rate than was intended.

The number of persons on the obligatory insurance registers for December 31st of each year has been increasing as follows:[7]

Year	Industry, Etc.	Agriculture	Total
1930			8,655,658 [a]
1931	8,482,894	794,858	9,277,752
1932	9,259,660	927,216	10,186,876
1933	9,635,264	1,034,831	10,670,095
1934	9,797,808	1,107,112	10,904,920

[a] Approximate.

Altogether, compulsory insurance now embraces approximately 11,000,000 insured persons and their dependents. However, contributions are being actually paid for considerably smaller numbers— about 6,300,000 in industry, etc. and about 640,000 in agriculture, or slightly less than 7,000,000 altogether. The compulsory feature of the law seems not yet to have become entirely effective.

The insurance plan operates under the control of the Ministries of Labor and Finance and the (consultative) Superior Council of Social Insurance. In each *département* (province), insurance is administered by a *service départementale* or *interdépartementale* (a decree-law of July, 1935, establishes *services regionaux*) and, under these, by the primary insurance funds (*caisses primaires*). There is no statutory limit on the number of primary *caisses*; insured persons associated for geographical, occupational or social reasons may combine for the creation of a *caisse*, subject to provisions laid down in the law and in the ministerial decrees. The primary and provincial *caisses* are, in general, operated according to the mutual aid insurance law of April 1, 1898. Existing mutual benefit associations were permitted to qualify as primary *caisses* by meeting the new requirements as to organization and membership control. The primary *caisse* is administered by a council elected by the members; the provincial *caisse* is administered by a council of at least eighteen, including members who may be elected by the insured persons (one-half or less), two physicians chosen from a list presented by the medical association with which the *caisse* has entered into an agreement for service (or, failing such an agreement, chosen by the other members) and six representatives of employers chosen by employers of the insured persons. Temporarily, as a provisional measure, members of the council are not elected by the insured persons but are named by the Minister of Labor from nominations submitted by various syndicates, mutual organizations, etc.

Persons required to insure who do not become affiliated with a primary *caisse* of their own choice are allocated to a *caisse départementale* by the provincial *service* to which they are charged by reason of their residence.

The insured risks are divided between those, like sickness, maternity and death, which are organized on a "distributional" or "assessment" basis and those, like old-age and invalidity, which are carried on a "capitalization" or "accumulation" basis (see page 153). The worker has complete freedom of choice in selecting the *caisse* or society to which he prefers to belong. A *caisse* cannot reject him on grounds of age or ill health. The distribution funds must maintain local offices and may not spend more than 3.5 per cent of their receipts for administration. Part of the income from contributions, needed for the payment of benefits which are expected to fall due within a short time, is assigned to the primary and departmental *caisses*; the remainder of the income goes to a Central Guarantee Fund where it is held in trust. The provisions for financial administration, protection against potential deficits in the primary funds, etc., are very complex. Their analysis is omitted because they have no direct bearing upon the purposes of this chapter.[3]

Until recently, the law permitted self-employed persons (and those who had been insured under the compulsory provisions but who became self-employed) to take out insurance voluntarily, provided they were French citizens under sixty years of age and their income was not in excess of the maximum specified in the law. These persons could insure for any or all risks covered in the law, except that their total contributions could not exceed 10 per cent of income. Persons who had been compulsorily insured but whose incomes had come to be in excess of the statutory limit had been permitted to insure voluntarily against all risks if their wages did not exceed the statutory limit by more than 2,000 francs. If the excess of their income was more, they could remain insured against death, invalidity and old age. The insurance funds could protect themselves against an excessive proportion of bad risks by requiring certificates of health from all *voluntary* subscribers except those who had been compulsorily insured. Married women who were not gainfully employed could insure against old age and complete invalidity, and against sickness or partial invalidity, by the payment of 10 francs a month. The insurance rates for voluntary subscribers were higher than for compulsory subscribers; there were no employers to divide contributions with them and their premiums were set higher in order to afford the societies financial protection against an excessive proportion of bad risks. This voluntary insurance, practised since 1930, was ended for non-agricultural workers by the decree-law of October 28, 1935.

Benefits of Sickness Insurance

Sickness benefits are furnished *in cash* and, *in a sense only, in the form of medical care.* The insured person is eligible to either kind of benefit only if he has at least sixty daily contributions* credited to

---

*Here and elsewhere it is customary to refer to "daily contributions." This phrase merely reflects the legal requirement that the contribution shall be measured as a percentage of the actual or average wage earned per day. In practice, contributions are paid at longer but stipulated intervals.

his account during the three months preceding the beginning of the illness.*

Cash Benefits. The definition of cash benefit is quite different in the industrial and agricultural insurance schemes. Whereas in agriculture the cash benefits for sickness, maternity, and death are, like the contributions, fixed irrespective of wages, the cash benefits in the case of industry and commerce vary according to the wage class to which the insured person belongs. Moreover, the conditions of award and the duration of benefits, both in cash and in kind, are in the case of agriculture left to be determined by the rules of the funds, whereas in industry and commerce they are determined by the law itself. Only in the case of invalidity and old-age benefits have provisions been the same for agriculture, industry and commerce.

In the insurance system for industry, commerce, and domestic service, a *cash* benefit of one-half the basic daily wage becomes payable to the insured person who is disabled by sickness so that he cannot continue or recommence his work, after a waiting period of five days of sickness for persons with less than three children or after three days for those with three or more children, and is paid up to a maximum of six months following the date of the first certificate of incapacity. This benefit ranges from 3 francs per day for workers in the lowest wage class to 18 francs per day for those in the highest. Cash benefits are reduced for hospitalized patients and are not paid if disability is due to an industrial accident (covered by workmen's compensation) or to a "culpable" illness. If disability continues beyond six months, the sickness benefit is discontinued, but the worker becomes eligible for an *invalidity pension* if he has been insured for the last two years and has had at least 480 daily contributions credited to his account.† (The invalidity pension ceases at age sixty, when the insured person becomes eligible to his old-age pension or annuity.) After fifteen days of illness the in-

---

*The decree-law of October 28, 1935, also specifies the minimum reserve which shall have been established from contributions.

†For those who entered insurance before age thirty, this pension is 40 per cent of the average wages earned since entrance to insurance; for others it is less.

surance fund pays for the insured person the cost of his premiums for old-age insurance (at one-half rate) and the insured has nothing to pay for this purpose.

In the event of death, the family of the insured, who has been insured for the year and has at least 60 daily contributions credited to his account during the three months preceding the beginning of his fatal illness, receives a funeral benefit of 20 per cent of the annual income, with a minimum of 1,000 francs plus 100 francs additional for each dependent child under age sixteen. In addition, widows of insured persons with at least three living children under thirteen years of age are entitled to a temporary orphan's pension for each child after the second under age thirteen. The orphans of an insured person, if under age thirteen, are entitled to orphans' pension (or up to age sixteen if attending school, receiving vocational training, etc.). Thus, in a proper sense, this is *a series of death benefits* rather than a *funeral benefit*.

The cash benefit in a *maternity* case includes the usual cash sickness benefit of 50 per cent of the basic wage for six weeks before and six weeks after confinement if the insured woman abstains from remunerative work during these periods; a nursing bonus of 150 francs per month for four months and a smaller bonus in each of the five succeeding months; and certificates to supply milk for the baby if the mother is unable to nurse her offspring. The maternity cash benefit is restricted to those persons who have been credited with at least 60 daily contributions during the three months preceding the presumed beginning of the pregnancy.

The *medical* benefit furnished under the French law is more like the German than the English provision in scope. It embraces treatment for the insured person, his wife and his children who are under sixteen years of age and who are not gainfully employed, for all illnesses, according to the need, and from the beginning. There is no waiting period. Treatment need not be restricted to the services of a general practitioner; complete medical, surgical, and preventive treatment, and medicines and appliances are covered for six months in any one illness. These services may be received, according to the patient's need, in the home or in the office, clinic or hospital. It should be noted, however, that while treatment is *insured*, it is neither *guaranteed* nor *furnished*. The insurance funds (*caisses*) do not actually undertake to furnish medical care nor do they make specific arrangements for medical service. *The French insurance system merely insures the insured person against the costs of medical care* (and it will be seen later that it insures him against only a fraction of these costs). The insured person (or his dependent) obtains from his *caisse* a form which, when properly filled out and authenticated, identifies him as an insured person (or the dependent of one), purchases his medical service, pays for it, and then applies to his *caisse* for reimbursement of this expenditure.

Each *caisse* makes an agreement with the local medical association. This covers certain questions concerning free choice of doctor by the insured, identification of an insured person by a doctor by means of an insurance form, use of standard forms and common nomenclature in the fee schedules of the *caisse* and of the medical association, supervision of the local doctors by the medical association, etc. This agreement is binding upon each doctor who undertakes to serve insured persons of the local *caisse*, whether or not he is a member of this local medical association. The patient has completely free choice of physician and he may change his physician whenever he wishes to do so.

According to the legal interpretation given by the Superior Social Insurance Council, any doctor may attend insured persons whether or not he has agreed to the contract entered into by the medical association and the fund to which the insured person belongs. It is only necessary for a doctor to comply with the procedure laid down in the rules of the fund in treating the insured person for him to be authorized *ipso facto* if he is satisfactory from a professional standpoint. The professional supervision exercised by the medical association applies moreover to all doctors whether members of the association or not and whether or not they accept the terms of the contract. Thus, the funds do not have to draw up a list of doctors who are authorized to treat insured persons but rather to keep a list of doctors who by reason of proved misconduct are deprived of the right of treating insured persons.

It should be made clear that, unlike German or British practice, the insurance societies or funds do not remunerate the doctor, dentist, or hospital. The patient pays his own bills and is reimbursed by his insurance fund up to 80 or 85 per cent of agreed, standard rates for specified types of service.* This type of arrangement applies to services furnished by general practitioners, dentists, surgeons, other specialists, midwives, or hospitals, and to the costs of medicines and appliances prescribed by a physician. The law does not undertake to place any limit on the fees charged by physicians, dentists, hospitals, pharmacists, etc.; these fees are entirely a matter of private arrangement between the practitioner and the patient or between the institution and the patient. However, the insured patient is reimbursed by his *caisse* only according to a fixed scale of fees. The effect of the arrangement is to fix the maximum financial responsibility of the funds. If the patient actually pays his doctor the standard fee of the *caisse*, he is reimbursed 80 or 85 per cent (depending upon his wage class†), and he himself pays 15 or 20 per cent. If the patient pays a fee larger than the standard adopted by his *caisse*, that is his own concern; the amount he receives in reimbursement from the *caisse* is then a smaller proportion of his expenditure than if his fees had been as small as those fixed in the adopted fee schedule. In the case of hospital service, the *caisse* may pay its contributions direct to the institution instead of to the patient. Also, the *caisse* may arrange to pay the insured his "reimbursement" in advance, if he otherwise lacks money with which to pay for medical care.

*The reimbursements cited here and following are those which prevailed prior to the recent decree-law of October 28, 1935.

†The law specifies that insured persons in the two lowest wage classes shall themselves pay (i.e., shall not be reimbursed) 15 per cent and others in the higher wage classes shall themselves pay 20 per cent for professional services, and, regardless of wage class, shall uniformly themselves pay 15 per cent of the costs of pharmaceutical and other purchases (Art. 4, Par. 5).

The schedule of reimbursement has been changed by the decree-law of October 28, 1935 (Article 6). At present, the law requires the insured person to "participate" in the fee schedule of the *caisse* to the extent of 20 per cent; he is now reimbursed by the *caisse* uniformly, regardless of wage class, 80 per cent of the fee schedule. The same "participation" (20 per cent) applies to medicines, except that the "participation" is increased to 40 per cent for prescriptions which cost more than 25 francs. The higher the cost of medicines, the larger the patient's share of the cost. This practice has been introduced to curtail the abuse of the scheme, especially in respect to the excessive prescription and use of patent medicines.

"Ainsi, la loi ne garantit plus les soins, mais seulement le remboursement d'une part des frais de médecine, qui est fixée par le tarif de responsabilité." (Antonelli)

In a typical agreement between the *caisse* and the medical association the doctors agree as to the procedures which will enable the patient to be reimbursed by his *caisse*. The doctor is obliged to give a certificate or receipt to a patient who has identified himself as one who is entitled to insurance medical benefit. In an ordinary illness, at the time of performing each medical act, the physician dates and signs the form and specifies the act in terms of an agreed code of symbols. He indicates the probable duration of the illness and his general advice (stay in bed, stay at home, etc.). At the time of the last medical act, the physician specifies the last day of sickness. The sickness certificate is accompanied by a form which the patient must deliver to the *caisse* within forty-eight hours following the first medical consultation. The sickness certificate is effective for a maximum of fifteen days and only for one illness or for concurrent illnesses. (The October, 1935, decree-law makes each of the first two certificates valid for eight days only.) If the illness lasts longer than fifteen days, the certificate must be renewed each fifteen days and must be delivered to the *caisse* for reimbursement at the end of the period to which it applies. In the event some new sickness develops during the fifteen-day period but after recovery from the first, a new certificate is necessary. Thus, the physician supplies the patient with a record of the medical acts performed and with a certificate of incapacity for work. The first enables the patient to secure partial reimbursement from his *caisse* for the costs of medical care; the second furnishes the proof that he is entitled to cash benefit during his incapacity for work. The medical certificate does not tell the nature of the illness or of the medical act performed. The diagnosis is a medical secret; the service rendered by the doctor is designated only by a code symbol which applies to a *class* of medical acts, all of which are of the same price in the fee schedule.

The administrative arrangements which are made necessary by this system of legal provisions and agreements are inevitably complex and cumbersome. Furthermore, the development of sickness records and statistics becomes almost impossible and it is not surprising that almost no such data are available after five years of operation.

To control the consequences of this local and decentralized method of establishing fee schedules, and the otherwise unlimited expenditures which the *caisse* may become obligated to pay for medical services, the law carries two provisions: (1) except for cases which require special treatment, for each day of sickness the total cost to the *caisse* for all medical and pharmaceutical treatment (exclusive of hospital care) shall not exceed 50 per cent of the average basic wage of the members of the fund during the preceding year; and (2) the central administration (the Minister of Labor and the Superior Insurance Council) is authorized to fix the fee schedule beyond which expenditures by the insurance funds will not be (reinsured or) reimbursed by the central Guarantee Fund (the so-called *Tarif de Responsabilité*). A *caisse* may (with government approval) set its own schedule higher than the *Tarif de Responsabilité* when its finances permit. The circular of instructions issued by the Ministry of Labor (August 24, 1930) in effect allows the *caisses* to spend approximately 100 to 130 francs a year per *person eligible* to receive medical care or 155 to 180 francs per *insured person*.

In principle, therefore, the individual is insured in a state-controlled fund against certain risks or losses, such as part of his wage-loss, and against some proportion of the costs of medical care during illness. Theoretically, the physician who furnishes medical care to insured persons has no direct financial or professional relations with the insurance system since he is paid by the patient. Actually, as will appear later, the situation is more complicated.

TOTAL INCOME AND EXPENDITURES

During the first nine months of operation of the insurance system (July 1, 1930, to March 31, 1931), the contributions of employers and employees amounted to 2.4 billion francs. The gross receipts from these sources were increasing toward a stable figure of approximately 300 million francs a month or 3.6 billion francs a year. It was estimated at that time that the system would continue to operate for eight and one-half million wage-earners at this level, equivalent at that time to approximately $144,000,000 a year. Total receipts, including the contributions of the government, were expected to attain a value of about 5 billion francs a year when a large proportion of agricultural wage-earners have come into the system and that one-fourth of the sum contributed by the industrial insured workers and their employers (850 to 1,100 million francs) would be consumed by sickness benefits. During the first full year (1931), contributions actually attained the value of 3.56 billion francs. Since then, during the period of continuing economic depression, perhaps with more unemployment and certainly with lower wages, contributions have declined somewhat. Income has actually been as follows (in millions of francs):

Year	Contributions	Public Subsidy	Total
1930 (6 months)	1,497	270	1,767
1931	3,562	540	4,102
1932	3,262	540	3,802
1933	3,271	509	3,780
1934	3,173	540	3,713

Contributions and other income apply in part against current (assessed) risks (sickness, maternity, etc.) and in part against future (capitalized) risks (invalidity, old age). Accordingly, only part of the total income is spent during the year of collection and the remainder is invested to meet future obligations. During the last full year for which data are available (1934), expenditures for the assessment benefits have been as follows:

CLASS	NO. OF FUNDS	EXPENDITURES IN MILLIONS OF FRANCS			
		Sickness	Maternity	Death	Total
Compulsory					
Industry, etc.	775	938.6	153.7	33.4	1,125.7
Agriculture	338	60.5	16.2	1.7	78.4
Voluntary					
Industry, etc.	38	0.1	a	a	0.1
Agriculture	160	7.3	1.1	0.1	8.5
TOTAL	1,311	1,006.5	171.0	35.2	1,212.7

a Less than 1,000 francs.

As against an expenditure for sickness benefits anticipated in 1930 to equal between 850 and 1,100 million francs, we find that in 1934 the total for sickness and maternity benefits actually came to 1,178 million francs. In the preceding years, the corresponding totals have been as follows:

1930–1931	870 million francs	
1932	1,042	" "
1933	1,104	" "

Cost of Medical Benefits

Social insurance under the national law is of such recent origin in France that it is difficult to attach very much weight to the costs incurred in the first few years. Furthermore, the costs which have been published for the various types of benefits are still provisional and there are still many uncertainties as to the number of persons who were actually eligible to receive the various benefits. The costs of the medical benefits may, however, be illustrated from the experiences with sickness and maternity insurance in the first twenty-seven months. The data summarized in Table 15 are based upon the records of 59 *caisses* with an average of 869,000 insured persons during the fifteen months October, 1930, to December, 1931, inclusive, and of 66 *caisses* with 984,000 insured persons during the calendar year 1932, being based upon records which were especially studied for the purpose of a trial evaluation.[8] These records are particularly interesting because of the very fact that they apply to the first period of a newly-created insurance system.

Expenditures began October 1, 1930, three months after the law came into effect. The number of insured persons, the number eligible to receive benefits, the volume of benefits and the costs rose from the beginning to values which at the end of 1931 had attained levels which were maintained without great change in 1932. The cost of medical benefits increased; but this was offset by the decline in cash benefits. All sickness insurance benefits combined cost $3.85 per insured person per year in the first fifteen months, and $4.64 in the calendar year 1932. Of the latter, 40 per cent ($1.87 per insured person) was consumed by the cash benefits and 60 per cent ($2.77 per insured person) by the medical benefits. Maternity benefits cost $0.88 per insured person in 1932, two-thirds being the costs of the medical benefits for mother and child. The two risks, sickness and maternity, cost $5.52 per insured person in 1932. The medical benefits for sickness and maternity cost $3.34 per insured person in 1932. The costs of medical benefits cited here represent only expenditures made by the *caisses* and are therefore only about 80 per cent of the expenditures authorized for the insured persons under the established fee schedules of the *caisses*; the insured are not reimbursed for about 20 per cent of the authorized fees for the medical agents or the drug stores. (We shall see later that the fees of doctors are actually considerably more than the authorized fees of the insurance societies. Hence, the sums cited in the tables are much less than 80 per cent of the expenditures actually made by the insured persons.)

TABLE 15

EXPENDITURES FOR SICKNESS AND MATERNITY INSURANCE IN FRANCE

Based upon the Experiences of 59 *Caisses* in 1930–1931 and of 66 *Caisses* in 1932

EXPENDITURES[a]	TOTAL		ANNUAL COST PER INSURED PERSON[b]		PER CENT	
	1930–31	1932	1930–31	1932	1930–31	1932
SICKNESS INSURANCE	$4,177,200	$4,565,700	$3.85	$4.64	100.0	100.0
Medical benefits	1,861,300	2,723,600	1.72	2.77	44.6	59.7
Physicians' fees	780,300	1,223,800	0.72	1.24	18.7	26.8
Surgeons' fees	118,400	160,100	0.11	0.16	2.9	3.5
Medicines, etc.	753,700	948,400	0.70	0.97	18.0	20.8
Hospitals, etc.	208,900	391,300	0.19	0.40	5.0	8.6
Cash benefits	2,315,900	1,842,100	2.13	1.87	55.4	40.3
MATERNITY INSURANCE	701,200	867,900	0.65	0.88	100.0	100.0
Nursing and medical benefits	419,400	563,300	0.39	0.57	59.8	64.9
Cash benefits	281,800	304,600	0.26	0.31	40.2	35.1
SICKNESS AND MATERNITY—TOTAL	4,878,400	5,433,600	4.50	5.52	100.0	100.0
Medical benefits	2,280,700	3,286,900	2.11	3.34	46.9	60.5

a Exclusive of administration costs. The data have been compiled from the report by Pernin.[8] For the periods to which the data apply the franc has been taken equal to 4 cents.
b 868,759 insured persons in 1930–1931; 983,793 in 1932. The costs per insured person are expressed on an annual basis. The data for October, 1930, to December, 1931, inclusive, have therefore been adjusted to a twelve-months' period *pro rata*.

In the first years of operation, the administrative authorities have been especially concerned with the relations between the expected and the actual costs. It was therefore very gratifying to them that the actuarial expectations were substantially validated in 1932 when the monthly social insurance costs had already begun to develop stable characteristics. Some benefits have cost more than was expected and others less; for example, medicines proved to be more costly and hospitalization less costly than had been anticipated. In the aggregate, however, the costs were not far from expectation and were less than the portion of the contributions which may be legally allocated to sickness benefits.

TABLE 16

A COMPARISON OF MEDICAL COSTS: FRANCE, GERMANY, ENGLAND AND WALES, AND THE
UNITED STATES

EXPENDITURES[a]	PER INSURED PERSON	PER ELIGIBLE PERSON
Actual expenditures for insurance medical benefits in France (66 *caisses*, 1932)	$3.34	Less than $3.34[b]
Average expenditure by legal sickness funds in Germany (1933)	8.87	4.86
Average expenditure for insurance medical benefit in England and Wales (1934–1935)	3.96	3.96
Average private expenditure by representative families in the United States (1928–1931)		
Family income under $1,200	7.80c	8.12d
Family income from $1,200 to $2,000	10.14c	12.16d

a Exclusive of administration costs under insurance.
b No data available but obviously less than $3.34 (the corresponding figure in the first column) because there are more "eligible" than "insured" persons by (roughly) 100 per cent.
c Expenditure per wage-earner or salaried worker.
d Expenditure per person in the family.

To gauge the significance of the sums provided for medical benefit, consider the comparisons shown in Table 16.

The amount potentially available for insurance medical benefit in France ($6.20 to $7.20 per insured person*) would exceed the actual expenditure in England and Wales but would still be less than the actual expenditure in Germany. The French fund could therefore permit a more generous provision of medical benefit than is provided in England and Wales and a more restricted benefit than in Germany, because fees for individual services are of about the same size in France as in Germany and Great Britain.† In 1932, however, the actual expenditures (by the *caisses*) for medical benefits in France were less than the British expenditures (the British expenditures were $4.69 per insured person in 1931 and declined to the figure shown in the table for 1934–1935), and were only 30 per cent

*1932; assuming the franc equals 4 cents.

†For example, the capitation fee which is paid to British insurance doctors has been equivalent to an average of 56 cents per service. This may be compared with 12 to 17 francs (at 4 cents per franc, 48 to 68 cents) paid by insurance funds per consultation in France.

of the German expenditures in 1929 ($11.21 per insured person) and 38 per cent of the German expenditures in 1933.

This comparison of insurance expenditures *per insured person* will be misleading unless their limitations are kept in mind. In England and Wales only the insured persons are eligible to receive the benefits, and the expenditure (shown in Table 16) applies to medical benefits only for these persons; in France and in Germany, however, both insured persons and their dependents are eligible and the expenditures cover medical care for both groups. It is therefore more significant to deal with the expenditures *per eligible person* than *per insured person*. Even costs *per eligible person*, however, contain elements of incomparability because they lump insured persons and dependents equally, despite the fact that in France insured persons and their dependents are eligible to equal, but in Germany to unequal, medical benefits. If the expenditures *per eligible person* are compared despite this limitation, it is found that in all three of these European insurance countries insurance expenditures for medical benefit *per eligible person* are less per person than the private expenditures made by families of comparable income in a representative American group. Or, to put the matter conversely: *in the purchase of medical services, American families of small means spend more (per person) from their private purses than is spent for medical care for insured persons and their dependents by the insurance institutions of France, Germany, or England and Wales.*

Although this observation is significant, its implications must not be carried too far. The comparisons are limited by several inherent difficulties of interpretation:

1. In addition to medical services which are purchased privately or which are furnished as insurance benefits, the poor are supplied medical services without direct charge by official and non-official agencies supported by tax funds or by charity or by both. It is not known whether the costs of such free care are greater (per capita) in the United States or in the insurance countries.

2. Fees for medical and hospital services are generally larger for comparable services in the United States than in the insurance countries and the same nominal sum generally purchases more medical care in these insurance countries than in the United States. This will be obvious to any American who scans the schedule of fees upon which the individual funds (*caisses*) in France are reimbursed by the General Guarantee Fund (*Tarif de Responsabilité*) or the fee schedules in use in German sickness insurance.

3. There is unfortunately no record of the expenditures made from their private purses by insured persons for medical care purchased as a supplement to or as a substitute for insurance services. If these expenditures were substantial, they might or might not bring the insurance expenditures which have been cited up to or nearly up to those cited for people who purchase medical services privately. There are no facts on these points and we cannot accept personal opinions as a substitute for the facts, however vigorously these opinions are expressed. The problem cannot be settled until reliable data become available.

Expenditures for medical benefits from the beginning of social insurance up to the present year may be illustrated from the costs of the principal insurance fund of Paris, the largest local sickness fund in France (and in Europe) with about 1,356,000 persons nominally affiliated with it and having approximately 1,100,000 insured members who actually pay contributions, and serving both them and their dependents.* The general distribution of expenditures, for sickness and maternity benefits only, for *La Caisse Interdépartementale Assurances Sociales de Seine et Seine-et-Oise,* is shown in Table 17. It will be noted that sickness benefits consume about 85 per cent and maternity benefits about 15 per cent of the total.† These proportions are the same as those which obtain for the *caisses* covered by the data shown in the preceding table. The sickness benefits are divided approximately 60 per cent and 40 per cent between medical

---

*Lacking exact data on the number of insured persons and dependents, it is not practical to express the costs on a *per-capita* basis.

†If death benefits were included, the distribution would be: sickness, 80 per cent; maternity, 15 per cent; and death, 5 per cent.

TABLE 17

THE COSTS OF SICKNESS AND MATERNITY INSURANCE IN PARIS

Expenditures by *La Caisse Interdépartementale Assurances Sociales de Seine et Seine-et-Oise*, 1930–1934*

BENEFITS	EXPENDITURES IN MILLIONS OF FRANCS			
	1930–31[a]	1932	1933	1934
TOTAL	185.42	145.08	145.33	128.73
Sickness benefits	150.22	117.77	121.62	109.23
Medical	84.12	70.23	77.29	69.93
Cash	66.10	47.54	44.33	39.30
Maternity benefits	35.20	27.31	23.71	19.50
Medical and nursing	8.25	7.79	6.68	5.56
Cash	26.95	19.52	17.03	13.94

*Compiled and computed from *Rapport du Bureau au Conseil d'Administration*, January, 1935. Data restricted to compulsory insurance.

[a] Fifteen months, October 1, 1930 to December 31, 1931.

and cash benefits. And this also agrees with the experience shown in Table 16. However, the maternity benefits for the metropolitan population in Paris are divided about 28 per cent for medical and nursing and about 72 per cent for cash benefits, as against (roughly) a reverse relationship between these two classes shown in Table 16.

It will be noted in Table 17 that medical services for the sick consumed 69.93 million francs in 1934 and that medical (and nursing) services for maternity cases consumed 5.56 million francs in the same year. How these sums were spent appears in some detail from Table 18. Of the sickness services, two-thirds of the costs (46.70 millions) apply to services for the insured persons themselves and one-third (23.23 million francs) to services for dependent wives or husbands and dependent children; of the maternity services, about 55 per cent (3.08 million francs) apply to insured women and about 45 per cent (2.48 million francs) to dependent wives of insured men. Both for sickness and maternity, the largest single class of expense is hospital care (including other institutions for the sick and convalescent). For cases of sickness, medicines and appliances cost more

TABLE 18

MEDICAL BENEFITS IN SICKNESS AND MATERNITY INSURANCE IN PARIS

Expenditures by *La Caisse Interdépartementale Assurances Sociales de Seine et Seine-et-Oise*, 1930–1934*

MEDICAL BENEFITS	EXPENDITURES (in millions of francs) FOR BENEFICIARIES OF THE SPECIFIED CLASSES			
	All	Insured Persons	Dependent Husbands or Wives	Children
SICKNESS INSURANCE—TOTAL	69.93	46.70	9.43	13.80
Physicians' fees	15.31	9.58	2.04	3.69
Surgeons' fees	5.17	3.39	0.76	1.02
Medicines, etc.	19.33	12.78	2.88	3.67
Dental care	5.37	4.43	0.79	0.15
Hospitals, etc.	24.55	16.37	2.94	5.24
Miscellaneous	0.20	0.15	0.02	0.03
MATERNITY—TOTAL	5.56	3.08	2.48	—
Physicians' fees	2.44	1.35	1.09	—
Surgeons' fees	0.05	0.03	0.02	—
Medicines, etc.	0.24	0.14	0.10	—
Hospitals, etc.	2.80	1.54	1.26	—
Miscellaneous	0.03	0.02	0.01	—

*Compiled and computed from *Rapport de Bureau au Conseil d'Administration*, January, 1935. Data restricted to compulsory insurance.

than physicians' services and nearly as much as physicians' and surgeons' services combined. Dental care accounts for a substantial but minor amount of the total expenditures. (These figures are exclusive of specific preventive and public health expenditures to which reference will be made later.)

GENERAL COMMENT

The French system of sickness insurance provides against the loss of wages caused by incapacitating illness and against the costs of medical care. Thus, like other national systems, it furnishes a measure of protection against both of the major financial risks created by illness. Like other national systems, the protection against wage-loss is only partial: the sickness benefit is fixed at 50 per cent of wages. Unlike other national systems which have been described, it does not undertake to furnish medical care; it undertakes only to provide insurance against the costs of such care. Furthermore, the arrangements whereby the *caisse* agrees to reimburse medical costs have three important limits upon the insurance protection: (1) the schedule of reimbursement is fixed according to a specified tariff of costs, not according to what the insured person actually pays; (2) the patient must pay part of the costs himself; and (3) the total costs, to the *caisse*, per day of sickness, is limited by the average basic wage of the persons insured in the *caisse*. To appreciate the significance of these limitations, we must turn back to their origins.

The benefits which are furnished by an insurance fund to the assured person are given in exchange for his contributions. The conception of strict insurance (*l'assurance individualiste*) envisages assuring to the individual money to replace a loss of money; when insuring against sickness, the insurance provides a guarantee against the costs of sickness and not against the sickness itself. The conception of social insurance (*l'assurance sociale*), however, envisages assuring to the individual protection against the risk of sickness itself, and not merely against the costs of sickness.

When the French legislature first began to formulate social insurance, it accepted the concepts of social insurance, particularly in respect to the social risks arising out of sickness and maternity and, in lesser measure, those arising out of invalidity; and it conserved the principle of strict insurance only for the risk of old age. This is evident in the first text of the law proposed by the government; in case of sickness or invalidity, the insured person was entitled to medical and surgical care, medicines, etc., and, in the event of incapacity, cash benefit. This proposal underwent some modification in successive drafts of the law. But when the law of 1928 accepted the principle that the patient had the right of free choice of doctor, the law also limited the obligations of the *caisse* by specifying that *benefits in kind* shall be limited by agreements as to costs. This modification in principle was then further emphasized in the law of 1930 which no longer guaranteed care but only reimbursement of a part of the costs (i.e., it dropped the provision of *benefits in kind*). To protect the *caisses,* there was written in first the provision that the patient shall pay part of the cost, second the limit on the total cost to the *caisse,* and finally (*l'amendement Thoumyre*), the provision fixing the limit of the forfeiture to be paid by the *caisse* per day of sickness in the event it cannot effect arrangements for medical care with the local medical association. Thus, by means of these reservations, the law of 1930 totally modified the character of the *benefits in kind* which were originally contemplated by the legislature and substituted another *benefit in cash.* Why did this happen? The answer lies in the attitude of the organized medical profession of France towards the relation of the doctor to social insurance and in the political influence which the profession was able to exert.

The profession took its stand for:

1. Freedom of every licensed doctor to undertake the treatment of insured persons and their dependents,
2. Free choice of doctor by the insured,
3. Freedom in the prescription of medicines,
4. Payment of the doctor by the insured,
5. Payment according to the medical act,
6. Preservation of privileged communication, and
7. Discipline of doctors by the profession.

It would take us far afield to review the basis of each of these "principles" or the fierce battles which have been waged over them. It must suffice to point out that: the 1st, 2nd, 3rd and 7th are intended to preserve the physicians from "lay control" and to assure them fair and free competition among themselves; the 4th and 5th are alleged to be essential to the maintenance of the "intimate, personal relation between doctor and patient"; the 6th is supposed to preserve the cherished confidential relation of doctor to patient and, in the social insurance debates on this point, revolved primarily about the refusal of physicians to reveal the diagnosis or the nature of the insured person's illness or the treatment furnished.* So much ink has been spilled over these "principles" that it is impossible to do the subjects justice in any brief account.† For our present purposes it is sufficient to report that the French medical professions, with their large representation in the legislature, won their demands. The law of April 30, 1930 (Article 4, paragraph 2) specifies that the patient has free choice of doctor (*L'assuré choisit librement son praticien*) and other provisions in the law (and in the decrees) assure the physicians their independence from any restraints or co-operative arrangements which social insurance might require. As has already been noted, the physician has no relation with the *caisse* or the insurance system, except to give the insured patient a record certifying the performance of a medical act and indicating the general nature of the regimen he has ordered, whether or not he has prescribed medicine, and his judgment on the patient's capacity for work. These principles remain intact in the decree-laws of October, 1935.

The administrative arrangements under which the medical benefits are provided in France were, in large measure, dictated by strongly organized medical professions, guided by the experience of their professional colleagues in countries with older insurance systems.[10] Presumably, these regulations adopted in France are therefore largely "what the doctor wants." Nominally, there is complete professional freedom from lay control, complete maintenance of the prized "personal relation" between doctor and patient and of the confidential relation upon which the French physicians place so much emphasis. As in the German, British, and other systems, the physician still has the dual task of providing care and of certifying disability for cash benefits. But in certification for cash benefit the French

---

*It goes back to the historic stand of French physicians objecting to the reporting, to the official authorities, of "reportable" diseases or of the cause of death on a death certificate.

†The interested reader is referred to reference No. 9 at the end of this chapter and to THE WAY OF HEALTH INSURANCE, by A. M. Simons and Nathan Sinai. Chicago, The University of Chicago Press, 1932, pp. 88–100.

physician need only certify the existence of disability; he is never required to reveal even his diagnosis. Thus, he is given much broader responsibility than is accorded his German or British colleague.

There is neither compulsion for physicians to undertake insurance practice nor to accept insurance patients; and the patient is assured free choice or change of physician on every occasion when he seeks medical care. The practitioners have neither salaries nor capitation fees. From their point of view, the insurance system operates merely to enable patients to spend more for medical care because reimbursement (within specified limits) is guaranteed. The fraction of the agreed medical fee which is not reimbursed to the patient is intended to discourage frivolous and excessive requests for service. Standard fee schedules, used as the basis of reimbursing the patient and of limiting the medical expenditures for which the central fund will reimburse the *caisse*, are intended to limit the maximum responsibilities of the *caisse* and to hold within reasonable bounds the professional charges. Thus, as a matter of fact, the financial independence and responsibility given to the doctors are offset by automatic checks which operate to make the medical benefits niggardly to the patient and, through these restrictions, inadequately remunerative to the doctor.

It must be obvious that the key to the entire arrangement for medical care is the fee schedule of the *caisse* and its relation to the charges made by the doctors. In many places, fee schedules were established by the *caisses* by taking account of the minimum scale of fees which had been quite openly adopted by organized local groups of doctors. In Paris, the minimum fee commonly charged is larger than the adopted insurance fee. "In some localities there seems to be strong evidence that the doctors increased their charges after the new law went into effect because of the greater capacity of their patients to pay. In these cases, therefore, the system operated to increase the income of the doctors from each patient rather than to reduce the burden upon the patients by the full amount of the subventions. In addition, of course, the system has aided the doctors by making it possible for more patients to come to them for treatment."[8]

It soon became evident that the greatest source of dissatisfaction among the insured persons with medical benefit arose out of the fact that the difference between the reimbursements paid by a *caisse* and the fees charged by the doctors was so large as in effect to provide a substantial nullification of the insurance itself. Two types of adjustment have been made: (1) the medical societies revised their schedules of minimum fees downward; and (2) the central insurance authorities first empowered the *caisses* to raise their fee schedules in excess of the reinsurance schedule (*tarif de responsabilité*) when their finances permit (circular of March 19, 1931) and later increased the fees in the reinsurance schedule itself (1933, 1934). Thus, the minimum fee schedules of the medical societies and the reimbursement schedules of the *caisses* have been brought somewhat closer together. This entire arrangement, however, maintains a sharply drawn issue in France between (a) the purposes of social insurance to furnish insurance against sickness, and (b) the financial interests of the doctor. The reason for the persistence of the conflict is almost self-evident when one compares the *minimum* fees fixed by medical societies and the fee schedules of the *caisses*. For example, such a comparison for Paris, 1935,[11] in respect to some typical medical services listed in the schedules, shows the following:

	Medical Society[a]	*Caisses*[b]
Office visit	25 fr.	12.00 – 15 fr.
Home visit (day)	30	12.00 – 17
Home visit (night)	80	28.00 – 34
Intravenous injection	30	14.40 – 18
Lumbar puncture	100	48.00 – 60
Consultation	60	28.80 – 36
Delivery (simple)	1,000	240.00 – 300

[a] Minimum fee.
[b] The lower figure is the rural and the upper figure the urban fee.

It will be noted that the *minimum* fees established by the medical society are in general about twice the fees accepted by the *caisses*. The *caisses* reimburse the patient for only 80 to 85 per cent (prior to October, 1935; now for only 80 per cent) of the fee listed in their schedule. Thus, if the patient is charged by his doctor only the minimum fee, he will generally be reimbursed something between 33 and 50 per cent of his payment to the doctor. If he is charged more than the minimum, his reimbursement is even less. In spite of reductions in the fee schedules of medical societies and increases in the fee schedules of insurance funds, the patient himself pays a very substantial part of his medical costs. Hence, any illness which involves frequent, long-continued or expensive services may bring burdens of medical costs despite social insurance in France.

Although the French system has been in operation only five and one-half years, it has been evident since its first year that the conjunction of medical and cash benefits brings the same difficulties which are common in other countries where this joint provision obtains. "That granting the patient full power to change his doctor whenever he wishes creates temptations for hard-pressed or unethical doctors to certify malingerers as ill in order to retain their patronage, is of course obvious. It can be checked in part by the funds, but only in part. Perhaps the best thing that can be said for the whole system of medical provision under the act is that it is the type which least arouses the opposition of the doctors."[3]

The method of remuneration adopted in France was what the professions wanted. But now that they have it, they are beginning to be less certain it is what they want. Each *caisse* must guard its treasury and balance its budgets. If it does not take appropriate measures, it finds itself exposed to serving as a large financial reservoir into which any unscrupulous physician, in collusion with an unscrupulous insured person, can dip his net. It is therefore not surprising that the *caisse* has developed protective devices. When the insured patient presents a certificate to show that he has paid for medical service and is entitled to reimbursement, usually no question is raised and no complex check-up is invoked if the amount is small and the illness of short duration. But when the bill is large or incapacity for work is certified or the prognosis is for a long-continued illness, or the certification of incapacity is repeated once, twice, three times, the record is examined. What is the history of the case? What was the nature of the illness? What did the doctor say about it? What kinds of services were rendered and how many?

In some cases, a few inquiries are sufficient to settle all doubts, to justify the *caisse* in accepting the certificates, and to pay reimbursement for medical benefit and—when the patient is gainfully occupied but incapacitated—to pay cash sickness benefit on account of lost wages. In many cases, however, this is far from sufficient. And with hundreds of thousands of such experiences occurring during the year, the problem before the *caisses* becomes of enormous magnitude. The outcome has been the development by the large *caisses* of medical staffs and elaborately equipped facilities for the examination of patients—partial and complete physical examinations; independent diagnoses and prognoses; X-ray and laboratory examinations; special urological, dermatological, dental and other examinations, and consultations, etc. Thus, the *caisses* find themselves engaged on a large scale in checking the work of the individual private practitioners. While it is probably true that in France more than in any other large compulsory insurance country the plan of sickness insurance has operated to entrench the individual private practice of medicine, it also is true that there, more than elsewhere, it has led to the most extensive system of supervision over such practice of medicine.

In Paris—and perhaps in the large cities generally—about 50 per cent of the cases are investigated, and in about 60 per cent of these the patient is examined by the physicians of the *caisse* to check on the record. Medical supervision, investigation, hearings, etc., "bureaucracy," conflicts of opinion on medical issues, conflicts of judgment on costs—these and other difficulties have not been avoided by the French system of remunerating the doctor. On the contrary, by the victory of dictating the system of remuneration and of assuring all patients completely free choice of doctor, the French doctors achieved stringent limitation of fees, a complex and cumbersome fee schedule, necessity for close administrative supervision, conflicts with insurance authorities, and a considerable loss in public esteem. The confusion which has followed upon this Pyrrhic victory seems to have exceeded what occurred in Germany with salaries, per-capita payments and fee schedules, and is certainly vastly in excess of what has been customary in Great Britain under per-capita payments.

A saving feature of the present situation is the growing practice whereby the supervising physician for the *caisse* (*le médecin controleur*) confidentially makes available to the patient's doctor the findings from the control examinations. This is in the interest of better medical care for the patient and improved quality in medical practice.

It should be emphasized that in principle the French doctors won independence from the insurance authorities and freedom from lay control. In point of fact, however, they won a system which constantly requires the lay authorities and the doctors whom they employ to check, verify and supervise the work of the private doctor and the charges he makes to his insured patients. The supervision is not direct—in the sense that the private doctor does not perform his professional work under the nominal supervision of the insurance officers—but it is there none the less, in the guise of review of the doctor's certificates and the complaints which are referred to the medical societies. This is true of both his certification of disability (for cash benefits) and his certification of the patient's payment of fees (for reimbursement by the *caisse*). The medical profession is apparently satisfied with the general arrangements provided by the law. On closer inquiry it is found, however, that the physicians are bothered by the system of payment and are fearful of the lengths to which review and indirect supervision will develop. They are already apprehensive of the "preventive medicine" which is being practised by the *caisses*, although many leaders in the profession have become reconciled—and some even enthusiastic—over the possibilities of preventive practices. This deserves further explanation.

In the first place, the sickness insurance funds are charged by law with the responsibility of taking all necessary steps to prevent illness. In accord with this principle, and in recognition of the financial as well as social savings which may be effected by the prevention of disease, the large *caisses* have shown a commendable interest in preventive medicine and have made substantial expenditures for this purpose (especially through subventions to existing independent agencies engaged in public health work).

In the second place, the sickness insurance *caisse* is charged to take all proper measures within its resources to prevent sickness from leading into invalidity. In a sense, there is a conflict of interest between the sickness and the invalidity insurance funds: it is to the interest of the sickness fund to have the patient well (and back at work) as soon as possible; it is to the interest of the invalidity fund to have him treated as thoroughly as possible in order to reduce to a minimum the probability that the illness will lead to subsequent invalidity. To reconcile these somewhat conflicting interests, the sickness insurance fund has been charged and authorized to presume that each illness or disability which lasts two months may lead eventually into an invalidity and to take such special measures and to use such specially equipped institutions as may be most effective in curing the illness or disability and in preventing the development of invalidity. In consequence, the *caisses* devote substantial sums to carry out these preventive services. Where there is a tendency on the part of individual doctors to keep patients under their individual care for the six-months' period in an illness during which reimbursement of medical costs is guaranteed, the *caisses* attempt to discover through their own staffs and their own diagnostic facilities the nature of the illness and whether or not the patient needs care more substantial than can be furnished by the individual doctor. Early cases of tuberculosis, for example, are discovered in this way and are referred to the anti-tuberculosis authorities and may be transferred if the patient agrees to special establishments for the care of the tuberculous. Similarly, patients who need special orthopedic or other special care are discovered as early as possible and are reassigned from the individual doctor of choice to the competent agency.

It is widely charged (in France as well as in other countries) that sickness insurance has generally failed to prevent or reduce illness, even when it alleges to be "health insurance" rather than "sickness insurance." In the operation of the French scheme of furnishing medical benefit there is evident in a simple and clear fashion the apparent conflict of financial interest between the individual, private practitioner engaged in treating the sick, and the public authority charged with the prevention of illness. This conflict has been becoming increasingly acute because the sickness insurance funds have been actively interested in prevention and are spending considerable sums in carrying on preventive work. This is all the more striking because public health activities (in the sense in which they are understood and actually practised in the United States) are relatively backward in France.

It is frequently argued that the British system whereby the physician receives a fixed annual sum for each patient, no matter how much service is rendered, tends to interest him in preventive medicine and to discourage excessive and unnecessary treatment, and that the French system, based on fee-for-service payment, restricts preventive practice and encourages excessive treatment even beyond that which normally occurs in non-insurance practice because the patient is guaranteed reimbursement. Whether professional practice will succumb to the temptation and will try to make of the insurance system a means of exploiting the public, or whether unethical and anti-social practice will be held within bounds by professional control and by lay recognition of the mutual character of insurance, remains to be seen. For the present, it is at least certain that in France the medical professions have been partially freed from the burden of unpaid service for the poor; the fear of sickness costs has been partially lifted from many of the people of moderate means; and a new though limited opportunity has been provided both lay and professional groups to increase both the volume and the quality of medical service.

It has not been possible to avoid mention of an unfortunate relation between the financial interests of doctors and insurance funds. In all fairness it should be added that some leaders of the physicians have taken a strong stand to improve professional services and to encourage interest in preventive medicine. Furthermore, the medical societies are committed to the policies of supervising the work of individual practitioners and guiding them in coöperative relations with the insurance institutions. Whether or not this commendable stand will bear fruit, only future experience can tell.

REFERENCES AND NOTES

1. VOLUNTARY SICKNESS INSURANCE, Series M (Social Insurance) No. 7. Geneva, International Labour Office, 1927, 520 pp.

2. Antonelli, Etienne: LE DROIT DES ASSURANCES SOCIALES. (Volume I, considéré par rapport aux individus; Volume II, considéré par rapport aux organismes.) Paris, 1932–1933, 262 pp.; 253 pp.

3. Douglas, Paul H.: THE FRENCH SOCIAL INSURANCE ACT. Philadelphia, Annals of the American Academy of Political and Social Science, 1932.

4. a. ASSURANCES SOCIALES: Textes complets de la loi sur les assurances sociales (loi des 5 avril 1928, 5 août 1929, 30 avril 1930, 31 mars et 28 juillet 1931, et 31 mars 1932) et du Règlement général d'administration publique (décrets du 25 juillet 1930, du 22 septembre 1931, et des 15 février, 21 mars, 15 et 21 avril, 1932); Ministère du Travail et de la Prévoyance Sociale, Paris, 1931;
   b. Recueil Général des Textes concernant les Assurances Sociales: Loi, Règlement, Décrets, Arrêtés, Circulaires, Conventions; Ministère du Travail et de la Prévoyance, Paris, 1931;
   c. Loi sur les Assurances Sociales du 30 avril 1930 et Règlement d'Administration Publique: Textes mis à jour au 1er mai 1935; also Décrets-Loi des 28 et 30 Octobre 1935, Modifiant le Régime des Assurances Sociales (L'Union des Caisses d'Assurances Sociales de la Région Parisienne), Paris, 1935;
   d. SOCIAL INSURANCE (Legislative Series) ACT (France, 5). Geneva, International Labour Office, 1930;
   e. Antonelli, Etienne: GUIDE PRATIQUE DES ASSURANCES SOCIALES (3rd ed.). Paris, 1931;
   f. Cibrie, P. and Hilaire, C.: GUIDE PRATIQUE À L'USAGE DES MÉDICINS ET DES SYNDICATS MÉDICAUX. Paris, 1933;
   g. HEALTH INSURANCE (Monograph Three). New York, Metropolitan Life Insurance Company, 1933.

5. INTERNATIONAL SURVEY OF SOCIAL SERVICES, Series M (Social Insurance) No. 11. Geneva, International Labour Office, 1933, pp. 197–270.

6. The franc is taken equivalent to (variously) 4 to 6.67 cents, according to its value in the period to which data on costs apply. When sickness insurance was first initiated in 1930, the franc was worth 3.92 cents. It is about 6.6 to 6.7 cents now.

7. Jacquier, Paul (Ministère du Travail): Rapport sur L'Application de la Loi des Assurances Sociales. *Journal Officiel,* March 12, 1935; *also* preliminary report for 1934, L'Union des Caisses d'Assurances Sociales et de la Caisse de Réassurance.

8. L'ÉQUILIBRE FINANCIER DES CAISSES PRIMAIRES: LES PRESTATIONS (Annexe: Les Résultats financiers des Caisses au cours de l'exercice 1932) by Pernin, XIIIth Congrès National des Allocations Familiales et des Assurances Sociales. Paris, May, 1933, pp. 129–144.

9. Newsholme, Sir Arthur: INTERNATIONAL STUDIES ON THE RELATION BETWEEN THE PRIVATE AND OFFICIAL PRACTICE OF MEDICINE, *op. cit.,* Volume II (see page 70).

10. See, for example, the publications of La Confédération des Syndicats Médicaux Français; the French medical journals; the debates of the French Parliament, etc.

11. ANNUAIRE OFFICIEL DU SYNDICAT DES MÉDECINS DE LA SEINE, 1935, pp. 77–80; Tarif de Responsabilité, L'Union des Caisses d'Assurances Sociales de Répartition de la Région Parisienne.

CHAPTER XII

"VOLUNTARY" SICKNESS INSURANCE IN DENMARK
With Supplementary Notes on the Recent Change to a
Combined Compulsory–Voluntary System

Introductory

HEALTH insurance in Denmark has been of special interest because of the widely held opinion that Denmark has probably been more successful than any other European country in the administration of a national voluntary system. With this consideration in mind, the Danish system was selected for study.

On May 20, 1933, while this study was in progress, Denmark adopted three consolidating Acts which recast the national program of social insurance. A number of important changes were made in sickness insurance, chief among these being the provisions which make registration with a sickness fund and the payment of certain specified contributions compulsory for all resident citizens who are between 21 and 60 years of age. Enrollment for sickness insurance ceased to be voluntary in Denmark when these Acts came into operation October 1, 1933, although—as will appear later—active sickness insurance retained certain essential voluntary features.

Despite this change, a description of the "voluntary" Danish system and an analysis of its operation in the past is still pertinent to this study. Before the new Acts were passed our observations had already led to the conclusion that the Danish system had been voluntary in so far as membership was not *legally* required, but had had many compulsory features; the elements of compulsion have been social and economic. The shift to a system which has certain elements of

241

legal compulsion was therefore especially interesting. In the following pages, the Danish system is first described and its operation analyzed in terms of its form prior to the passage of the new Acts. Later, at the end, there is added a brief account of the changes made by the Acts of May, 1933, and certain data bearing upon the effects of the Acts on the scope of the insurance scheme.

THE INSURANCE SYSTEM PRIOR TO THE ACTS OF MAY, 1933

The Background of Sickness Insurance

Denmark has a total population of approximately 3,600,000 persons, of whom about 1,500,000 are gainfully employed. For administrative purposes, the country consists of twenty-three county districts—Copenhagen, and twenty-two other counties. In 1931 about 1,728,000 persons or about 50 per cent of the total population and about 65 per cent of the adult population were members of the state-recognized, sickness insurance clubs or societies. This is the largest proportion of a population directly covered by sickness insurance in any country with either a voluntary or a compulsory system, and even this figure underestimates the total coverage of the insurance system because it does not take account of the children (under fifteen years of age) of members, who are also covered by the benefits. It is estimated by the authorities that between 85 and 90 per cent of the persons eligible to insurance are actually insured. At the end of 1932, the last full year under the old system, there were 1,736,000 persons embraced by the system of sickness insurance. Somewhat more than 50 per cent of the members are women.

To understand the development of social insurance in Denmark, it is essential to keep in mind certain fundamental characteristics of the country. Denmark is small and the population is homogeneous in race and religion. Elementary education has been compulsory since 1814. Though the population is largely agricultural and individualistic, the people have long been accustomed to coöperative buying and selling, and to the operation of a central administration which has supervisory power over local authorities in health as well as in economic matters.

The country has for a long time had a complete system of municipal and county hospitals serving the poor without charge (at the cost of the municipalities) and rendering care to others at fixed fees which depend upon the type of accommodations used. In the municipal hospitals of Copenhagen, for example, the charge is 1.20 crowns ($0.32) a day in the wards; in other hospitals, 4 to 5 crowns ($1.07–$1.34) a day. These charges generally cover all types of services rendered, including medical care. For insured persons the fees are paid by their insurance societies at a 50 per cent discount; for those too poor to maintain their insurance, the charges are paid by their municipalities. Other persons pay their charges privately. The hospital physicians are salaried officers.

Since 1914, district health officers have been relieved of the duty of furnishing medical care to the poor. Instead, district physicians are employed on a full-time or a part-time basis. Persons afflicted with infectious disease are entitled to care without charge if they enter the special hospitals available for this purpose. Nearly all surgery and a large proportion of all medical care in serious illnesses are furnished in hospitals. General hospitals are erected by the local communities and, so far as fees fail to cover operating expenses, are supported by these communities out of tax funds. Public health, hospital, and private practitioners have been accustomed to work together coöperatively, efficiently, and with comparatively little friction. Thus, *Denmark has a substantial and long-established system of public medical service apart from but serving to supplement its sickness insurance system.* It is probable (though detailed data are not available) that the expenditures from tax funds for hospital and medical services are about equal in amount to the expenditures for medical benefits furnished through the insurance system.

The voluntary formation of sickness insurance societies had been growing during the nineteenth century in Denmark as in other countries. In the latter years of that century, when the need for expansion of social insurance became pressing, the country did not follow the German model. Instead, it developed a program based upon the principle of voluntary insurance, with the additional provisions of state subsidy for persons "without means" and state supervision over the societies which were to be approved and subsidized. When the enabling act came into force in 1892, the country already possessed about 1,000 benefit societies with a membership of more than 100,000 persons. Since 1892 many changes have been made. The provisions of the years 1928–1933 will describe the system substantially as it operated prior to the revisions introduced by the Acts of May, 1933.[1-4] In general, the latest available statistics apply to the calendar year 1931 and 1932. Although the data for 1933 are available, they are not very useful for our purposes in analyzing experience of years prior to the recent reorganization, because the new Acts became effective October 1, 1933, and the experience of the fourth quarter is merged in the official reports with that of the first three quarters of the year.

Membership and Contributions in the Sickness Funds

The state recognizes and aids those sickness insurance funds or societies which restrict their membership to particular trades or particular localities, submit their records to official inspection, abide by the government regulations, and admit to membership any "poor" person ("without means"*) between the ages of 14 and 40. (Orphans may be entered at any age under 14. Funds may fix a higher age limit than 40, but in practice all funds have this limit.) No person may be a member of more than one society. Sickness insurance is not restricted to gainfully occupied persons; the wives of such persons and any other persons may become insured if they meet the statutory requirements in respect to being "without means" and in respect to health. Wives are not insured by virtue of their husbands' insurance; they must become insured persons in their own right. Government

---

*Persons who are "without means" in the statutory sense are considered "poor" for the purposes of social legislation in Denmark.

aid is not limited to "workers" in the ordinary sense of manual workers, but applies equally to other persons in the same economic circumstances, i.e., farmers, artisans, tradespeople, civil service employees, and others "without means." Members' dependent children who are under 15 years of age are automatically covered in respect to the benefits furnished by the insurance system. The approved societies may admit to membership but receive no state aid for persons whose means exceed the limit prescribed by the state.

The economic limits set by the government for insured persons who are eligible to receive state aid vary from place to place but not in respect to occupation, and may be revised every year. The income limit is equal to the annual income of skilled workers at full employment. Lately the limits in respect to *income* have been between $750 in rural districts and $1,126 in and near Copenhagen (with additional allowances of $80 for each dependent child under 15), and in respect to *capital* between $2,600 for persons without dependents and $3,750 for persons with dependents.[5]

The contributions of insured persons also vary from place to place with the insurance society and from year to year, being dependent upon the size and the scope of the benefits furnished by the several societies. In 1931 the average was about $5.12 per member for the year. *Employers make no contributions for insured persons.* The state contributions consist of: (a) about 54 cents during the year per member whose income did not exceed the legally specified limit; (b) one-fourth the cost of providing the most important benefits to these members during the year;* and (c) three-eighths of the excess cost of the benefits provided to members who entered a society with impaired health, over and above the cost of benefits to members who entered in good health. In the aggregate, state contributions have amounted to about one-fourth of the total costs. In addition, the

---

*State aid of this category which is made in respect to medical care could not formerly exceed a total of $643,000. Therefore, this state contribution actually amounted to only about 15 or 16 per cent of the cost of medical benefits, instead of 25 per cent. We shall see that this limit in respect to state expenditures for medical care was abolished by the 1933 Acts.

societies receive from the tax funds of local governments: (a) hospital care at not more than one-half the normal charges; (b) three-eighths of the excess cost of benefits for impaired persons; and (c) voluntary grants which in 1931 equalled about 17 cents per member.

The law makes three provisions for the person who has been a regular state-aided member and whose means improve so that they exceed the specified limits for members "without means." (1) Such a person may retain regular membership, if the rules of his society permit, by paying in addition to the prescribed contributions a sum at least equal to the state contributions for other members whose income or wealth is less than the statutory limit.* If such a member again comes to have an income (or capital) below the limit, he becomes an ordinary member eligible to receive benefits and his society receives state aid on account of his membership. (2) The member with improved means has the privilege of transferring membership to a "continuation fund" which admits members "with means" and he may in adverse circumstances again transfer back to a state-aided fund. (3) He may remain a "non-regular" member of his society, i.e., he is not eligible to benefits but retains his right to become a "regular" member with full right to benefits if his means should decline below the statutory limit.

In 1925 there were 1,583 local funds, 53 trade funds, and 11 industrial funds with an average membership of 890 per fund and an aggregate membership of 1,479,000 or 63.2 per cent of the adult population. Between 1925 and 1931, the number of funds changed very little (1,592 local, 43 trade, and 10 industrial funds), but the total membership increased to 1,728,000—i.e., the average number of members per fund has been increasing. In the total number of members there were included about 25,000 non-regular members (not eligible to benefits) and 9,437 regular members with means.

The insurance funds are (voluntarily) combined, on a geographical

---

*This provision for regular members whose incomes have come to be in excess of the statutory limit is in practice scarcely used; there are now only about 6,000 members in this category.

basis, into "Central Unions" and these in turn are united in a national organization, "The Confederation of Central Unions of Sickness Funds in Denmark." Through this confederation the various funds have developed a central agency for coöperative negotiations with the government authorities and have worked out agreements whereby their members are given the right of transfer from one sickness fund to another, irrespective of age or health and without entrance fees or waiting periods. They have even worked out agreements with similar agencies for transfer of members with insurance funds of Norway and Sweden.

CASH AND MEDICAL BENEFITS

The benefits provided in case of sickness are (a) cash and (b) medical care. The legal minimum for cash benefit is 11 to 13 cents per day and the maximum four-fifths of the member's (or of all members') average daily wage up to a limit of $1.61 per day. Cash benefit may be paid up to a maximum of 26 weeks in twelve consecutive months; all benefits are limited to a maximum of 60 weeks in three consecutive years. The limitations upon sickness benefits may be indicated as follows:

1. No benefits are payable during the first six weeks of membership, except when due to an accident;
2. Cash benefits (in partial replacement of wages) are not payable for illness lasting less than four days (individual societies may extend this waiting period to seven days). However, for illnesses lasting longer, the benefit is payable as from the day on which the society was notified of the disability (incapacity). (Medical benefit is available from the beginning of illness without any waiting period);
3. Cash benefits are not payable for illness due to a "culpable" condition (fighting, drunkenness, etc.);
4. Cash benefits are not payable for illness during which the member receives his regular wage or in which benefits equal to his regular wage are provided from other insurance;

5. Cash benefits are not payable for illness in which the member receives benefit under the Workmen's Compensation Act; and

6. Cash benefits are not payable for illness contracted during an epidemic when medical care is provided at public expense (this provision may not be invoked without the approval of the supervising public authorities). (This limitation on benefit was abolished by the Acts of 1933.)

Before an insured person may receive cash benefit (in partial replacement of wages lost on account of incapacity to work) his incapacity must be certified to the insurance society by his physician. When the society doubts the continuance of an insured person's incapacity, it stops paying this benefit. The insured has the right of appeal to the director (the government supervising authority) who may make a finding of fact. The society has no right, however, to question a doctor's specific judgment on the existence or continuance of incapacity. Inquiries in Denmark indicate that these provisions work efficiently and harmoniously.

Medical benefit prescribed by law includes free medical attention in the home and in the physician's office, and hospital and sanatorium care, both for members and for their dependents who are under fifteen years of age. In addition, the funds may, under prescribed conditions, provide additional care such as specialist services, clinic care, dentistry, medicines and appliances, home nursing, convalescent care, etc. When the furnishing of medicines was made a permissible benefit, its popularity resulted in rapidly increasing costs. The law was then amended so that the society may not pay more than three-fourths of the cost of medicines; the member must pay at least one-fourth. This provision was partially effective in checking the excessive prescription and consumption of medicines, but the total cost of medicines has been steadily increasing. The state makes no contributions toward the cost of medicines.

Maternity benefit is prescribed for all funds and includes medical attendance. For members who have been contributors for at least ten months, it includes cash benefit of 1 crown (27 cents) or more per day for not more than ten days after childbirth and ordinary medical care thereafter. (The maternity benefits were altered by the Act of 1933; see page 260.) Prior to October 1, 1933, the sickness funds generally granted a maternity benefit of 3 crowns a day in Copenhagen, of 2 crowns in the provincial towns, and of 1 or 2 crowns in the rural districts.

No funeral benefits may be provided except as a contract of private insurance between the fund and an insured person. In practice, however, the funeral insurance society and the sickness insurance society are often managed by the same board, even though they remain separate legal entities in accordance with the Act of March 27, 1929.[2]

Medical service is provided by physicians working under agreements which are of two kinds. Outside of Copenhagen, the insurance institutions have no authority to select physicians; all physicians in good standing who report to the regional section of the Danish Medical Association that they are willing to serve, may be remunerated for services to insured persons. In Copenhagen, on the contrary, the doctors are engaged by the insurance societies. Physicians are remunerated either according to a fee schedule for the services they render or on a flat rate at so much per insured person per year (capitation fee). The total expenditures to physicians during a year are approximately equally divided between those who serve on an attendance and on a capitation basis. Special payment provisions are made for the care of chronic patients, for those requiring surgery, for night calls, travel charges, etc. When payment rests on a capitation basis, special payments are limited to very few services and are made according to an agreed fee schedule.

In Copenhagen, the patient does not have entirely—but he does have very substantial—free choice of doctor; the city is divided into three main districts and fifteen sub-districts, and he may choose among the local contract physicians in his main district. "Free choice" by the patient is limited, however, by the fact that no physician may accept more than 1,500 persons as potential patients. In the provinces, the patient generally has free choice of all physicians in the town or within a radius of ten kilometers if the physicians are paid on a fee schedule, or he has entirely free choice of his physician for the coming year if they are paid on a capitation basis. Where the physician is paid on a capitation basis, the patient cannot as a rule change his doctor during the year except for good and sufficient cause.

There are no legal provisions to settle disputes between sickness funds and their members, but in practice such disputes are submitted to, and are settled by, the supervising governmental authorities. Disputes between patients and doctors are settled by hearings before the chairman of the local physicians' association and the officers of the fund, and appeals may be taken first to a joint medical and lay council, and, since 1929, may be carried to the Minister of Social Affairs.

Hospital care is provided in the local government hospitals and the cost is paid by the insurance funds at agreed rates. The hospitals are operated on high standards of quality and yet economically, so that this type of service is provided at comparatively small cost. Specialist services are often furnished under contracts of service between sickness societies and the specialists. Prescribed medicine is an optional benefit. In 1931, 1,050 societies furnished pharmaceutical benefit, most of them bearing one-half of the costs incurred. The medicine may be purchased by the patient from any licensed pharmacy. The patient pays at least one-fourth the cost (the actual proportion varying with the society) and the pharmacy receives the remainder from the insurance society.

Nearly all physicians in Denmark, except the specialists, engage in insurance practice. Negotiations concerning professional matters are conducted centrally between the government authorities, representatives of the National Association of Sickness Funds, and representatives of the Danish Medical Association. The Medical Association, having enrolled all except less than a dozen physicians, is fully representative of insurance doctors.

MORBIDITY AMONG INSURED PERSONS

There were, in 1931, 1,692,674 members ("without means") entitled to the benefits of sickness insurance.[6] Of these, 806,257 were men and 886,417 were women. The number of days of sickness in respect to which benefit was paid is shown in the following tabulation:

	Men	Women
At home	2,524,000	2,780,000
In hospitals	1,325,000	2,167,000

In addition, benefits were paid for 1,098,000 days of sickness among children in hospitals. The ratio of benefit days at home to days in the hospital was 1.9 for men, and 1.3 for women. According to customary American experience, this volume of hospitalization would be considered high. Thus, as against an usual experience among non-insured persons of less than 1 day of hospital care per person during a year, the Danish experience shows 1.7 days for men and 2.5 days for women. These relatively high figures may be attributed to the comparatively low cost of hospitalization, to the necessity for hospitalizing cases which cannot readily receive modern care in homes which are small and unequipped with those facilities which are desirable adjuncts of the sick-room, and to the general popularity of hospital care among all classes of the Danish population. That the figures do not indicate high sickness rates, or morbidity rates made excessive by the desire of insured persons to receive benefits to which they are entitled, is evident from the average duration of sickness in which benefit is paid (Table 19).

To evaluate these averages, consider the fact that in the sickness surveys conducted in the United States by the Metropolitan Life Insurance Company among some 570,000 white persons of both sexes and all ages over one year[7] it was found that among the persons of wage-earning ages (15 years and over) males lost 8.3 days and females 8.4 days a year. A number of other surveys[8] show variously

TABLE 19

AVERAGE DAYS OF SICKNESS IN RESPECT TO WHICH BENEFIT WAS PAID,
DENMARK, 1926–1932

YEAR	MEN	WOMEN
1926	4.4	5.4
1927	4.6	5.5
1928	4.6	5.4
1929	4.8	5.5
1930	4.5	5.4
1931	4.8	5.6
1932	4.8	5.9

from 6.6 to 7.6 days of disability or days lost from work per person during a year. A national commission (appointed by Mr. Hoover) estimated that "The 42,000,000 men and women gainfully employed probably lose on an average more than eight days each annually from illness disabilities, . . ." A study conducted by the Committee on the Costs of Medical Care[9] shows that among representative white families with incomes under $2,000 the average annual disability is about 8.2 days per person. This figure applies to all persons and all ages. Special tabulations restricted to gainfully occupied persons (ages 15–64 inclusive) show 10 days of disability a year per person among those in families with annual incomes under $1,200 and 6.4 days per person in families with $1,200 to $2,000 per annum. For both of these income classes combined, the weighted average is 7.5 days per person. When days of disability occurring after 26 weeks of disability within the year are excluded, the averages become 8.3 and 5.7 per person in the two income classes respectively, or 6.4 for the two classes combined in appropriately weighted proportions. If now the average days of disability per person on account of the first 3 days of disability are excluded, the average is reduced from 6.4 to 5.3. This last figure should now be increased by the average disability occurring during the first 3 days in such disabling illnesses as last longer than 3 days. The amount of this increase is difficult to measure but is nearly 1 day per capita. The figure of 5.3 is then increased to approximately 6 days per capita per year. This figure may be com-

pared with the data shown in Table 19, because the days of sick (cash) benefit are restricted in Danish insurance to a maximum of 26 weeks within twelve consecutive months and are paid (from the day of notification) for disabilities lasting longer than 3 days. Certainly there are no indications here that the average days of disabling sickness in respect to which benefit is paid to insured persons in Denmark is high.

INCOME AND EXPENDITURES

The general trend of costs may be illustrated by the data of recent years. Income from all sources and expenditures for all the purposes of sickness insurance, expressed per insured member, have been as follows:

Year	Income	Expenditure
1920	$5.58	$5.50
1925	7.89	7.66
1926	7.75	—
1927	7.57	—
1928	7.80	7.27
1929	7.03	7.34
1930	7.31	7.51
1931	7.71	7.51

Income increased about 2 per cent and expenses about 4 per cent between 1931 and 1932. Income has generally exceeded expenditures by a sufficient margin so that the state-recognized sickness funds have maintained reserves which are approximately equal to the cost of a year's operation.* This may be illustrated by the principal items in the balance sheet for the year ending December 31, 1931:

	Per Member
Income	$7.71
Expenditures	7.51
Net total assets (December 31)	6.26
Reserves	6.15

*The law requires that the contributions of members shall be such as will be sufficient to meet the claims on the fund and to form a reserve equal to the average annual expenses in the last three financial years.

It will be recalled that the income of the sickness funds is derived from various sources. The description of the administrative arrangements may not have made clear, however, that the net effect is to retain the essential characteristics of a *contributory* plan. This becomes evident when the income of the sickness funds is examined in respect to the sources of income. Thus, for example, the income for the calendar year 1931 was derived as follows:

	Per Cent
Contributions of members	69.5
Compulsory subsidies of the state	23.7
Interest on investments	2.8
Voluntary subsidies of communities	1.9
Miscellaneous income	2.1
TOTAL	100.0

Cost of Medical Benefits

An analysis of expenditures reveals the costs of the several benefits furnished by the sickness funds. The figures for the calendar year 1931 are shown in Table 20.

There are three points of special interest in these figures: (1) The medical benefits consume nearly three-fourths of the total funds. Indeed, if the administration costs are divided *pro rata* between the cash and the medical benefits, the medical services account for 80 per cent of the total expenditures. This may be compared with 69 per cent for Germany (1933), 38 per cent for England (1934) and about 60 per cent for France. *More than perhaps any other national system, Danish sickness insurance provides medical care rather than cash benefits.* This emphasis upon insurance against the costs of medical service rather than upon reimbursement for wage loss may be an important element in the apparent administrative success of the system.

(2) The costs of medical benefits are distributed in Denmark much as in other insurance countries where medical benefit is broad in scope or as in the private medical expenditures of poor

TABLE 20

EXPENDITURES FOR SICKNESS INSURANCE IN DENMARK, 1931

EXPENDITURES	PER INSURED MEMBER	PER CENT
TOTAL	$7.51	100.0
MEDICAL BENEFITS—TOTAL	5.41	72.1
General practitioners	2.19	29.1
Specialists	0.28	3.7
Hospital care	1.48	19.7
Medicines	0.80	10.6
Dental care	0.22	3.0
Home nursing	0.10	1.4
Maternity	0.13	1.8
Miscellaneous	0.21	2.8
CASH BENEFITS—TOTAL	1.34	17.8
ADMINISTRATION	0.76	10.1

families in the United States. This becomes evident when the data cited above are recast (being restricted to the comparable fractions) and are compared with figures cited in other chapters (page 100).

	Denmark (1931) Per Cent	Germany (1933) Per Cent	United States (1928–1931)* Per Cent
ALL MEDICAL BENEFITS	100	100	100
Physicians	46	40	45
Hospitals	27	30	22
Medicines	15	18	21
Dentistry	4	11	8
Other	8	1	4

*Representative families with annual incomes of less than $1,200.

(3) The cost of administration in Denmark in 1931 may be compared with the same item (for the same year) in other insurance countries:

Cost of Administration (1931)

Denmark	$0.76 per person	10.1 per cent of total
Germany	1.69 " "	9.0 " " " "
England	1.61 " "	14.7 " " " "

Although smallest in absolute amount, the per-capita expenditure for administration in Denmark represents a similar proportion of the total insurance expenditures.

There is general agreement among impartial observers that in Denmark the administrative arrangements operate to the mutual satisfaction of the public, the insurance societies, and the professions. Disputes are said to be infrequent and over-certification of disability comparatively unusual. Unemployment, as elsewhere, does increase sickness certification, but to a minor degree.[10] The explanation for this seems to lie in the fact that the cash benefits are comparatively small and offer little temptation to those who might otherwise be inclined to malinger. Invalidity insurance, which applies to most persons who carry sickness insurance, involves the societies and the physicians in possibilities for friction and antagonism. It is reported, however, that the difficulties are largely avoided because of wide understanding among the public of the mutual nature of the insurance and because of the high character of the medical practitioners.

Nearly all physicians engaged in general practice are insurance practitioners. With approximately 2,000 such physicians, there is one for each 870 insured persons (and their dependents). The total insurance expenditures for medical services rendered to insured persons by general practitioners ($2.19 per member) are equivalent to an assured income of approximately $1,900 per physician. This is considered a substantial remuneration from insurance practice in Denmark.

General Comment

It appears from all evidences that Denmark has had a successfully operating system of sickness insurance for the poor and for the people of small means. However, it is difficult to accept the usual characterization of this as a *voluntary* system. Although membership in the insurance societies has been legally optional, there have been many indirect compulsions upon the citizen to join. Even prior to the Acts of May, 1933, the extensive scheme of state aid provided in effect a strong economic incentive. In addition, there have been other indirect compulsions. If through failure to become insured a person becomes a public charge because of sickness, he might lose his right to vote, and if he has received relief from the municipality during the three preceding years he might forfeit his claim to an old-age pension. Non-insured persons must repay municipality relief when able to do so and, if below the statutory limit in respect to income and capital, may not marry without the consent of governmental authorities. It would therefore be more accurate to refer to the Danish system not as voluntary but as a "state-subsidized 'voluntary' system." This is, of course, not intended to imply derogation of its usefulness or effectiveness. On the contrary, we would emphasize that it stands out among the national systems for its emphasis upon medical rather than upon cash benefits and for the apparent effectiveness with which its administration is conducted.

CHANGES MADE BY THE ACTS OF MAY 20, 1933
(Effective October 1, 1933)

The principal changes made in the Danish sickness insurance system by the Acts of May 20, 1933, may be reviewed briefly.[11]

Scope. The new laws require: (a) that every Danish citizen (or other person residing in Denmark) is eligible to enter a fund; and (b) that every Danish citizen between the ages of 21 and 60 is bound to *register* with either a sickness or a continuation fund, if not already a regular member of one or the other, and to pay contributions *as a member with dormant rights* in order to maintain the right to enter a fund at a later date. Persons who fail to comply with these provisions lose their right to old-age pension and are subject to fine. In addition, every citizen who is required to *register* for sickness insurance is also required to enter invalidity insurance and to pay contributions therefor.

Admission to Insurance. As formerly, only "poor" persons may be admitted to a sickness fund as regular members entitled to benefits. Selection is to be carried out according to the tax registers, and according to statutory limits on earnings which fluctuate with the wage index and which are to be fixed annually by the Minister of Social Affairs. This limit must correspond to the average wage of a skilled worker employed throughout a year. The sickness funds must continue to admit to membership any member of a continuation fund whose income has fallen below the statutory limit for a "poor" person.

Continuation funds (sickness associations of persons with means which exceed the statutory limits) must admit all persons between 14 and 40 years of age who are not "poor" persons and who comply with other requirements in respect to health. They must also admit, without respect to age or health, those who have been regular members of sickness funds and who cannot remain in these funds because their incomes have come to exceed the statutory limit for "poor" persons. Inasmuch as persons whose means exceed the statutory limits and who are over 40 years of age cannot be admitted to a continuation fund as members with dormant rights, and cannot be transferred from such membership to regular membership, they must apply to state-recognized sickness insurance societies. They are admitted to these societies as members with dormant rights and may become regular members when their means fall below the statutory limits. As formerly, a sickness fund may maintain a separate (accounting) section for those who are not "poor," as long as the section has not less than fifteen members.

It is important to recognize that while registration as a member with dormant rights is compulsory, enrollment as a regular member is still state-aided voluntary insurance. An individual cannot have invalidity insurance unless he is a regular member or a member with dormant rights of a state-recognized insurance society or continuation fund.

Conditions of Benefit. The right to receive benefit remains subject to a qualifying period of six weeks (except in case of accident). This period does not apply to the children of insured persons who become regular members before the age of fifteen. The qualifying period for maternity benefit remains ten months.

A regular member who has drawn benefits to the limit becomes, as formerly, a member with dormant rights. Restoration to regular membership generally requires, as formerly, a qualifying period of twelve months and then only if the insured person is, to a certain degree, capable of work according to medical testimony. However, the waiting period of six weeks does not apply to a member who has been restored to full rights at the end of the qualifying period. During the period when he is not entitled to benefits from the insurance fund, the insured person may receive municipal aid without disqualification as a voter.

The relation between receipt of benefits from a sickness society and from municipal authorities is rather complicated and requires further explanation. Cash benefits from the society may not continue for more than 26 weeks within twelve consecutive months. However, the member who has received the maximum cash benefits to which he is entitled from his society, may—if he continues to be incapacitated—receive cash benefit of a corresponding size from his municipality during the remaining 26 weeks of this twelve-month period. Then, upon the beginning of the next twelve-month period he can again receive 26 weeks of benefit from his society and 26 weeks of benefit from his municipality. At the end of the second twelve-month period he is eligible to only 8 weeks benefit from each of these sources. Having now exhausted his ordinary rights to 60 weeks' benefits, he can apply to become again a regular member of the sickness society while being also simultaneously entitled to apply for his invalidity pension. If the incapacitated person has received medical benefit *simultaneously* with cash benefits for 60 consecutive weeks (cash benefits for 26 weeks from his society, then for 26 weeks from his municipality, and then for another 8 weeks from his society), he has exhausted his rights to benefits and can try to become again a regular member of the sickness society and can also apply for his invalidity pension. He may further receive medical benefit from his municipality while receiving his invalidity pension; he may even receive medical benefit from the invalidity fund—especially if the fund considers that medical aid may contribute to restoring his capacity to work.

Benefits in Cash and in Kind. These benefits remain substantially as before. Maternity benefit, however, now consists of: (1) service of a midwife and, if necessary, of an obstetrician; (2) cash benefit for 14 days, equal to the ordinary cash sickness benefit; and (3) for women employed in specified industries, a special cash benefit for 6 weeks before and 3 to 6 weeks after parturition.

The regulations of a sickness fund may require the members to insure against the costs of burial. In such cases the burial fund must reinsure these risks.

Contributions. The provisions remain substantially as before. Registered members with dormant rights are required to pay 2 crowns ($0.54) a year up to the end of the year in which they become twenty-five years of age, and 2.5 crowns ($0.67) thereafter. The subventions from state and local governments are essentially unchanged, except that the total amount which the state may spend as subvention to the sickness insurance societies for medical services is no longer restricted to 2.4 million crowns ($643,000).

Organization, Administration, and Relations with Doctors. There are no important changes in these respects. The law continues to provide for the supervision of the funds and for the creation of a Council (its members elected in equal numbers by the National Association of Sickness Funds and by the Danish Medical Association) for the arbitration of disputes between a fund and the doctors.

Thus, in substance, the new laws leave the system of sickness insurance unchanged in all fundamental respects except that all citizens must register with insurance funds as members with dormant rights if they are not already regular members, and must pay small, fixed contributions in order that they can later (voluntarily) become regular members entitled to benefits. The new provision for compulsory registration applies to persons who have not been regular members because their income (or capital) exceeded certain statutory limits defining "poor" people and to those who, though being "poor," have failed to exercise their rights to regular membership. Those who are required to register (i.e., all Danish citizens between the ages of 21 and 60) must, however, make contributions for invalidity insurance.

The Acts of May 20, 1933, came into effect on October 1, 1933, and prescribed that the newly established obligations must be fulfilled before October 1, 1934, by all persons who were between 21 and 60 years of age when the law came into effect and otherwise within three months after attaining the age of 21 years by persons who were under that age. The effect of the new Acts was to bring substantial increase in the number of persons insured against sickness. In the state-recognized sickness societies, there were 1,840,000 regular members (entitled to benefits) on December 31, 1933, and 2,100,000 on December 31, 1934. In previous years the average annual increase had been about 40,000; in 1934, the increase was 260,000. Taking into account the changes since October 1, 1933 (the effective date of the new Acts), there has been an increase of nearly 280,000 insured persons as a direct consequence of the Acts. At the end of 1933 there were about 20,000 members with dormant rights, and at the end of 1934 about 170,000. In the same period, the regular membership of the continuation funds increased from 75,000 to 100,000, and the membership with dormant rights from zero to 10,000. Taking all together, sickness insurance now embraces 2,380,000 members. In addition, the 38,000 persons employed on the state railroads and who are members of the special railroad sickness fund are (by an Act of March 27, 1934) embraced in the same governmental sickness insurance supervision as applies to other persons. Thus, some 2,418,000 persons are protected against the risks arising out of sickness in Denmark. This is equivalent to about 90 per cent of the population over 14 or 15 years of age.

Thus, under the new Acts:

    a. *Registration for sickness insurance is compulsory;*
    b. *Insurance against invalidity is compulsory;*
    c. *Entrance as a regular member, or transference from sickness insurance with dormant rights to active insurance, remains voluntary.*

The Danish system of sickness insurance originated in voluntary mutual insurance associations of poor people, passed through the stage of state-supervised and state-aided "voluntary" insurance funds, and has now entered the category of combined compulsory and voluntary insurance. The new Danish system is—like the German, British, French and other systems—chiefly a "poor" man's insurance. Unlike other voluntary insurance systems, the Danish system requires protective insurance "with dormant rights" for all citizens between 21 and 60 years of age. This is a significant innovation in the history of sickness insurance.

REFERENCES AND NOTES

1. For a more extensive description consult VOLUNTARY SICKNESS INSURANCE, Series M (Social Insurance) No. 7. Geneva, International Labour Office, 1927, 520 pp. *See also* the three following references.

2. For the texts of the recent Danish laws concerning health insurance, consult the publications of the International Labour Office, Legislative Series 1927, Denmark 6B (Act of July 14, 1927); 1929, Denmark 1B (Act of March 27, 1929). For the Acts of 1933, consult *Industrial and Labour Information,* 1933, xlvi, p. 403; xlvii, p. 213.

3. For a brief description of the system, *see* THE NATIONAL SICKNESS, INVALIDITY AND FUNERAL INSURANCE IN DENMARK, by the Commissioner of Recognized Sickness Funds. Copenhagen, 1932, 36 pp. Detailed data appear in the reports of the Director for 1931, 1932 and 1933.
   Newsholme, Sir Arthur: INTERNATIONAL STUDIES OF THE RELATION BETWEEN THE PRIVATE AND OFFICIAL PRACTICE OF MEDICINE, *op. cit.,* Volume I (see page 70).

4. HEALTH INSURANCE (1931), Monograph Three (*revised edition*), and SOCIAL INSURANCE LEGISLATION (1932), Monograph Four. New York, Metropolitan Life Insurance Company, 1933 and 1932.

5. In this chapter, for the purpose of the statistics cited, the crown (krone) is taken equivalent to $0.268. The 1935 value was about $0.220.

6. Detailed data on morbidity, costs, etc., were supplied by the International Labour Office (Geneva), bringing up to 1931 tables contained in their Report No. 7 (see reference No. 1 above). These statistics were verified by the central government authority in Copenhagen. For the purposes of this chapter, the data have been rearranged and expressed in units more directly comparable with data appearing in other chapters.

7. The sickness surveys are reviewed briefly in THE MONEY VALUE OF A MAN, by Louis I. Dublin and Alfred J. Lotka. New York, The Ronald Press, 1930, Chapter VIII. For more detailed data, consult the original surveys or the summary prepared by M. L. Stecker: Some Recent Morbidity Data. New York, Metropolitan Life Insurance Company, 1918, 28 pp.

8. Reviewed briefly in THE PRINCIPLES OF VITAL STATISTICS, by I. S. Falk. Philadelphia and London, W. B. Saunders Company, 1923, Chapter V.

9. Falk, I. S. Klem, Margaret C. and Sinai, Nathan: THE INCIDENCE OF ILLNESS AND THE RECEIPT AND COSTS OF MEDICAL CARE AMONG REPRESENTATIVE FAMILIES. Chicago, The University of Chicago Press, 1933, pp. 77 and 79. The figure cited from this study is obtained by applying the weighted average incidence of disabling illness among persons in the income classes "under $1,200" and "$1,200–$2,000," i.e., about 0.5 per person during a year, to the average duration of disability (16.4 days) per illness involving any disability.

10. Cf. INTERNATIONAL STUDIES ON THE RELATION BETWEEN THE PRIVATE AND OFFICIAL PRACTICE OF MEDICINE, op. cit.

11. Adapted from Industrial and Labour Information, 1933, xlvii, pp. 213–218, cited in reference No. 2 above, and from information supplied by the Director of Insurance, Copenhagen.

PART THREE

❧

CHAPTER XIII

SOME CONCLUSIONS FROM HEALTH AND SICKNESS INSURANCE IN FOREIGN COUNTRIES

OUTSIDE of the United States, most progressive countries of the world have attempted to provide through insurance against the uncertain financial burdens of sickness. In the preceding pages the results of our studies on health or sickness insurance in a number of these countries have been recorded. On the whole, the subject has been treated as though this form of insurance were a discrete and definitive unit. While this practice has been generally followed, it has not been adopted altogether; at a number of points attention has been directed to the fact that health insurance does not stand alone and that it is only one element in the larger manifold embraced by social insurance. The account has repeatedly dealt with the actual administrative interrelations between health insurance and other forms of social insurance such as maternity, invalidity, accident, or old-age insurance, and has often had occasion to refer to direct and indirect relations with still other forms of social insurance such as unemployment or survivor's insurance.

Health insurance is a part of social insurance. It was conceived in the same forces and has grown and evolved in the same soil. The underlying force is the quest for security. Social insurance has now served for many decades as a technique whereby hundreds of millions of people, themselves without substantial capital and earning small or modest incomes, have been given some measure of financial security against the major economic risks of life and living. The treatment of health insurance, more or less apart from other forms of social insurance, has been a procedure of convenience to the extent that we have been studying only one part of an organic whole. Yet, in so far as the part has had an identity separate from that of the whole, has dealt with problems peculiar to its own field and has embodied procedures uniquely important to its own necessities, its separate study has been justified.

Social insurance in general, and health insurance in particular, arose out of broad social necessities. Dealing with individual and communal problems, it has been inevitable that the technique of social insurance would be dynamic and functional, not static and unchanging. Indeed, the first lesson to be learned from the world's experience with health insurance is that it *is* dynamic and that it *is* adjustable to the life of its times. One sometimes hears the criticism that the technique of health insurance is still imperfect, that no nation has yet devised the ideal scheme, and this, it is argued, is attested by the frequent changes which are still being made after more than half a century of experience. How much more serious would the converse be—if it could be properly argued that health insurance has been fixed as in a mold and has not been adjustable to those social changes which half a century has brought—changes whose broad outlines are known to every tyro of social history! Health insurance is a social institution. Its design can attain a final and "perfected" form only in a static society.

Nor is it sufficient to give to health insurance its proper place only in the field of social insurance. In the one direction, it is related to invalidity, unemployment and other forms of social insurance. In another direction, however, it is related to social structures which are not insurance but which are, nevertheless, safeguards erected by society to serve social functions. Because of the nature of the risks with which it deals—without regard to the contributory scheme through which it is financed—health insurance touches and overlaps the administrative areas of public health and public welfare; it is related to these through common elements in the functions which all three are designed to serve but it is distinct because it is a *con-*

tributory insurance where the other two are *tax-supported public services*.

The common element in health insurance, public health and public welfare is the fundamental risk of sickness with which all three must deal. Health insurance has traditionally been marked off from public health, from a functional point of view, by the line which separates the treatment of disease in the individual from the prevention of disease in the entire community. But changes in the medical and sanitary sciences have been obliterating this line of separation. Increasingly, because of the changing nature of health problems, the public health authority has been coming to be concerned with the individual, at the same time that the early diagnosis and care of illness in the individual have been coming to be an increasing concern of the community. Similarly, the rôle of disease in creating poverty and dependency has been receiving increasing attention among the authorities charged with the administration of public welfare. Every attempt to treat the cause and not merely the symptom of individual need for public assistance tends to emphasize the rôle of disease as a cause of insecurity and to impress upon the public welfare agencies the common bond which unites efforts to prevent disease with efforts to prevent dependency. Thus, health insurance (and, therefore, social insurance) becomes interlocked with public health and public welfare, both conceptually and administratively.

Social insurance first arose in its modern form out of the needs of a changing society whose life was quickened and affected in a thousand ways by the forces of industrialization and urbanization. The form which social insurance has taken in one country is different in many respects from the form it has taken in another. This, which is true of social insurance in general, is true of health insurance in particular, as has been evident from the description presented in earlier chapters. A large proportion of the preceding pages has been devoted to distinguishing the particular system of health insurance which prevails in one country from the particular system which obtains in another. Now when undertaking the task of collating the observations, it is difficult to generalize conclusions without particularizing a catalogue of exceptions. However, certain broad tendencies may be discerned and some general conclusions may be drawn, and these are deserving of special mention because of the very fact that they emerge as common threads.

1. First, and above all other trends, health insurance in Europe has been moving steadily from voluntary to compulsory systems. Not all voluntary schemes have already gone over to the compulsory stage, but the trend in this direction has been clear and uniform. Where voluntary schemes still exist, there are generally direct or indirect compulsory features and these are being strengthened and multiplied. No country which has once established a compulsory system has ever gone back to a voluntary system.

2. Sickness insurance has dealt first with the wages lost through disability and second with medical service. From their inception, sickness insurance schemes have been designed to meet the needs of wage-earners of small means. Generally, but not everywhere, the programs have been progressively expanded to embrace larger fractions of the population than were at first included, reaching upward on the economic ladder to include workers with somewhat larger earnings than were originally covered by the laws. But European systems of health insurance, with only minor exceptions, still restrict the insured to employed persons, and generally to those with small earnings and little or no capital. In some countries the industries and occupations embraced by health insurance have not changed very much, but in most there has been considerable increase in the breadth of the coverage.

3. In almost every country which has had experience with a system of national or regional sickness insurance, there have been evident the following tendencies:

a. To maintain the cash benefits which are guaranteed as reimbursements for wages lost on account of disability but not to expand these benefits very much, after they have come to be available for a maximum of six months' incapacity in a year, except so far as upward readjustments in the size of the benefits have been made necessary by advancing wage levels;

b. To place increasing emphasis upon *medical* rather than *cash* benefit, especially by providing medical service instead of furnishing cash with which to purchase the service;

c. To expand the variety of medical benefits, attaining in some countries a broad scope so as to include all important kinds of professional care;

d. To expand the population eligible to receive insurance medical benefit by covering the dependents of the insured persons; and

e. To increase the active participation of the insurance system in measures concerned with the prevention of disease.

4. The large diversity of arrangements through which the insurance contributions are paid testifies to variety in the principles under which the systems are conceived and in the local conditions under which they must operate. In most cases, the state assumes only regulatory and supervisory functions; the insurance funds are usually contributed by employers and employees who share the costs. In Denmark and in some other countries, the state makes substantial contributions towards the costs of insurance benefits. (In Denmark, federal and local governments combined contribute about 25 per cent of the health insurance income.) But in Denmark, it should be recalled, employers make no contributions for their employees. Tax support rests on the principle that the health and welfare of the wage-earning class are a responsibility of the entire state and the costs of preserving health, of meeting the financial consequences of sickness, and of curing disease among the poor should be paid, at least in part, by the people of larger means. It still remains true, however, that health insurance is primarily a mutual, contributory form of insurance. It should be emphasized that, taken by and large, it is financed mainly by the contributions of the insured persons, with or without the help of contributions from their employers. Tax support is either absent or is a minor feature, and in some leading insurance

countries where there has been tax support this has been decreasing rather than increasing.

The absence of tax support for health insurance in some countries and the decline of such support in others raises a question on the extent to which health insurance is *social* insurance. In the writings of some students of the subject, the *social* aspect of insurance is related to the transfer of the costs from the beneficiaries in the low income brackets to other citizens (non-beneficiaries) in more privileged, economic classes of society. If we accept this point of view, health insurance is social insurance in a country like Great Britain (where general tax funds account for about one-seventh of the cost) or in Denmark (where they account for about one-fourth), to the extent that the general tax funds used in the health insurance budgets are derived from income groups not entitled to the benefits of the insurance scheme. Conversely, in the sense of this argument, health insurance is not social insurance in Germany and in other countries where tax funds do not enter the budget. The school which holds these views also argues that the contributions of employers—in countries where there are such contributions—are not substantial social contributions because they are passed on by industry to consumers and, for the most part, are paid eventually by the employed persons covered by insurance; employer contributions are social contributions for the insured persons to the extent that industry passes them on to consumers who happen not to be covered by the insurance scheme. This school of thought argues that the social function of social insurance can be discharged if a substantial part of the cost is contributed by tax funds raised through the taxation of incomes in the upper brackets so that social insurance becomes a device for the partial redistribution of income.

Health insurance has not been primarily an instrument for the distribution of income. Even if its total costs in a program of maximum scope, including both cash and medical benefits, were charged against non-beneficiaries, it would involve a sum equal to about 6 per cent of the earnings of the beneficiaries. This is not to imply that health insurance has not effected some redistribution of income, for it has; it means that this has not been the main or primary function of health insurance. How health insurance has operated to redistribute income was noted, for example, in Chapter VI; in Germany, where insured persons have paid two-thirds and their employers one-third of the costs, the shift in emphasis from cash to service benefits has had the effect of furnishing benefits according to *the need* rather than according to *the size of contributions*. In this respect, there is some redistribution of income *within* the insured population. The same phenomenon occurs in any scheme in which contributions are not proportioned according to the number of persons (the insured individual and his dependents) eligible to receive benefits. In such a case, the insured person who is without dependents helps to pay the costs for the insured person who has dependents.

To argue or to imply that the social function of health insurance is measurable by its effects upon distribution of income is to set up a straw man. There are other social functions which have no necessary relation to the partial allocation of costs to tax funds or to employers. The pooling of funds for a group of persons so that each of them is assured protection against the insured risk (loss of wages or costs of medical care or both) under a government-supervised, non-profit scheme is, in our opinion, the fundamental social attribute of health insurance. Judgment on its social usefulness can stand or fall on this principle, apart from its rôle in relation to the distribution or the redistribution of income.

5. Even in countries where so-called "voluntary" schemes operate, the government regulations provide that the insurance societies or "funds" shall be under the sole control of employers and employees if both contribute to the costs of insurance or under the exclusive control of insured persons if their employers do not make contributions. In Great Britain, control is vested entirely in the insured, despite the fact that employers and employees make contributions. It seems eminently fitting that those who contribute the funds or those for whom they are contributed shall control the policies. Com-

mercial or profit-making associations are not admitted as insurance carriers. This is grounded on the sound principle that there should be no profit motive in insurance against sickness in a legally required insurance or even in a government-supervised, voluntary scheme, and that there shall be no independent intermediary between the insured person and the physician or other medical agent who agrees to provide service in time of illness. The insurance societies (funds, *Kassen*, *caisses*, etc.), entrusted with the details of local administration of health insurance, are essentially democratic institutions of the insured persons. Medical practitioners and institutions furnishing insurance benefits are responsible either to the people whom they serve or to associations of the people, not to business men who sell insurance for profit.

6. All national sickness insurance plans have been conceived in the interest of the public welfare and to improve the public health. Yet in some insurance countries there is a more or less sharp separation between the insurance and the public health authorities. To be sure, there is often effective coöperation between the two, and this is greater in some countries than in others. There can be no doubt that sickness insurance has contributed to improvement in the public health, though not as substantially as had been anticipated or predicted by advocates of the system. Nor is this surprising, since the emphasis of the systems was for a long time upon cash relief rather than upon medical care. Today, though the medical benefits have been increased, curative rather than preventive care is, of course, still the main task. This is inherent in sickness insurance, because the treatment of disease is necessary. Even in an ideal program, based upon the sound application of present-day knowledge and skill, treatment would involve ten or fifteen times as much money and as much work as prevention.

It is an interesting historical fact that the sequence of relations between cure and prevention has been substantially the same in all national health insurance systems. When a national program is first established, curative rather than preventive care is the first and the more pressing necessity. After this objective is attained and a system has been provided to furnish medical care for those who fall sick, attention begins to focus upon the prevention of disease and disability. Increasingly, but still inadequately, sickness insurance tends to become health insurance. This sequence is neither essential nor unavoidable; sound conception of a system, with due regard to history and experience, would take adequate account of both preventive and curative functions from the very beginning.

When taking stock of the preventive health functions of sickness insurance, attention should not be focussed merely upon those classes of activity which are traditionally associated with public health departments of government. There are more ways of preventing disease and contributing to the health of a community than by registering births and deaths, purifying water supplies, recording reported cases of communicable disease, or by other *community* activities. A system which provides wage-earners with one-half or two-thirds of their accustomed income during the period when disabling sickness makes them unable to work, which supplies them or their dependents with the services of a doctor without delay and without worry about the costs, which assures them medicines prescribed by a doctor, essential dentistry, hospital care, nursing or other services, which furnishes the gainfully occupied women maternity care and gives them one-half to two-thirds of their wages when they abstain from gainful employment for the month or six weeks before and after childbirth and which furnishes maternity care to the wife of a wage-earner, which provides prenatal and postnatal care, diagnostic aids and facilities for the physician who suspects tuberculosis or some other condition whose accurate diagnosis requires the aid of extensive and expensive equipment—any system with these and other benefits found in the well-developed sickness insurance schemes of Europe makes profoundly important contributions to the public health. To be sure, not all insurance schemes furnish all of these benefits, but most of them furnish many of these services. These may not have been labelled public health benefits; they may go by the more humble name of medical benefits. But they are public health services none the less.

There is a curious paradox to be noted. In the United States the formal community activities of public health agencies have been developed further than in most European sickness insurance countries. Yet it is only now being recognized in the United States that many fundamental health services cannot be made effective until the wage-earner and his family are assured the income necessary for subsistence during periods of unemployment (whether the unemployment is caused by lack of work or by sickness) and are enabled to buy or otherwise obtain medical care.

Elsewhere in this volume attention has been called to the fact that Germany has a system known as "sickness insurance" and Great Britain one known as "health insurance." In the light of present considerations, it must be clear that, in a fundamental sense, any well-designed system of "sickness insurance" is *ipso facto* a system of "health insurance."

When health insurance was first designed in some countries, there was not always close administrative coördination with public health administration. In succeeding years it has often been difficult to develop such coördination after administrative procedures become established and fixed. It would therefore seem that such coördination were better devised at the inception rather than later. However, if coördination is to be effective it must be real rather than nominal. There are a number of European countries in which nominal coordination exists, but in which the visiting observer searches almost in vain for signs of close or real participation between the authorities charged with the two classes of activity.

Nevertheless, and despite these observations, the evidence is overwhelming to the effect that the practices of "mutual assistance" and of "public health" have been drawing closer and closer together. Indeed, in a number of insurance countries increasing attention is being given to the proposal that public health and health insurance should be unified in a single public medical service.[1]

7. As one studies the history of health insurance, one is impressed with the large part of the discussion which is devoted to the problems associated with the administration of the medical benefits. The actuarial and financial authorities have had to face difficult questions; and in various ways they have solved or circumvented their problems. But the medical issues seem to have been of another kind. What are the reasons?

Prior to the beginning of British health insurance (1911), the medical professions of many countries manifested little or no interest in the subject when their systems were first being established and the insurance programs were generally instituted without the adequate consultation or advice of these professions. In consequence, many arrangements were introduced which hampered and irritated the physician in his professional work or were financially unfair to him. Many procedures in health insurance practice were indifferent to the doctor's concept of independence in professional action; they restricted him in his traditionally free and confidential relation with his patients; they tended to discourage him because low tariffs or small capitation fees compelled him to assume a large volume of work for a meager financial return; they tended to demoralize him because the dual responsibility of furnishing medical care and of certifying disability for cash benefits demands a constant distinction between serving God or Mammon. Not all of these circumstances prevailed anywhere in local insurance areas; some of them prevailed everywhere in insurance countries.

There was noise and stir and bustle and bickering about income and methods of payment for professional service. But the chief source of irritation between insurance societies and insurance doctors lay much deeper. It was grounded upon the unavoidable antagonism of the professions to any form of "lay control." Even in Germany, where the complaints against inadequate remuneration were loudest, the incomes of physicians were—with due regard to differences in the costs of living—as good as they were in the United States in the same years. In England, where satisfaction has perhaps been greatest among insurance physicians, physicians' incomes have apparently been increased and have been made more stable by insurance.

When the British system of National Health Insurance was adopted in 1911, the government had the advantage of consultation with the British Medical Association (although, to be sure, in the eleventh hour of the legislative program). As a result, the medical relations established in this system were, on the whole, mutually satisfactory to all parties concerned and—with modifications subsequently adopted—provided a basis of coöperative work which more than twenty years of experience has only succeeded in strengthening. It is generally agreed that the British consultative procedure between the government and the medical professions has been largely responsible for the amicable conditions which have, on the whole, characterized the provision of insurance medical benefit.

Against the British experience we must set the French experience. When compulsory health insurance was finally adopted in 1929–1930, the medico-political influences were extremely strong. Provisions were written into the law at the behest of the professions which, even in the few years which have elapsed, have proved largely unsatisfactory to the professions themselves and have largely nullified some basic purposes of the insurance system.

European experience seems to show that the design of a health insurance system should be *counselled* by the professions but *determined* by the representatives of the public. It is to the evident advantage of both groups that an even balance be kept between the interests of the professions and of the people who are to be served. Neither group should exploit the other.

The struggles to throw off "the yoke of lay control" have been bitter, in part because of misunderstandings, in part because it is in the nature of the case difficult to change the administrative arrangements once they have been established. Now that large experience has accumulated, it seems clear that problems of this kind are better and more equably solved before rather than after a system is inaugurated. This is an important lesson from European experience.

Lest an erroneous impression be left on this subject of professional relations in insurance and on lay control of medical practice, the following paragraphs may be quoted from a review which cannot be accused of neglecting the interests of the professions.[2]

The slogan "free choice of doctors" has been the rallying cry of the medical professions in many a hard fought battle with the societies. It has come to symbolize the entire complex of personal relations between individual patient and practitioner, with income determined by competition. . . .

The societies seek to restrict the freedom of choice to practitioners upon whom they can depend to protect the interests of the society. They wish to be able to discharge (which means to blacklist) any doctor who exceeds their ideas of liberality in care, in prescribing, and especially in granting certificates of incapacity.

"Free choice" of practitioner is much like "free competition" in industry in that neither has ever existed, although both are constantly invoked. Both suppose that the purchaser has a complete knowledge of all the services and goods available and the ability accurately to judge their respective merits. But it is a constant complaint that city-dwellers at least seldom know anything whatever about the comparative qualifications of the practitioners in their locality and, in case of an emergency, are forced to ask the neighbors or have recourse to the telephone directory, while rural residents have few among whom to choose. It is quite probable that, from the point of view of the patient, there is much more free choice, because more intelligently informed, among the insured in Great Britain, where the list of available practitioners is posted in the post-office for general comment and information, than in the cities of the United States.

It is very seldom indeed, in recent years, that one hears any request from patients for "free choice." Only the physicians demand it, and there is some reason to believe that the societies are not wholly wrong when they charge that this demand, like the analogous one for "free competition" in industry, is loudest among those who wish to use somewhat questionable methods of competition. It has already been mentioned that extreme liberality in prescribing and granting certificates of incapacity is the easiest way to build up an insurance practice. There is no denying the fact that absolute freedom to change doctors puts a weapon in the hands of unscrupulous patients with which to reward unscrupulous doctors. It is also equally true that a sharply restricted choice, directed by the societies, brings about very harmful "lay control."

Such a situation enables the societies most effectually to compel practitioners to give the sort of "economic service" that will conserve the insurance funds and to yield their scientific judgment to the demands of the society officials. It introduces most of the old familiar evils of the "voluntary" stage and the "lodge doctor."

8. The insurance doctor has had the dual responsibility of treating the sick and of issuing certificates of incapacity. It is often said that the difficulties involved in discharging these dual functions are largely due to the inept administrative interferences of the insurance societies. Yet it has been noted that the difficulties were almost as serious in Great Britain, where the insurance doctor has no direct relations with the Approved Society, as in Germany, where (until recently) he was employed by the *Krankenkasse*. It seems more probable that the underlying cause of the trouble has been not the relation of the doctor to the insurance carrier, but the inherent conflict between the two functions with which the doctor has been charged.

The problem of over-certification of disability has apparently been largely solved in some insurance countries by: (a) partial separation of cash and medical benefits (as in England); (b) effective supervision by non-competing, salaried medical officers (as in the case of the Regional Medical Officers of England and the *Vertrauensärzte* of Germany); and (c) strength and independence of the practitioners (as in Denmark). Obviously an even better solution—if it can be given practical form—would be the complete relegation to unemployment insurance of cash benefits for unemployment due to sickness. No country has tried this; yet it would be a vastly significant experiment, especially if it made use of the experience of countries which have had effective professional supervision of professional functions and whole-time salaried medical officers to assume (certification) responsibilities which should not be borne by physicians engaged in active practice.*

9. It should not be lost from sight that the disputes between the insurance authorities and the organized medical professions have always been over details, not over the fundamental principle on which national health insurance systems rest. In addition to what has already been said on this point in preceding chapters, the following paragraphs may be quoted from Simons and Sinai:[3]

> . . . a very thorough search of the available sources of information has failed to find a single condemnation of such systems with a request for a return to private practice. . . .
>
> We can truthfully say that in no country having insurance does the organized medical profession ask its abolition, that insurance does not necessarily lower the income of the physicians and dentists, and that a long and world-wide view shows a constant decline of lay control in the management of medical service in insurance systems.
>
> The demand for medical representation on the administrative side hits at the heart of the matter. There is nothing so highly mystical about the economic and social problems involved as to bar such representation. On the contrary, once the cash and service sides are separated, the rest is an extremely simple problem in administration.
>
> British and French experience, and the judgment of recent official investigators from countries contemplating the introduction of health insurance, gives sound reasons for the conclusion that every step in the direction of separation of these functions and increasing the power of the medical professions in the control of insurance institutions has brought greater satisfaction on the part of patients, public, and practitioners.

10. It is almost gratuitous to add that giving medical groups the opportunity for leadership and consultative responsibility in formu-

*The British Columbia health insurance act, passed by the legislature March 31, 1936, is entirely restricted to medical care. It is possible that this is a step in the direction suggested above.

lating and administering an insurance scheme will not solve all the problems and certainly not all the financial problems. The economic difficulties have another source and call for another solution. They are the consequence not of organization and administration, but of the fundamental economic weakness of the insured populations.

In ordinary private practice, comparatively few physicians serve only the poor. With the prevailing tradition of a sliding scale of fees, remunerative practice among those who are in better circumstances supplements the physician's income from his poor patients. In European insurance, however, with membership generally (though not always) limited to the low income classes and the fees adjusted to their financial means, the physician engaged in insurance practice must provide a large—sometimes a too large—volume of service in order that he may earn a decent livelihood. So long as the contributions from the insured or from the insured and their employers are insubstantial by comparison with the ordinary medical expenditures of the well-to-do and the rich, insurance practice must remain a poor-man's practice. The economic outlook of the insurance doctor must, in a large measure, be colorless or even discouraging unless the average *per-capita* sum available to pay for the medical care of the insured persons is substantially increased through extension of insurance to include more than the low income classes of the population.

To these considerations must be added another. American experience demonstrates that medical costs, especially because of their variable and uncertain size, are burdensome for individuals or families with incomes up to at least $3,000 and even up to $5,000. European insurance practice rarely applies to those families whose workers earn more than $1,500 or $2,000 (in equivalent purchasing power). The nature of medical costs demands that insurance should include at least those with incomes up to $3,000. This is especially desirable because those whose incomes fall between $1,500 and $3,000 (approximately 42 per cent of all natural families in the United States in 1928) would require practically no financial assistance from employers or the state to enable them to pay for reasonably adequate medical care. They need little more than an efficient system of pooling their funds. Thus, from the point of view of the people's need and also to the end that there should be sound financial support of the professions, the insured population should be more comprehensive than is the case in European practice.

The restriction of sickness insurance to the low income classes has had another unfortunate result. It has traditionally concentrated attention upon the purpose of providing financial subventions for the poor through the contributions of employers or the state, or both. For a long time it tended to divert attention from the greater needs —to eliminate variation and uncertainty in medical costs and to eliminate the burden of these costs by distributing them among large portions of the population. Sickness insurance should be much more than a form of poor relief; it should be, as it can be—and as, in considerable measure, it has come to be—a form of social insurance for self-sustaining people.

The objectives contemplated here cannot be attained unless the contributions are fixed proportional to income. If they are fixed uniform in absolute amount, they must be either determined by what the poorest among the insured persons can pay or they must be fixed at a higher level and require proportionately large contributions from the employers of the poorest or from the state. If contributions are fixed as a percentage of earnings, then it is practical to cover a broad range of income classes, to make the contributions proportional to ability to pay, and to accumulate an average contribution per insured person which is sufficient to provide substantial benefits and at the same time pay adequate remuneration to those who furnish medical services.

11. Experience demonstrates the need for an increase not only in the fraction of the population eligible to sickness insurance where this is still restricted, but also in the scope of the medical benefits. The need for insurance against the costs of medical service arises from the uncertain and highly variable nature of these costs. This

need applies to all economic classes except the highest. The responsibility for variations in costs is broad and rests upon all four of the principal medical services—those furnished by physician, dentist, nurse, or hospital. Distribution of the costs of one or two or three of these types of service reduces the probability that sickness costs will be burdensome or catastrophic for a particular family; but insurance for less than all four services solves only part of the problem. In many European countries health or sickness insurance was designed without recognition of this important fact, or despite it, on the ground that half a loaf is better than none.

In Germany and in Denmark, for example, the scope of medical benefits has become broad and tends to embrace all important services (except tax-supported hospital care, including the service of staff doctors in the hospitals); but in Great Britain and in some other countries national health insurance has been primarily restricted to the home and office practice of general practitioners of medicine and to the provision of prescribed medicines. Voluntary hospital insurance on a large scale has evolved in some countries to supplement the limited benefits of compulsory insurance. In Great Britain, both professional and lay students of insurance practice urge the expansion of insurance medical care to embrace consultant and specialist service, laboratory and other diagnostic aids, dentistry, nursing, ophthalmic care, hospital and other institutional service, physiotherapy, and other subsidiary services.

In the interests of economy, efficiency and effectiveness of service, as well as in the interest of meeting the true need of the people, the scope of insurance medical benefit should be sufficiently broad to cover all necessary medical care and should be intimately correlated with other health services. In this connection it should be kept in mind that a program of comprehensive medical benefits must be correlated with the broad scope of the insured population. When insurance is restricted to low wage classes, broad medical benefits are financially impossible unless there is large financial assistance from employers, the government, or both.

12. It would divert us from the intention of this summary if we should attempt to review the findings of our studies on the costs of health insurance in various countries. As a consequence of many differences in the systems of different countries, the costs vary a great deal. In every case, these costs are not more—and, in general, are less—than the private expenditures of comparable American families. This is true whether these costs are measured in absolute amount or as a percentage of income. In every insurance country health insurance has been solvent despite great fluctuations in employment, costs of living, and economic conditions generally. The reason for the financial strength of health insurance is easily discovered: sickness is treated as a distributive and not as a capitalized insurance risk so that both contributions and expenditures are adjustable from one fiscal period to another, without need or regard for any capital except comparatively small operating reserves. Health insurance has been outstanding as that form of social insurance which above all others has been financially sound, even through periods of social and economic upheaval.

13. The diverse characteristics of health insurance organization testify not only to the different circumstances under which social insurance has evolved, but also to the highly varying conditions under which it operates. The principle of mutual contributory insurance against the risks arising out of sickness has been found applicable under flexible, administrative arrangements which permit adaptation to different local conditions. In almost every national system, the central administration has carried the responsibility of *supervising* financial, executive, and judicial functions but has left the *operation* of these functions largely in the hands of democratic, local associations of the insured persons. This has meant that in most countries both contributions and benefits have been adjustable according to the means of the local groups of contributors. In Great Britain, where contributions have been uniform for all persons covered by the system, flexibility in benefits has been only partially attained through the use of the disposable surpluses of the Approved

Societies. Through close supervision and the use of equalization or reinsurance funds, financial solvency of the local groups has been safeguarded without excessive restraints on the flexibility of the system.

14. During more than fifty years of experience with large-scale national systems, medical benefit furnished through compulsory health insurance has not become "state medicine" or "public medicine." In so far as governments have contributed a small part of the costs (and it has been seen that tax support has declined rather than increased), there has been "socialization" of costs. But above all, health insurance has remained primarily a system whereby the contributions of insured persons (and, commonly, of their employers), with or without tax support, have gone into a common pool from which to pay cash benefits and to remunerate private practitioners of medicine, dentistry, etc., as well as hospitals and pharmacies. The point deserves emphasis; the medical benefits of health insurance have been furnished through the private practice and not through the "socialized" practice of medicine. From this point of view, health insurance has been a bulwark against the socialization of medical practice because it has financed the private practice of medicine, especially the private practice among the poor and among the people of small means—the particular classes whose medical services some people argue should be "socialized." This, according to one's point of view, is the strength or the weakness of health insurance.

Opinions differ whether the practice of medicine should remain primarily a private activity or should become mainly a public function. There can be no doubt, however, that health insurance has operated to strengthen the position of private practice in the insurance countries. It is fair to venture the opinion that without insurance, public medicine would be further advanced in these countries than it is now. In a practical and significant sense, health insurance has been the alternative, not the forerunner, to public medicine in particular sectors of social welfare.

Another significant effect of health insurance upon the practice of medicine is that it has also tended to entrench the *individual* practice of medicine. To those who hold that the rational and effective practice of modern medicine requires coördinated groups of general practitioners, specialists, technicians, etc., rather than individual practitioners, it will seem that the way should be opened in the health insurance of the future to the practice of groups as well as of individuals. This is a larger subject than can be pursued at this point; but we would call attention to this important problem which students of health insurance must be prepared to face.

15. It is difficult to draw clear and unambiguous conclusions from European insurance experience with methods of paying for insurance medical services. Many different procedures have been followed under diverse conditions. Numerous evidences indicate, however, that both the insurance authorities and the medical professions have much to gain and little to lose in following the British practice of leaving to the professions broad choice in the method of remuneration. Among *per-capita, per-illness,* and *per-attendance* procedures, each has its advantages in particular circumstances, though the *per-capita* procedure seems on the whole the most satisfactory to physicians and the simplest for the administrative authorities. Whatever the method of remuneration, the total sum of money available from the pool of insurance funds for remuneration of doctors must be fixed, but this total sum should be subject to periodic adjustment by a competent body upon which doctors are adequately and effectively represented.

16. As a corollary to what may be said about the method of paying for insurance medical services, it may also be observed that because the medical professions play a large and significant rôle in health insurance, they should be accorded administrative responsibilities coördinate with the importance of the work they do. All European experience testifies that the professions should have a strong and authoritative voice in the design of the arrangements under which they must serve. The French experience, though comparatively

short, nevertheless makes it clear that the strength of the professional voice should not exceed proper and reasonable bounds.

Finally, lest this review of European sickness insurance leave misapprehensions, the proverbial one word more. In the nature of the case, a review of the kind attempted in the preceding chapters tends to devote disproportionate space to controversial questions in relation to those upon which there is unanimity of opinion. This is an error which is almost invariably made in writings on sickness insurance and which, in a measure, is unavoidable in the nature of the task. The proof of the error rests in this: one of the unique characteristics of contributory health insurance and the one which attests most unequivocally to its beneficent function is that no country which has ever tried it has given it up. The march of events has always been from voluntary insurance of narrow scope, small contributions and meager benefits to compulsory insurance of more embracing scope, larger contributions and more generous benefits. The enlarging programs have had a sound economic basis because the increasing costs have been voted by representatives of those who make the contributions.

A large volume of evidence, which scarcely needs further review, attests the value of social insurance. However, the attacks which are still made in the United States upon the value of the medical benefits justify a few lines on this point. It has become almost a pastime, among the critics of the medical benefits, to quote from the writings of Dr. Erwin Liek who has been one of the most severe critics of sickness insurance in Germany. It is therefore fitting to close with the following passages[4] in which Dr. Liek gives his judgment—founded upon his own experience—of the advantages which sickness insurance has conferred upon the German people:

> Has sickness insurance been useful to the insured person? Undoubtedly. Among our poorer classes, in the families whose existence depends on daily earnings, a serious illness, especially of the breadwinner, was formerly a grave menace to the family.

Old doctors tell moving stories of the terrible effects of a long illness: a modest competence destroyed, happy human beings plunged into misery and want. Sickness insurance has brought about a radical change. . . . In 1904, when I was an assistant in the Danzig municipal hospital, sickness insurance had not been applied to agricultural workers. . . . What did we see in the hospital? Numerous old dislocations, badly united fractures, chronic inflammations, all of which had either not been treated at all or treated by quacks. All that was changed from the moment that the agricultural workers became compulsorily insured. . . . Only a fool or a malevolent person could deny the remarkable progress we have made since the adoption of social insurance.

These views can be duplicated from the authoritative writings in every insurance country.

REFERENCES AND NOTES

1. McCleary, George F.: NATIONAL HEALTH INSURANCE. London, H. K. Lewis & Co., Ltd., 1932, p. 177; or Social Insurance Medical Services, by A. Tixier. *International Labour Review,* February, 1934, xxix, p. 181.

2. Simons, A. M. and Sinai, Nathan: THE WAY OF HEALTH INSURANCE. Chicago, The University of Chicago Press, 1932, pp. 96–97.

3. *Ibid,* pp. 113–114.

4. As quoted by Dr. McCleary (NATIONAL HEALTH INSURANCE, *op. cit.,* p. 162) from E. Liek: DIE SCHADEN DER SOZIALEN VERSICHERUNG UND WEGE ZUR BESSERUNG. Munich, 1928.

CHAPTER XIV

SOME LESSONS FROM WORKMEN'S COMPENSATION INSURANCE IN THE UNITED STATES*

INTRODUCTORY

THIS review of European experience with health insurance has led to a number of observations which may have value when contemplating plans for group payment of sickness costs in the United States. To what extent can these observations on European experience be tested against American experience? In the United States there is no national or state system of general health or sickness insurance; but there is compulsory sickness insurance in the special field of workmen's compensation, all other forms being of a voluntary nature.

Many so-called voluntary schemes contain effective compulsory features; but these are economic and social, rather than legal, compulsions. Indeed, even some of the state workmen's compensation programs are nominally voluntary, though in effect compulsory. It has already been seen that voluntary (health or sickness) insurance plans have nowhere in the United States become very widespread or far reaching. Although the number of persons covered in these plans is considerable, it is still only a very small fraction of the people to whom the costs of sickness are burdensome.

American compensation practice is more limited than national sickness insurance, in respect to both the population and the disabilities covered. It is, nevertheless, a large system of insurance, witness

*For more detailed studies on workmen's compensation, the interested reader should consult the first fifteen general references listed at the end of this chapter. The report issued by the Bureau of Medical Economics of the American Medical Association[15] has been used extensively and freely in the preparation of this chapter.

the fact that in recent years the annual expenditure for medical care under compensation insurance has been about $77,000,000.[16] This sum is about one-half the amount spent for medical benefits by legal sickness insurance "funds" in Germany ($149,000,000 in 1933), but is larger than expenditure for medical benefit under national health insurance in Great Britain ($52,000,000 in 1934), and exceeds the insurance medical expenditures in other countries.

Although workmen's compensation legislation has followed an independent line of evolution, it takes its origin in the same social forces which led to the national health insurance laws. The industrial revolution brought such serious maladjustments as to compel first humanitarian factory legislation, and later more and more specific regulation of the conditions of labor.

> Out of the old personal relations of master and servant, custom, crystallized into the common law, had built up three basic principles or "defenses" to protect the employer against actions for damages growing out of accidents to his employees. The first of these was the "fellow servant" doctrine which absolved the employer from all responsibility if the injury was due to the actions of a fellow servant.* The second was the "assumption of risk" which held that any person seeking employment assumed the risks of the occupation. The third was the principle of "contributory negligence" which required the injured employee to prove that no oversight or carelessness of his had contributed to the happening of the accident.[17]

When the factory began to take on its modern form and became complex beyond anything conceivable in preceding centuries, these defenses no longer had substantial justification. The worker became largely incapable of protecting himself against the negligence of his fellow employee, nor could he gauge and assume the risks of his occupation; neither could he or others always tell when he was contributing to his own injury. In the event of a work accident or an occupational disease, the worker often or commonly became helpless

*Some authorities would hold that this statement in the passage quoted here is too broad. It may be more accurate to say that the fellow-servant doctrine absolved the employer if the injury was due to the *negligence* of a fellow servant.

to find redress. A growing multitude of sick, injured and crippled was thrown out of industry to be supported and maintained by the charities of society. The circumstances became so terrible that they dictated their own remedy.

Slowly, but inevitably, the legal basis of compensation for work accidents was shifted and the courts gradually established an equality between employer and employee which improved the latter's chance of receiving financial recompense if he became the victim of a work accident. The movement began abroad with the English reform acts of 1846. Employer's liability was established by the German act of 1871, the English act of 1880, and the state laws enacted in the United States between 1885 and 1895. The injured workman still had to prove negligence on the part of the employer and he had to deal with the insurance companies which the liability acts had brought into being and which, for a premium, took over the employer's risk.

Then came the era of suits and litigations. The injured workmen tried to collect damages from insurance companies whose premiums and profits depended upon how successfully they avoided (or evaded) payments of liability. For example, an investigation of how the system operated in Wisconsin[18] showed that of $1,025,000 paid by employers to liability insurance companies in 1911, scarcely $300,000 reached the employees or their dependents. Under this system, it soon came to be recognized that the improvement in the worker's state was almost negligible.

Most accidents remained uncompensated and even employers rebelled against the bickering, legal entanglements, rising costs and increasing discontent engendered by liability insurance. Employer and employee demanded that the United States follow the example of European countries and advance from the *liability* to the *compensation* stage. Liability for damage was to be replaced by prompt and adequate economic relief through a fixed, specified, equitable, automatic schedule of compensations for the injured worker or his dependents. Work accidents were to be charged against the industry and the product of its labor. The legally prescribed contributions of employers were to provide a fund for the proper compensation of those who were disabled or incapacitated in the course of their employment.

Under the influence of public indignation and with the forceful leadership of President Theodore Roosevelt, the first workmen's compensation law was passed by Congress in 1908 to cover workers under the federal jurisdiction. In 1911, ten states passed similar laws; by 1916 there were thirty-one states with compensation insurance; and a few years later all but four states had enacted similar legislation. At this time, only two states are left without workmen's compensation laws—Arkansas and Mississippi.*

One effect of the federal emergency relief program of 1933 was the addition *in effect* of four million persons to the population covered by the United States Employee's Compensation Act of 1916. These persons became entitled to medical and hospital care for such injuries as they sustained in the performance of duty and for occupational diseases. Nominally, they were not covered by the Compensation Act; in reality, they received the benefits of the Act through executive provision. In October, 1935, it was announced that workers employed on Works Progress Administration projects are entitled to disability or death compensation for traumatic injuries incurred while so employed. The rates of compensation are similar to those provided in the act of February 15, 1934.[19]

Of the forty-four states with laws prior to 1935, workmen's compensation insurance is strictly compulsory in only twelve states; in thirty-two states the law is *nominally* elective. In effect it is practically compulsory in all forty-four. Besides removing the employers' defense under the liability laws, most laws assume acceptance on the part of employers unless they file specific objection. These procedures were used to escape the rulings of the courts which had declared the early compulsory compensation acts unconstitutional because they violated the "due process" clause of the Constitution.

*Workmen's compensation laws were enacted in Florida and South Carolina in 1935.

In forty-two states the compensation acts are administered by appointive commissions or individual commissioners, instead of by the courts as under liability insurance. Usually, appeals from the rulings of the commissioners to the courts are allowed only under specified conditions and only on points of law. In some states the acts cover only "hazardous" or "extra hazardous" industries and generally exclude from their jurisdictions domestic employees, farm laborers, casual or intermittent employees, those working for employers with less than a specified number of employees, and the railroad workers who are subject to federal jurisdiction. To be compensable, injuries must as a rule arise out of, and in the course of, employment. Some of the acts make compensable all injuries received in the course of employment. In 1931, ten of the state laws, the Federal Government, and the District of Columbia included occupational diseases, some covering practically all diseases in this class, others only certain occupational diseases specifically listed in the schedules of the acts.[20] By 1934, twelve states covered occupational diseases at least in part.[21] A revision of the New York State law, enacted March 26, 1935, makes "any and all occupational diseases" compensable.

When the various state laws were in process of formulation, there were vigorous battles fought over the nature of the insurance carrier. Many employers, fearful of strong state control, fought against exclusive state funds and insisted upon the right to meet the law's requirements through self-insurance (upon providing acceptable evidence of financial responsibility) or through employers' mutual insurance companies. The existing commercial insurance companies fought for permissive legislation which would allow competing private insurance carriers. The laws which were finally passed generally permitted self-insurance, stock and mutual insurance companies, and state funds. Indeed, the insurance companies had so much influence on legislation that they left the stamp of their methods and procedures not only in the laws generally, but even in the laws of a few states where commercial companies were finally excluded from competition with exclusive state funds.

In 1931, seven states had exclusive state funds, eleven had state funds and competitive private insurance carriers, and twenty-six permitted private companies or self-insurance, or both. The insurance premiums vary from state to state, from industry to industry, and from company to company. They are presumably determined by the benefits provided by law and by the hazards of the industry. Rating systems attempt to judge each employer's specific risk according to the hazards of the industry and the frequency of accidents in his establishment.

The years in which the compensation acts were being adopted and the immediately succeeding years were marked by hectic political battles, by campaigning, chicanery, corruption and strife. As might have been predicted from European experience, the medical professions remained generally aloof from all this—largely indifferent, uninterested, and uninformed. A majority of the early laws provided only the most perfunctory medical service for the injured workingman despite the fact it was inevitable that nearly every case which was to come under the jurisdiction of the acts would involve a medical opinion. Nevertheless, the laws were framed largely without benefit of medical counsel and their administration was placed exclusively in lay hands. Until 1934 only one state had a physician member on its compensation commission. (As will be seen, the new New York State law, which came into effect July 1, 1935, gives to physicians one-third of the representation on the industrial council which is charged with broad advisory functions in the administration of workmen's compensation.)

In the forty-four states in which insurance against industrial accidents has been made in effect compulsory for employers, the early experiences of European compulsory health insurance and workmen's compensation practice have been passed in review. Though in a sense seen in the miniature, this field of American experience has displayed all of the tribulations of the larger European stage. Blunders in administrative organization, excessive lay control of professional practice, inadequate medical service, insufficient and unfair remuneration of medical practitioners, excessive costs and wasteful management, exploitation by commercial insurance carriers, malingering by workingmen, frauds by physicians, shyster practices by lawyers—they are all in the record. The full story is a long one. For present purposes it must suffice to focus attention upon the provision of medical benefits under a class of laws which may be considered to be compulsory insurance against certain costs of sickness.

Cash and Medical Benefits under Workmen's Compensation

Workmen's compensation legislation was designed primarily to furnish cash benefits. Under the specifications of the early acts, these benefits were small and, in general, inadequate to meet the expressed objectives of the laws. With the march of the years there has been a steady liberalization of these benefits. This was accomplished by larger allowances in the percentage of wages used as the basis to calculate compensation, by increases in the minimum wages which the laws use as such a base, and through increases in the cash benefits which are specified in the schedules of compensation for specific injuries. Liberalization was also accomplished through decreasing the waiting period (i.e., the interval between the occurrence of an accident and the day on which disability becomes compensable), and by increasing the scope of the coverage, especially by the addition of occupational diseases to the list of injuries which are compensable. Simultaneously, the benefits under the compensation acts have been enlarged through increases in the scope of the medical benefits and in the maximum amount of money which may be used to pay for medical service in a particular case.

The laws display very wide variations in the compensation paid for total or partial disability. The awards for total disability are based upon computations which assume, in different states, from 40 to 70 per cent of the wages normally earned by the injured worker. The amounts of the weekly compensations are usually prescribed between minima and maxima, the largest allowances ranging up to $25 per week. If total disability is temporary, compensation is payable only during its duration; if total disability is permanent, it is payable for from 208 weeks (in the Philippines) to life (in eighteen states). However, many laws specify that the total amounts payable shall not exceed certain fixed sums. Compensation for partial disability varies similarly. If one wishes to discover how inadequate cash compensation usually is and how far it fails in compensating the injured worker, he has only to study the records. Or he can compare the arbitrary compensation schedules of almost any jurisdiction with scientific estimates of the value of human life.[22]

When originally conceived, the compensation acts were based upon the theory that work accidents are chargeable to the cost of producing the products of industry. It was further recognized and recommended by the legislative investigating bodies that the costs of work accidents should be kept to a minimum and that workmen's compensation should provide the fullest medical relief and indemnity commensurate with wage-loss.[6] In the face of these recommendations in principle, the medical benefits which were originally provided in the acts were grossly inadequate. In the early stages of compensation history, twenty-two states limited medical care to what may be provided within thirty days, and twenty-four fixed $100 as the maximum sum which might be expended on all medical services furnished in a particular case. Five states provided no medical care in their first enactments.

Although the scope of the medical benefits was later increased and some of the inadequacies were eliminated, there developed many difficulties in the administration of medical care. In large measure this was due to the fact that the technique of providing medical care was part of a system which had been designed primarily to furnish cash benefits, not medical care. But the medical benefits have become so important that the whole program has been gradually changing. Many compensation commissions have come to recognize that the purposes of workmen's compensation are: first, prevention of industrial accidents and injuries; second, the provision of medical service; and third, cash compensation. This change in viewpoint is of fundamental importance in understanding the costs and the present limitations of the compensation acts.[23]

The effect of niggardly medical provisions was to deprive many injured workmen of the care which would have moderated disabilities and which would undoubtedly have prevented many injuries from becoming permanent disabilities. A few years of experience demonstrated that the truly significant opportunity of workmen's compensation was to give the injured workman good medical care. This was even more important than merely giving him a cash sum and permitting him the discretion of spending it as he would. *Restoration rather than compensation became the keynote.* Accordingly, began the period of expansion in the scope of medical benefits.

Connecticut was the first to give unlimited medical care to injured workmen. By 1932, fifteen jurisdictions (state, federal, and the possessions) had no money or time limits on the medical care guaranteed under their compensation acts, and several other states had so amended their laws that in effect the medical provisions were without legal limit of either time or money. A compilation as of May 1, 1935, shows twenty-three states with unlimited medical provisions.[24] Mr. Ethelbert Stewart, of the United States Bureau of Labor Statistics, estimated recently that the physicians and hospitals of the United States received some $72,000,000 annually in payment for services rendered under compensation acts. The Research Staff of the Committee on the Costs of Medical Care estimated, from entirely independent data, that industry spends about $79,000,000 a year for medical care.[25] And, as has already been noted, the Bureau of Medical Economics of the American Medical Association has more recently placed this estimate at $77,000,000.[16] These sums represent, of course, very large increases over the amounts spent in the early years of compensation history.

The liberalization of medical benefits has been won step by step over the objections of groups whose attention has been fixed more or less exclusively upon the size of the expenditures. Insurance companies especially, and in some cases state funds, have raised objections against the efforts to enlarge the scope of medical benefits. The complaints of the commercial companies actively engaged in compensation insurance have been bitter because, they have alleged, every increase in the cost of medical service is "a cut into their profits." Some insurance companies and many industrial employers have, however, begun to realize that it is good business and real economy to provide more and better medical care. Nevertheless, most of the companies look askance at each advance in compensation medical costs and use their large influence to hold the cost of these services to a minimum.

The significance of medical benefit to the industrial worker can be gauged by weighing the relative frequency with which medical, as opposed to cash, benefits are furnished. Accurate data on this point are not readily available. Yet it is known that, in 1920, of all recorded accidents only 2.86 per cent were of such severity as to require the payment of cash compensation. In 1930 this proportion was even lower, 1.55 per cent. In all other recorded cases, if any benefit was provided, it was medical benefit only. Workmen's compensation administration is based upon a system designed primarily for the provision of cash benefits (less than 2 or 3 per cent of the cases which come to the attention of the authorities) and not for that large part of the 97 or 98 per cent of the cases which receive only medical attention.

It has been estimated[26] that there are 90,000,000 industrial accidents in the United States annually and only 3,000,000 are of sufficient severity to involve lost time beyond the day or work-shift during which the accident occurred. Various estimates agree in placing the number of *fatal* industrial accidents among persons covered by workmen's compensation, in a year of so-called "normal" employment, at 20,000 to 25,000 per annum. As against about $400,000,000 spent annually in the administration of workmen's compensation and in the cash and service benefits furnished, the full cost of industrial accidents to employers and employees is not far from $5,000,000,000 annually.[27]

Cost of Administering Workmen's Compensation Insurance .

The program of workmen's compensation legislation evolved out of the difficulties which prevailed under liability insurance. The compensation laws make all accidents arising out of, and in the course of, employment (and, in some states, some or all occupational diseases) compensable according to definite schedules. It was intended that the laws should remove the risks and uncertainties of litigation; and, in considerable measure, they accomplish this result. The insurance problem is therefore greatly simplified by comparison with that which existed under liability insurance and makes possible a clearer and more accurate actuarial basis for insurance practice.

One would therefore expect that workmen's compensation insurance would be practised with comparative economy and that administration and other overhead or insurance-carrying costs would be relatively small. But this is not the case. *Of every dollar of premiums collected during recent years in workmen's compensation insurance, 42 cents was spent by, or remained with, the carriers; 38 cents was paid in cash to the injured workers, and 20 cents was paid to doctors and hospitals.*

It would be an easy task to propose a division of funds more equitable to industry and the consumer who pay the costs and to the workmen for whose benefit the system is designed. Cash benefits and medical care for the injured worker are the objectives of workmen's compensation. It is for these purposes that the premium dollar should be spent. Yet 42 cents of each dollar collected in premiums dwindles away and only 58 cents remains to furnish the benefits.

It may be properly recognized, on the one hand, that the provision of medical and cash benefits under workmen's compensation presents some difficult and complicated problems which do not appear in the administration of cash and medical benefits under health insurance (i.e., whether an injury occurred in the course of the employment and whether caused by the employment). On the other hand, there are numerous problems in health insurance which do not appear to an equivalent degree in workmen's compensation (i.e., the record-keeping of insured persons, the certification of dependents eligible to receive benefits, the certification of all cases of incapacity, etc.). Yet as against an insurance-company overhead cost of 42 per cent of the total funds under workmen's compensation, we have these figures for the administration costs in European health insurance:

Germany (1929)	6.5 per cent
(1933)	10.0 " "
Great Britain (1934)	15.5 " "
Denmark (1931)	10.1 " "
France—legal limit for the *caisses*	3.5 " "
—legal limit for all insurance agencies	5.6 " "

It has been seen in earlier chapters that the administration of health insurance is not as efficient as it might be; yet by comparison with prevailing practices under workmen's compensation in this country, the administrative agencies under health insurance seem to be paragons of efficiency. Attention has already been called to the inadequacy of the sums available for medical benefits under compensation insurance and we shall return to this subject later. At this point it should be noted that if any considerable savings were effected in the compensation insurance overhead costs and these savings become available to pay for medical benefit, vast improvement in these benefits could become possible because the insurance overhead costs have been more than twice as much as the costs of medical benefits.

COMMERCIAL EXPLOITATION

Workmen's compensation insurance coverage is written by four types of carriers, radically different in their efficiency to dispense the funds which they collect from employers of labor. The following figures represented in recent years (and perhaps still represent) the fraction of total premiums retained by the insurance carrier.[28]

Stock companies	38.0–42 per cent
Mutual companies	20.0 " "
Competitive state funds	10.6 " "
Exclusive state funds	4.0 " "

Carl Hookstadt reported that: "The total saving to insured employers of the United States (1922), if all were insured in exclusive state funds, would be over 30 million dollars annually."[28]

Commonly accepted rules have permitted 41.5 per cent of the premiums collected by the insurance companies to be used for expenses. This figure includes:

Acquisition	17.5	per cent
Claim adjustment	8.0	" "
Auditing of payrolls	2.0	" "
Factory inspection	2.5	" "
State and federal taxes	4.0	" "
General administration	7.5	" "
TOTAL	41.5	per cent

In some cases these overhead costs have actually attained 45 per cent. In spite of this situation, many or most casualty insurance companies have denied that they make profits from compensation insurance. Of course one cannot have insurance of any kind without some overhead cost. No matter how efficiently managed, it costs money to manage money, whether the benefits are provided in cash or in services. The objection is not that there are overhead costs, but that they are too high.

From the figures cited above, showing the large spread between the overhead costs of the exclusive state funds at the one extreme and the commercial stock companies at the other, it is obvious that the nature of the insurance carrier which operated in a particular state was not determined entirely by considerations of economy. Indeed, there is reason to believe that the true spread in overhead costs has been even larger than appears in the figures cited above, because legal obstructions have in some instances hampered the efficient operation of exclusive or competitive state funds.

It was originally intended that workmen's compensation should operate in such fashion that 75 to 90 cents of every dollar contributed by employers should reach employees or their dependents. On the basis of health insurance experience one would have expected (or hoped for) at least this much. Yet, as the facts show for the years cited, of the average premium dollar collected, less than 60 cents reached the eventual beneficiaries in cash or in valuable service.

The casualty insurance companies have sometimes taken a stand of strong opposition against state funds, whether competitive or exclusive, on the ground that the commercial companies were in the field before the enactment of the compensation laws. Some have maintained that they had a vested interest upon which the state cannot encroach without, in effect, practising confiscation. The opponents of the commercial companies have denied this, contending that the historical facts are as follows:

> a. The laws were designed with the intention that compensation insurance should be vested in state or in employer-mutual funds;
> b. The commercial companies opposed the legislation and therefore forfeited the right to practise under it and to be entrusted with its administration; and
> c. Compensation insurance is compulsory and collectivistic in character. The compensation premium is really a tax, the proceeds of which are distributed by a state commission for the benefit of injured workmen and their dependents. No private organization has a right to even part of a tax.[29]

It has been pointed out that the situation in workmen's compensation insurance has been as if the state farmed out to private interests, at a price, the rôle of collecting and spending its taxes for education or public protection. "We are inclined to forget," said Carl Hookstadt, "that a compensation law is a *workmen's* compensation law. It is not an employers' compensation law, nor a physicians' compensation law, nor an insurance companies' compensation law, nor a compensation law for the benefit of those who administer the law. It is for the employee and the interest of everyone else should be subordinated."[30]

Workmen's compensation insurance is compulsory and no amount of competition or education or other sales effort can in the aggregate change the total amount of insurance written in a state. Sales efforts may increase the business of one company as against another, but to the people of the state, 17.5 per cent of premiums spent for acquisition costs represent non-remunerative expenditures to support these competing companies.

This argument is intended only to emphasize that any sums which are spent in excess overhead could be spent for purposes of greater social significance, especially for those whose lot the compensation laws were designed to improve, through larger cash benefits and medical services.

Although there are difficulties in the administration of state funds, "even their most hostile rivals have ceased to circulate rumors of their approaching bankruptcy, and their cost of administration has probably reached as low a point as, and in some cases even a lower point than, is consistent with efficiency. The charge on the premiums for the cost of administration varies from nothing in Nevada, where the interest on the investment of the surplus meets all charges, to from 10 to 15 per cent in a few of the funds."[31]

ACCIDENT PREVENTION

When compensation legislation was being conceived and in the days of its infancy, there were great hopes for a vast program of accident prevention. Much was said on this score and large promises were made. It is, therefore, a sad commentary that it is not even possible to discover how much has been accomplished in this field. Accident statistics are so inadequate that one cannot discover to what extent the intention to develop an effective instrument for accident prevention has met with success.

There is no doubt that the program of compensation legislation has resulted in the prevention of many millions of industrial accidents. There is equally little doubt that there has been a good deal left undone in this field. Both may be chargeable to workmen's compensation practice. In many factories and in many places it has been cheaper to prevent accidents than to pay for their consequences; in other factories and in other areas it has apparently been cheaper to pay compensation than to prevent the accidents.

If the costs of compensation insurance and the costs of the benefits increase, a more effective program of accident prevention may be expected. There is ample room for improvement. It is alleged by some investigators that accident rates are probably higher in the United States than in any other industrial country of the world. It is argued that, per million of population, almost twice as many persons are killed by accidents in the United States as in France or Japan and more than twice as many as in highly industrialized Great Britain.[32] Whether or not this conclusion rests on unassailable data, there is no doubt that the industrial accident rate in the United States is unnecessarily high and that workmen's compensation insurance has fallen far short of all that was expected of it in the field of accident prevention. Nevertheless, its accomplishments should not be ignored or underrated. Apart from its functions as a measure for social reform, workmen's compensation has had far-reaching public health effects. Professor W. G. Smillie of Harvard has recently referred to the latter in the following words:[33]

> . . . As a direct result of *workmen's compensation laws* there has been a tremendous development in industrial sanitation and an improvement in the methods of medical supervision of industrial workers.
>
> The large insurance companies, particularly those that deal in industrial group insurance, have done more to improve the health of the industrial worker than any single agency, governmental or otherwise. This aid has been given both directly to the industry itself, through expert advice, and indirectly to the worker by the simple method of raising group premiums in hazardous industries. The industry is compelled to protect the worker by suitable means in order to lower its insurance premiums.

Professional Relations

Some of the commissions which investigated workmen's compensation before the laws were enacted recognized that in actual practice the larger part of administration would be medical and not legal. Yet, as matters developed, the legal, technical and financial aspects were permitted to overshadow the medical, and apparently to the detriment of the entire program.[34] Only a small fraction of compensation cases involves legal judgments, board hearings or cash payments; a much larger proportion requires some medical care. Nevertheless, the fundamental concept in the administrative scheme is the organization of machinery for the distribution of cash benefits.

Medical relations seem to be neither much better nor much worse under state funds than under private companies. Apparently, according to some who have studied this subject, what counts is not so much the public or private nature of the insurance carrier as the representation of the medical professions in the administrative authority.

The largest variable in the budgets of the casualty insurance companies has been the cost of medical benefit. It is therefore not surprising that these insurance companies have attempted, so far as this was possible, to hold medical costs to a minimum and also to fix them by contract. It is charged that the companies have tried to restrict compensation physicians to those who would serve the companies' needs, that is, hold medical service to the smallest volume and the lowest costs. There seems to be little doubt that the companies have been especially interested in engaging those physicians who could be counted upon to give opinions (on the extent and severity of injuries) which are favorable to the companies in cases involving cash compensations. Consequently, there has been some tendency towards the selection of compensation physicians on the basis of a commercial need which applies to less than 5 per cent of industrial injuries, i.e., to those cases which involve cash compensation.

Throughout the history of professional relations under workmen's compensation runs the same thread which was discovered in our analysis of European health insurance. No matter how closely the

beads are strung, the thread shows through. The compensation practitioner has had to serve two functions: provide medical care and
render a supposedly impartial, professional judgment upon which
cash benefits are to be paid.

The compensation laws provide, directly or indirectly, that the
employer shall furnish medical care to injured employees. This provision has been interpreted to mean that the employer has the right
to select the physician or surgeon who shall furnish the service. The
employer generally assigns this right to his insurance company.
Hence, the company has the choice of doctor. As we have already
noted, the company has tended to choose doctors who would work
expeditiously and inexpensively from the point of view of the company. Not without reason, in the choice of doctors many or most of
the companies have been far more interested in the cheapness of
the professional work than in its quality or effectiveness from the
point of view of the injured employee. There has grown up a system
in which the intent of the law to provide medical care to the injured
workman has come into conflict with the financial interests of the
insurance companies. There are grounds for the contentions of labor
organizations and of the American Medical Association that many
company-appointed physicians have diminished compensation costs
not only by agreeing to provide care for inadequate fees but by
hurrying workers back to their jobs and by understating the severity
of disabilities when they testify before the compensation commissioners. Casualty insurance companies deny that they attempt to
influence doctors in these matters. The record does not always substantiate their claims. It is very gratifying that there have been many
evidences, especially in recent years, of a different outlook on the
problem by some of the companies which have interested themselves
in the advantages of high-grade medical services and in the welfare
of the injured workman.

The complaints of doctors have been vigorous and vociferous.
Unfortunately for their case, many will question whether they "come
into court with clean hands." Compensation practice is avoided by

most physicians because it involves them in "red tape" and because it requires special knowledge of the administrative techniques or special competence in the treatment of injuries. The abuses of compensation practice therefore tend to be restricted to a fraction of the medical profession. But this fraction is not small. It may be justifiable to say that the medical professions could afford to apply to their colleagues rather than to the insurance companies a large proportion of the diatribes which they issue against abuses in compensation practice. If one wishes to see how doctors have utilized to their own advantage some of the abuses which prevail under workmen's compensation, he has only to delve into the records on the organization of industrial clinics designed to operate under blanket contracts with employers or insurance companies.

The subject may be illuminated by the facts brought to light by the Cullman Committee[35] appointed in 1931 to review medical and hospital problems in connection with the workmen's compensation law in New York State. A cross-section of litigated cases was studied. Each claimant had for a period of months or years been under the treatment of a physician chosen by the insurance company or at a commercial clinic and, in most cases, had also been under the care of a physician of his own selection. Medical evidence was heard on each case from both the insurance company's and the claimant's physicians and then from an impartial specialist chosen by the State Department of Labor. The conflict of testimony is striking. In each case in which the physician had been chosen by the injured worker, the disability was laid to the accident. In the cases in which reports were furnished by physicians chosen by employers or insurance companies, this was denied in 75 per cent. The impartial specialists reported that the industrial accidents were responsible in 68 per cent of the cases, that the relationship could not be determined in 13 per cent, and that the accidents were not responsible in 18 per cent. In respect to ability to return to work, among cases in which the company physicians found 90 per cent able to work, the impartial specialist found only 25 per cent ready to resume their labors. The inquiries of the

Committee also disclosed "an astonishingly complicated and far-reaching racketeering outfit" which included a brokerage business in compensation cases, a "corrupt and unscrupulous machine" involving a chain of clinics, shyster lawyers, incompetent and inexperienced physicians and untrained nurses through which "it is easy to prolong periods of disability, pad medical bills, and even create cases out of whole cloth." The Committee recommended the outlawing of commercial clinics and the discontinuance of insurance company clinics. A year later, Mr. Cullman added that "the march of events has shown that a State monopoly of the writing of workmen's compensation is essential to the sound administration of the law."

The root of the evil is clearly not in the existence of the commercial companies nor in the practices of doctors, but in the system which exposes doctors to competitive price-cutting and which lends their uncertain and difficult economic lot to exploitation by the insurance carriers. The weakness of the medical professions in the face of financial pressure is the most serious objection to placing physicians in positions of administrative responsibility. There may be some ground for the fear that such responsibility might be abused through the excessive apportionment of funds to pay medical fees. Obviously, the physician should receive his proper place in the design of an administrative responsibility, to see that professional questions are solved on professional grounds and that professional practice receives proper opportunity and fair remuneration. Beyond this, the history of workmen's compensation does not indicate that the physician holds any special promise of administrative wisdom or courage.

It was concluded in the discussions of health insurance that "free choice of doctor" should, so far as possible, be preserved to the patient. It was also discovered that not every argument for free choice is dictated solely in the patient's interest (see page 279). It is nevertheless gratifying that the stringent limitations on free choice which were common in compensation practice a few years ago are now giving way to increasing latitude. It is especially interesting that in a number of states the medical societies have successfully campaigned for the establishment of a "panel" system which requires the employer or the insurance company to designate in each locality physicians or surgeons from among whom an injured employee may choose his doctor. For example, an amending section of the Wisconsin law reads as follows:[36]

> The employee shall have the right to make the choice of his attending physician from a panel of physicians to be named by the employer. Where the employer has knowledge of the injury and the necessity for treatment, his failure to tender the same shall constitute such neglect or refusal. Failure of the employer to maintain a reasonable number of competent and impartial physicians ready to undertake the treatment of the employee and to permit the employee to make choice of attendant from among them shall constitute neglect and refusal to furnish such attendance and treatment.

More recently (December 31, 1933), a similar proposal was offered by the Medical Committee on Workmen's Compensation Insurance appointed by the Governor of New York.[37]

> It is the opinion of your Committee that the principal abuses as they affect the workmen are due primarily to the manner in which medical service is at present provided, and that they can be corrected only by granting the injured workman the right to choose a physician under certain limitations and safeguards designed to assure medical service of adequate competence, and to protect the employer and the insurance-carrier against excessive costs. . . .
> In order to establish adequate medical safeguards, physicians are to enroll for workmen's compensation work by registering their training and their qualifications with the medical society of the county in which they reside, or with a board designated by the county society. When making their applications for enrollment they will agree to limit their professional activities under this act to those conditions which a general practitioner is competent to treat, or in the case of specialists, which lie within their special field. The requirement of enrollment as well as all other provisions of the proposed act includes physicians engaged in physiotherapy, X-ray and other diagnostic laboratory

work. The medical society or the board designated by it is to recommend to the industrial commissioner that the physician be authorized to render medical care under this act, and the recommendation and the certificate of enrollment or authorization will specify the character of the medical care which he is qualified and authorized to render. . . .

Upon the recommendation of the county medical society or of the board designated by it, the commissioner will issue certificates of enrollment to qualified physicians which will specify the character of medical care which the physician is authorized to render under this act. . . .

Obviously, if there were general agreement on the fees or some other suitable basis for payment, and if doctors became well-informed on the technique of serving in workmen's compensation cases, all licensed physicians in a community who wished to do so could serve on these "panels." This trend is especially significant because it originates in proposals of the medical profession.

The proposals developed by this Medical Committee were embodied in legislation which has since been enacted by the Legislature of New York State (March, 1935). Under the new law, the injured employee, not his employer, is given the right to select the physician; the medical societies are afforded an opportunity to nominate physicians who, with the approval of the compensation commissioner, may engage in compensation practice; and the enlarged Industrial Commission (with one-third medical representation) is empowered to establish a schedule of minimum charges for services rendered by physicians.

This line of evolution suggests for consideration and study that medical care for industrial accidents and occupational diseases should become part of a general scheme of medical service. In such a scheme, the employer of labor should make contributions sufficient to pay for the medical care of cases which are properly chargeable to industry. His contribution should go, not into a special compensation fund, but into a general fund for the payment of medical service and the physicians should treat these cases without distinction from cases

which are non-industrial in origin.* From the point of view of the
patient to be served, the only distinctions which are sound and valid
are those which provide that each patient will be served by a practitioner who is competent to furnish the type of care which the case
requires. Such arrangements seem essential if free choice and professional responsibility are to be encouraged and industry is to bear
its fair share of the costs.

Not a little of the trouble over professional relations in compensation practice hinges on payment for medical service. To the professions, this matter is, for obvious reasons, extremely important. It is
equally important to the insurance companies, because their costs
of operation are of three kinds:

1. Acquisition and other overhead,
2. Cash compensations to injured workers, and
3. Payments to doctors and hospitals.

In particular circumstances, the first of these varies little from year
to year and the second is, in general, bounded by schedules written
into the laws. The third, i.e., the costs of medical care, is the principal variable. The incomes of the insurance companies are fixed by
the size of premiums and these, in turn, are not easily changed.
It is therefore obvious that the net profits of the companies vary
nearly inversely as their medical costs. Hence, it is easy to see the
inevitable lines of battle between the professional groups and the
casualty insurance companies. These lines were tightened when the
limited bounds of medical care provided in the earlier acts were replaced by the more liberal—and in some cases unlimited—provisions
of the later or amended acts.

In workmen's compensation, as in other fields, physicians and
hospitals charge "what the traffic will bear" although this practice
may be disguised under a variety of traditions, customs, and appear-

---

*If the employer were expected to contribute only so much as would cover the costs
of medical care for industrial cases, it might be difficult to determine this sum. If he
were expected to make substantial contributions to the cost of a general insurance
system for medical care, the portion of his contributions applicable to medical needs
arising out of employment might be a point of secondary importance.

ances. In consequence, the payment for professional medical care has not been a peaceful affair. Demonstrations by insurance companies that doctors receive fees substantially like those earned for similar services in private practice do not contradict demonstrations by physicians that they are inadequately rewarded for their labors. It must be recognized at once that here is the same situation which we discovered in our analysis of health insurance abroad. And the answer to the paradox is the same here as it was there, i.e., though the sums available to pay for medical care have been increasing, the total has been and remains inadequate. The inadequacy in workmen's compensation is brought into sharper relief by the fact that a large part of the premiums collected from employers goes to pay for overhead costs. And, as was remarked before, much or most of this is a total waste so far as the supposed beneficiary, the injured employee, is concerned. He pays in reduced cash and service benefits for the competitive practices of those who are rivals for shares in a volume of insurance of which the total amount is fixed.

It may be, as the insurance companies contend, that the total amount of money available for medical payments (between $70,000,000 and $80,000,000) is inadequate to permit higher fee schedules than are now in use. Nevertheless, it is equally clear that, even if this were true, much higher schedules could be supported by the same insurance premiums if any appreciable part of the sums now spent on acquisition and other overhead costs of questionable value was devoted instead to the direct service of the injured worker. More than twice as much is apparently spent in overhead as in the payment for medical care. If the non-productive costs of stock and mutual companies were reduced to those of exclusive state funds—especially to those of the better administered state funds—and the savings were applied to medical care, there could result vast improvement in the quality and in the completeness of medical benefit, and almost complete elimination of those reasonable professional difficulties which are due to inadequate remuneration of doctors and hospitals. Not without reason is this point made again and again. It looms large out of the fog of misunderstanding which is everywhere evident in the writings on medical practice under workmen's compensation.

There are other sources of trouble in the relations of doctors and insurance companies. There are questions of medical secrecy, of the personal relation between doctor and patient, and a host of other issues which have become familiar from inquiries into the history of medical practice under health insurance. In workmen's compensation one finds the same types of difficulties which beset health insurance. Always one discovers at the bottom, as the principal causes of trouble, inadequate financial resources and the dual function of the physician—to provide medical care and to render judgments upon which another agency dispenses or withholds cash benefits. The objection against compelling the physician to serve a double function is even more serious in compensation than in health insurance practice. In compensation practice, the certification for cash benefits applies against "funds" in which a commercial corporation or some other "third party" rather than, as in health insurance, a mutual association of insured persons has a direct financial interest in the cash benefits.

Finally, one other phase of professional relations deserves comment. It will be recalled (see Chapter II) that organized medical groups serving organized industrial population groups have been fostered and encouraged by workmen's compensation. Contract practice is perhaps more common in the form of workmen's compensation medical practice (or, in some states, as a substitute for it) than in all other forms combined. There can be no doubt that some of the serious evils in corporate and contract medical practice have been encouraged by unfair and unethical agreements of service with insurance companies. It is, however, absurd to carry the implication in this point too far, because the same practices may be observed in hundreds of places where the contracts have little or nothing to do with workmen's compensation. The evils of contract practice and their unfortunate consequences for the professions and the public cannot be laid at the door of workmen's compensation. They are to be found wherever enterprising practitioners have succumbed to economic pressure and have compromised their professional standards for financial gain. What is significant is this: compensation has fostered and encouraged contract practice, and a system of inadequate remuneration of medical agencies has often directed contract practice into unfortunate channels. If the underlying economic situation were improved, there would be provided an increased opportunity for the development of forms of contract practice which could be as advantageous to the public as to the professions.

It seems doubtful that the ends conceived in these remarks can be attained merely by minor amendments of the compensation laws. The basic economic and professional relations require something more drastic. It is essential that the faults in compensation practice be not extended. General health insurance, if it comes, should be built upon its own properly designed foundation. It should not come through extension of workmen's compensation.

Conclusions

It is interesting first to quote at length the conclusions presented in the report of the Bureau of Medical Economics of the American Medical Association from its study of "Medical Relations under Workmen's Compensation":[15]

1. There should be absolute free choice of physician or surgeon by the injured worker among those competent to give the services required. That competence should be determined by professional standards and not by financial considerations.
2. There should be no solicitation or compulsion exercised on patients to compel them to enter into any scheme of medical care. Any deviation from this rule means that medical qualifications and consequent medical care are made subject to financial considerations.
3. All expenditures for medical care should go to those who give that care. There is no excuse for the presence of the profit taking promoter, organizer or entrepreneur between

the physician, surgeon, nurse, hospital or other agent giving such care and the patient who receives it. Every attempt to introduce such a third party has been proved wasteful and harmful.

4. There should be medical representation in all compensation institutions proportionate to the medical interests involved. Questions of a purely medical nature should be passed upon by those who have met the standards set up by law to determine medical qualifications and who alone have been pronounced capable of passing on such questions.

5. It is important that in every state medical society there should be an active committee devoted to the study of the problems of industrial medicine. Wherever compensation laws exist, this committee should be in close and continuous contact with the administrators of compensation, to the end that medical subjects be presented from the scientific professional standpoint and that all physicians may be kept fully informed of any questions at issue.

6. There should be greater consideration for the human side of accident prevention programs and the active participation of physicians in such work.

7. It is suggested that efforts be made through joint action of state medical societies and the compensation authorities to establish more equitable and uniform fee schedules.

It is not difficult to agree with most of these conclusions. It is difficult to believe, however, that anyone advocates *absolute* free choice of physician (first conclusion above) except as a counsel of perfection, even when the choice is limited among those who are supposedly "competent" to give the services required. Neither the insured worker nor any other person ordinarily has absolute free choice. He is always limited by geographical and economic factors and by legal restraints upon those who are permitted to practise. Furthermore, it may not be wise social policy that the insured worker should be given *complete* freedom to squander his or the employer's or the consumers' money as he wishes. *Reasonably* free choice, with due regard to the social obligations which are involved, should be adequate. When full recognition is given to the need for special technical competence required of those who should be available to care for the industrially injured, "free choice" properly requires limitation to a restricted list of specially certified practitioners.

It is difficult to agree with the authors of the report quoted above that the fifth of their conclusions "is really the only essential one and implies all the others." It may well be "that the form of legislation and institutions is of far less importance than their administration"; but it seems none the less clear that the essence of the matter lies in the first and third rather than in the fifth conclusion.*

If a system of workmen's compensation or other insurance which involves the provision of medical care guarantees reasonably free choice and avoids the necessity of having the entrepreneur, it has an especially valuable opportunity to serve in the interests of good medical care rather than of least costs. If a system does not have free choice of doctor and does permit the operations of profit-motivated insurance carriers, no amount of wise medical counsel will eliminate a fundamental conflict of interests. Further, the evidence has yet to appear that many state medical societies have shown that interest and devotion to workmen's compensation which would warrant the anticipation of the wise counsel for which the fifth conclusion (page 316) calls.

Several generalizations stand out clearly from our own analysis:

1. The scope of the compensation laws has broadened by extending the coverage to larger numbers and varieties of industries, by embracing (in twelve states) occupational diseases along with industrial accidents, by expanding the variety and by increasing the duration of medical services.

2. The emphasis has, to an increasing degree, been shifting from the provision of cash benefits (to replace wage-loss and for the purchase of medical care) to furnishing benefits in kind (medical care as a supplement to cash benefit for wage-loss), although cash

*This reference to the third conclusion quoted above bears particularly upon the first sentence of that conclusion. The last sentence—"Every attempt to introduce such a third party has been proved wasteful and harmful"—is more inclusive than I should be prepared to defend. I. S. F.

benefits still consume approximately twice as much money as medical benefits.

3. The worst evils in compensation medical practice may be traced to lack of adequate professional participation in formulating and administering the laws (or to lack of adequate provisions for professional safeguards in the administration of the medical benefits), and to exploitation for profit by commercial carriers. Some of the most serious abuses have been eliminated when (and where) joint medical and lay groups have arrived at agreements upon revised procedures; and many of the most objectionable features have been successfully eliminated in some of the states where commercial carriers are not permitted to operate.

To judge from much which has been written on workmen's compensation practice, one would gather that the entire program was foisted by some vague and elusive enemy of society upon employers, employees, physicians, insurance companies, and other participants. This impression is gained, in no small measure, from the fact that little is written about features of compensation practice which operate smoothly and much is written about matters which are controversial and unsatisfactory. Compared to an ideal state of affairs, workmen's compensation practice has been sadly defective. But compared to the precedent system of legal suits, damage claims and settlements, current practice represents a substantial improvement and is accepted as such by employers and employees.

As Simons and Sinai[88] have properly remarked, the extension of workmen's compensation to cover occupational diseases among industrial workers was effected by substituting the word "injury" for the word "accident" in earlier laws. "To make the change to a comprehensive health insurance law covering all industrial workers, it would, in most cases, be necessary to do little more than change the word to 'all diseases.' Doing this would at once extend all the evils as well as the benefits of a compulsory health-insurance system to a majority of workers in industry."

It is greatly to be hoped that no such expansion will be made.

Patching up old laws to meet new requirements is often a painful and ineffective procedure. It would be far better to conceive compulsory insurance on the basis of its own needs, with full regard to former experiences. Restriction to wage-earners would perpetuate evils and shortcomings already perceived in existing health insurance systems; placing the total burden of costs on industry for disease not directly related to occupation would create a fundamental inequity; building upon obsolete and inadequate administrative arrangements would bring newer and more disagreeable periods of legal, commercial and professional difficulties.

These remarks are not intended as a criticism of workmen's compensation practice. They are offered as a caution that if compulsory health insurance is inaugurated in the United States, it should be builded not upon this existing form of compulsory insurance, but upon a foundation adequately designed for the purpose.

REFERENCES AND NOTES

1. WORKMEN'S INSURANCE AND COMPENSATION SYSTEMS IN EUROPE (Twenty-fourth Annual Report of the Commissioner of Labor). Washington, Government Printing Office, 1909.

2. Frankel, L. K. and Dawson, M. M. (with L. I. Dublin): WORKINGMEN'S INSURANCE IN EUROPE. New York, Russell Sage Foundation, 1911.

3. Rubinow, I. M.: SOCIAL INSURANCE. New York, Henry Holt and Company, 1913, 542 pp.

4. Bulletins of the Bureau of Labor Statistics. Washington, Government Printing Office, many numbers, 1917 to date.

5. WORKMEN'S COMPENSATION ACTS IN THE UNITED STATES—THE MEDICAL ASPECT. New York, National Industrial Conference Board, 1923.

6. Downey, E. H.: WORKMEN'S COMPENSATION. New York, The Macmillan Company, 1924, 224 pp.

7. MEDICAL CARE OF INDUSTRIAL WORKERS. New York, National Industrial Conference Board, 1926.

8. Commons, J. R. and Andrews, J. B.: PRINCIPLES OF LABOR LEGISLATION. New York, Harper & Brothers, 1927, 632 pp.

9. Bowers, E. L.: IS IT SAFE TO WORK? Boston, Houghton Mifflin Company, 1930, 230 pp.

10. Kessler, H. H.: ACCIDENTAL INJURIES. Philadelphia, Lea & Febiger, 1931, 718 pp.

11. MEDICAL SUPERVISION AND SERVICE IN INDUSTRY. New York, National Industrial Conference Board, 1931.

12. Williams, Pierce (and I. C. Chamberlain): THE PURCHASE OF MEDICAL CARE THROUGH FIXED PERIODIC PAYMENT. New York, National Bureau of Economic Research, Inc., 308 pp.

13. Simons, A. M. and Sinai, Nathan: THE WAY OF HEALTH INSURANCE. Chicago, The University of Chicago Press, 1932, 250 pp.

14. Epstein, Abraham: INSECURITY: A CHALLENGE TO AMERICA. New York, Harrison Smith and Robert Haas, 1933, 696 pp.

15. MEDICAL RELATIONS UNDER WORKMEN'S COMPENSATION, prepared by the Bureau of Medical Economics. Chicago, American Medical Association, 1933, 158 pp.

16. *Ibid,* p. 97.

17. *Ibid,* pp. 7–8.

18. Commons, John R.: The Industrial Commission of Wisconsin. Its Origins and Methods. *The Survey,* January 4, 1913.

19. *Labor Information Bulletin.* Issued by the Bureau of Labor Statistics, U. S. Department of Labor (Washington), October, 1935, ii, No. 10.

20. OCCUPATIONAL DISEASE LEGISLATION. (A Committee Report.) New York, American Public Health Association, 1931.

21. For a review of recent legislation, *see Monthly Labor Review,* 1934, xxxviii, pp. 840–852; 1348–1361.

22. Dublin, L. I. and Lotka, Alfred J.: THE MONEY VALUE OF A MAN. New York, The Ronald Press, 1930, Chapter VII.

23. *Cf.* Connecticut Board of Compensation Commissioners, Report for 1927–1928; and Report of the Industrial Survey Commission of New York, Legislative Document 87, 1928.

24. Snick, J. J.: *Proceedings of the Casualty Actuarial Society,* May 24, 1935, xxi, p. 257.

25. Falk, I. S., Rorem, C. Rufus and Ring, Martha D.: THE COSTS OF MEDICAL CARE. Chicago, The University of Chicago Press, 1933, p. 9.

26. Heinrich, H. W.: Handbook of Labor Statistics, Bulletin No. 541. U. S. Bureau of Labor Statistics, 1931, p. 313.

27. *Ibid,* p. 315.

28. Comparison of Workmen's Compensation Insurance and Administration, Bulletin No. 301. U. S. Bureau of Labor Statistics, April, 1922.

29. Bulletin No. 212. U. S. Bureau of Labor Statistics, June, 1917; *ibid,* Bulletin No. 511, 1930.

30. Bulletin No. 281. U. S. Bureau of Labor Statistics, June, 1921, p. 188.

31. MEDICAL RELATIONS UNDER WORKMEN'S COMPENSATION, *op. cit.,* p. 45.

32. INSECURITY: A CHALLENGE TO AMERICA, *op. cit.*, p. 577.

33. Smillie, Wilson G.: PUBLIC HEALTH ADMINISTRATION IN THE UNITED STATES. New York, The Macmillan Company, 1935, pp. 256–257.

34. McSweeney, E. F.: Bulletin No. 248. U. S. Bureau of Labor Statistics, March, 1919, pp. 282–286.

35. *Monthly Labor Review,* 1934, xxxviii, p. 97.

36. MEDICAL RELATIONS UNDER WORKMEN'S COMPENSATION, *op. cit.*, p. 79. On California law, *see* Changes in the Compensation Law, by A. J. Pillsbury, p. 13.

37. Report of the Medical Committee on Workmen's Compensation Insurance. New York, December, 1933, pp. 8–10.

38. THE WAY OF HEALTH INSURANCE, *op. cit.*, p. 191.

CHAPTER XV

VOLUNTARY OR COMPULSORY GROUP PAYMENT OF SICKNESS COSTS IN THE UNITED STATES?

LONG academic battles have been waged over the issue between voluntary *versus* compulsory sickness insurance.[1] The principal conclusion upon which most students are agreed is aptly presented by Simons and Sinai[2] in the following words:

> Every attempt to apply the principles of voluntary insurance on a large scale has proved to be only a longer or shorter bridge on the way to a compulsory system. Every so-called "voluntary" system is successful in just about the proportion that it contains compulsory features, especially in selling and the collection of premiums. Such voluntary systems are of interest primarily because they set the pattern for the coming compulsory legislation. Many of the least desirable features of compulsory schemes were inherited from previous voluntary systems. This point is of paramount interest to nations still in the voluntary stage.

This conclusion is particularly germane in the light of the observations noted in the preceding chapters. It should be constantly borne in mind as the advantages of a voluntary or compulsory principle for a program of group payment in the United States are examined alternatively. With some emendation, the following arguments are selected from the writings of proponents of one or the other.[3] They are cited, at first, without prejudice as to their validity. We shall turn later to their evaluation.

PRINCIPAL ARGUMENTS FOR VOLUNTARY INSURANCE

Let us consider first the arguments which have been advanced for voluntary insurance. The substance of some is self-evident; others deserve comment and explanation.

1. Voluntary insurance can be established for small units of the

population, wherever homogeneous groups exist, and may be adapted strictly to the needs and the financial circumstances of the groups. It need not be one thing in a particular place because it must be this in another.

2. Voluntary insurance permits of establishment where and when it is desired; the system need not be crippled in one place by compromises with objecting groups elsewhere. It can wait for hesitant groups and can absorb them when they are prepared to undertake it.

3. The scope of the benefits can be adapted to the needs and demands of a particular group, to their financial means, and to the medical resources which are available locally.

4. Voluntary schemes which are organized to provide more than the barest essentials of medical service require the existence of *groups* of consumers and *groups* of practitioners. Inasmuch as both are already to be found only in cities and industrial areas, voluntary insurance is especially and chiefly applicable to such places.

5. "The majority of the Committee [the Committee on the Costs of Medical Care], although aware of the limitations of coverage and the possible difficulties of voluntary health insurance, nevertheless believe that the ultimate results will be far better if experience with actuarial and administrative details, and above all the evolution of group practice units capable of rendering rounded medical service of high quality, precede the adoption of any compulsory plan by a state as a whole.

"Their reasons for holding this position are:

"The maintenance of the quality of medical care is fundamental. Good service to the sick is worth what it costs; poor service is likely to be worth little or nothing. It is much more important to establish plans whereby complete and competent medical care will be obtained by a considerable section of the population, and later, on the basis of this experience, to work out ways and means of extending the same care to all, than to devise a more widespread plan which would furnish a medical service limited in scope and deficient in quality. In the main, foreign systems of compulsory health insurance have done the latter. The scope and quality of their services have improved with time, but America need not follow their mistakes either in policy or method. It is probably true that in the United States, except for some rural areas, a much larger amount of medical service is available, and is actually obtained even by low wage-earners, than was the case in any European country during the period when its health insurance system was developing. A plan which was aimed especially to bring in the low wage-earner and which was keyed down to his paying ability, would either have to be subsidized from the start by employers, by tax funds, or by both, to an unprecedented degree, or else it would provide a medical service more limited in scope or lower in quality than a large part of the population now receives.

"European practice has no doubt moved on from voluntary to compulsory insurance; but the former appears to have represented a desirable preparatory phase. To many members of the Committee, experience of European countries suggests that a certain development of voluntary insurance may be inevitable before the people of a country become sufficiently familiar with the principles involved to support adequately any legal requirement for insurance."[4]

To this statement five subscribing members (to the majority report) of the Committee added the following qualifying comments:

"We call attention to these significant statements embraced in the body of the report: 'Fortunately we have retained in this country a wholesome local responsibility for medical service. This fact means that opportunities exist for trying out many plans under various and variable conditions. . . . The Committee urges the broadest sympathy toward experimentation in promising fields, together with the most searching analysis of results.' We believe that experimentation along the lines of both voluntary and required health insurance, along with the other experiments in the group purchase of medicine should be promoted and carried on. In all likelihood, in certain areas of the country and for certain population and economic groups, required health insurance will be found to be more feasible and practicable than voluntary health insurance or vice versa.

"Therefore, we feel that the report should not emphasize or recommend voluntary health insurance over required health insurance, or vice versa, but that both plans or a combination of the two be equally recommended by the Committee for experimentation."

Further, the principal argument of the majority of the Committee on the Costs of Medical Care for voluntary—as against compulsory—insurance *at the outset* continues as follows:

"It is very desirable to develop strong, organized professional groups, each rendering comprehensive medical service, before insurance becomes compulsory. If health insurance is to operate most successfully, it must cover all forms of illness and include preventive as well as therapeutic care. Such an end can be attained more readily when the medical service is rendered by organized groups than when rendered by individual practitioners. Unless there has been ample previous experience in a state with group practice as a basis of furnishing medical service, any law for required health insurance would make individual practice and not group practice the legal foundation of the whole system. Such has been one of the chief disadvantages which European countries have faced under compulsory insurance. In Germany the recent trend toward group practice has been seriously hampered by the compulsory insurance law.

"There are also weighty administrative considerations against making health insurance compulsory as a general program for the United States. Compulsory insurance abroad has depended for its administration largely upon organized groups of employees, such as unions or coöperative societies. Their part in the administration has in some countries proved disadvantageous to quality and economy of service, partly because of the wide geographical dispersion of the membership, and partly because health insurance is likely to be a secondary interest of these organizations. Be this as it may, such industrial and coöperative associations are not sufficiently developed in most localities in the United States to include more than a small fraction of the population. It would be impossible, therefore, to use such organizations as the basis for administering compulsory health insurance. Usually it would be necessary to form new, local organizations. This would require a large amount of direct governmental administration, because the government would be the only available or recognized agency, capable of administering a compulsory insurance plan for the diverse and unorganized elements that make up the population of most American cities. European experience, particularly in those countries like Germany and Austria which have had comprehensive insurance plans for many years, shows that serious evils of competition and price-cutting may exist under a compulsory plan and, if so, are difficult to eradicate.

"Finally, it is probable that no legislature would pass a compulsory health insurance law unless it included, from the start, a combination of medical care insurance with cash benefits for income protection; but these two forms of insurance should not be combined."

In reference to the last point, it should be noted that cash and medical benefits have been more frequently separated under voluntary than under compulsory insurance. And, as has been noted in preceding chapters, the administrative separation of cash from medical benefits is a goal of high importance.*

6. Voluntary insurance offers special opportunities to retain the principle of direct contributions by individuals or families. This is significant because direct payment offers a constant reminder to the insured person that insurance is a mutual undertaking, and will tend to discourage malingering and excessive demand for service.

7. Voluntary insurance provides a guarantee against political interference and control. "It ought to be remembered that compulsory insurance will necessarily be subject to political control and that such control will inevitably destroy professional morale and ideals in medicine." (Minority Report, C.C.M.C.)[5] This type of caution argues for slow experimentation with voluntary forms of sickness insurance.

---

*The recently enacted compulsory law of British Columbia is restricted to medical benefits.

Principal Arguments for Compulsory Insurance

Now we may consider briefly the principal arguments which have been advanced on the other side. They run as follows:

1. Many undesirable practices develop in medical service under voluntary insurance, and these are evils of a sort which only governmental control in compulsory insurance can prevent or cure because they arise principally from competitive practice. Experience with large numbers of voluntary insurance plans in the United States shows that, in many of them, groups of practitioners facing competition with other groups and in order to attract patients from their competitors have reduced their fees to the point of impairing service; proprietary clinics with contracts of service for voluntary insurance organizations have taken advantage of the economic difficulties in which individual physicians find themselves, have employed them at inadequate salaries, and have loaded them with more work than they could possibly do well. Other proprietary groups have utilized for profit purposes excessive fractions of the income from premiums, leaving small reserves (or none at all) for emergency needs, have restricted the scope of service to the minimum, or have added undesirably restricting clauses to their contracts, and have accumulated no reserves for improvement or expansion of facilities or service. Commercial "racketeering" by voluntary insurance groups recently became a public scandal in California and required drastic action by law enforcement agencies.[6] Compulsion and government regulation are necessary to restrict sickness insurance to non-profit associations and to protect the public and the professions against commercial exploitation or undesirable competition among insurance practitioners.

2. It is argued by proponents of voluntary insurance that, in principle, the way to avoid unethical and otherwise undesirable practices in a voluntary scheme is to apply the indicated cures—namely provide medical care through larger, organized medical groups in which financial control rests jointly with lay and professional representatives —not to scrap the voluntary form of the organization. Unfortunately

for this point of view, it ignores the fact that voluntary forms of group payment go on while the organization of large and well-controlled medical centers remains a hope of the future. The crystallization of existing practice continues, while the desirable remedy in voluntary action is not yet even fashioned. Compulsory insurance under government control is the answer.

3. If a basis of payment equal to the needs of good medical care, if adequate remuneration of practitioners, if stability of income for hospitals and clinics, and if accumulation of reserves for emergencies are to be provided, the people with incomes above the level of dependency or of minimum subsistence must be brought within the scheme, and this can be effectively accomplished on a sufficiently large scale only through compulsory insurance.

4. Government control is essential where assistance from public funds is necessary for population units containing large proportions of poor families.

5. If people have the privilege of joining voluntary insurance groups or remaining outside the scheme, there will be a tendency for those who are in poor health to join and for those in good health to abstain. Compulsory insurance for entire units of population is necessary to provide against the adverse selection of medical risks or the administrative complications which would have to be introduced to protect the insurance fund against the accumulation of bad risks. Voluntary schemes which exclude bad risks exclude those who are most in need of medical care.

6. Though the Majority Report of the Committee on the Costs of Medical Care recommended voluntary insurance, it recognized the following arguments for compulsory insurance:

"Families with low or irregular incomes, even if they are self-supporting while employed, cannot usually be covered by any form of voluntary insurance. The experience with voluntary insurance in other countries has generally led to the conclusion that persons employed in small businesses or self-employed are also unlikely to enter a voluntary plan, unless they see a saving to them personally or a likelihood of better care. For these reasons, voluntary health insurance has been succeeded by compulsory insurance in most of the countries of western Europe.

"The use of the state's power of making membership in a sickness scheme obligatory for large groups of persons increases the population served and also reduces the administrative cost of securing and retaining members. The Committee recognizes that the distribution of the costs of medical care will not become widespread in some communities, or for certain sections of the population in many communities, unless there is legislation which makes the distribution of these costs compulsory."[4]

7. "Most European countries, one after another, have gone from a voluntary to a required system of insurance, but many of the evils of the voluntary system are carried over to the compulsory plan. Vested interests are built up under voluntary insurance which are very difficult to dislodge, even though they seriously hamper effective work. While it is true that the United States has few coöperative societies which could administer compulsory health insurance, this is a fortunate rather than an unfortunate circumstance. In European countries, such societies have almost completely outgrown their usefulness, so far as health insurance is concerned; but they still remain to clutter and confuse administration, and to prevent insurance statistics from being useful for public health purposes."[7]

8. "Voluntary insurance will never cover those who most need its protection. No legerdemain can bring into a voluntary system the unorganized, low-paid working group who are not indigent but live on a minimum subsistence income. Yet any plan that helps those with less serious needs and does not reach those whose needs are sorest does not solve the fundamental problems of providing satisfactory medical service to all.

9. "There is no innate antagonism between required health insurance and the development of organized medical service. On the contrary, such health insurance might be a powerful stimulus to the formation of organized groups. If health insurance covers all major

types of medical service, and if local communities are free to obtain medical service from organized groups, when such groups are available, the obvious benefits, economic and professional, of organized service will act as the most effective possible stimulant to the formation of such groups. The dangers of giving local communities this authority can be guarded against if all contracts are subject to approval by a state board that insists on fair treatment to the practitioners and the maintenance of good standards.

10. "Required insurance will undoubtedly be simpler and more direct to administer and, in the long run, more economical. There will be less tendency to create over-lapping agencies and to duplicate capital investment. Because a large proportion of the people will be included, it will be more stable.

11. "Governmental participation and regulation will undoubtedly be almost as necessary for voluntary as for compulsory insurance, if the worst abuses are to be avoided. Such participation will be more effective if it is started in the beginning."

To this point, eight members of the Committee who subscribed to the majority report submitted the following additional statement:

"We believe that an additional reason for the early adoption of required health insurance rather than voluntary insurance is that a system of required insurance encourages the development of higher standards of medical care of the patients included in such a system."

Exploitation in voluntary systems might be controlled by lay or professional or mixed groups. But there is room for difference of opinion on this point. Only the state can be both strong and impartial and can guarantee effective supervision.

12. Experience shows that voluntary insurance has come into being in the United States largely under industrial auspices. Though it has been honestly and effectively administered in many places, in many others it has provided an opportunity for an undesirable form of industrial paternalism, furnishing poor and inadequate service, and contributing further "to tie labor to the job." Indeed, in some states voluntary systems of industrial sickness insurance have been

exploited as a means of foisting upon the worker some of the costs of medical care for industrial accidents and occupational disease. Compulsory insurance and government control is needed to eliminate and prevent the further appearance of these vicious practices.

13. The costs of adequate medical care would exceed the financial means of families at least up to the $2,000 annual income level and in part up to the $3,000 level. In normal times, these income brackets include 50 per cent and 75 per cent, respectively, of all families. That such large proportions of the population have incomes inadequate to support adequate medical care is a consequence of the economic order. If the health of the people is a concern and responsibility of society, then society has a stake in assisting all to receive good medical care. This cannot be done except through financial assistance from government funds. Hence, a government-supervised plan of furnishing medical care is unavoidable.

14. It is argued that political control and consequent professional demoralization are inevitable under compulsory insurance. This has not happened in Europe, witness the fact that no responsible group, professional or lay, proposes to give up compulsory and revert to voluntary insurance. Instead, the proposals of all responsible groups are in favor of extending the scope of the medical benefits and expanding the insured population. Furthermore, many of the existing evils in European compulsory insurance are relics of the practices, agencies, insurance "funds," etc., inherited from the days of voluntary insurance.

EVALUATION OF THE ARGUMENTS

It is important to remember, in considering the shortcomings of either voluntary or compulsory insurance, that these must be evaluated not against an Utopia, but against the existing system of medical practice. The proponent for the one or the other cultivates the habit of showing the deficiencies in medical service which may be expected under the system he does not favor. Yet, shall we close our eyes to evils and inadequacies in our present-day scheme in the United

States, with its inability to deal with the incompetent practitioner, with its excesses of professional specialization, secret fee-splitting, unnecessary surgical operations for financial advantage, inadequate public expenditures because of the fee-for-service tradition, burdensome costs, inadequate remuneration of practitioners, and the neglect of tens of millions of people who receive no individual preventive service and no dentistry or whose illnesses go unattended?

As we review the needs and the arguments for one form of insurance or another, one point stands out in especially bold relief. The most important single objection to compulsory—and in favor of voluntary—insurance, which was advanced by the Majority of the Committee on the Costs of Medical Care and which determined their stand against "required" insurance, may be expressed in this form: there is no sound justification why the state should compel contribution of funds until there can also be an equivalent guarantee for the adequate performance of service. The hasty establishment of a compulsory plan would mean compulsion of contributions without guarantee of service beyond that which is provided by existing agencies. And this is insufficient ground to justify compulsion.

Against this weighty argument must be balanced the following: (a) *At the outset,* compulsory insurance need not call for larger funds than are now being spent in the private purchase of medical care; the objective at first is merely to distribute the burden of costs among groups of individuals and to replace variable and uncertain costs by fixed and certain contributions. (b) The "power of the purse" offers the strongest possible opportunities to press for improvement in the means of furnishing medical care; a compulsory system could be so organized that economic as well as other incentives are offered to practitioners to stimulate improvement of service. This, it seems, is an important type of argument for compulsory insurance: while offering a solution for the need to distribute the costs under government control, it simultaneously offers the means of increasing and stabilizing professional income, and of providing incentives to more efficient and more qualified service.

In following the Majority of the Committee, the ideal would be to recommend voluntary systems of group payment and utilize all possible means of *encouraging*—but not *requiring*—desirable forms of organized, efficient, group practice of the highest quality. Then, when the organization of medical service has progressed to the point where it is possible to guarantee the quality and sufficiency of service, the voluntary system should be made compulsory. But this is frankly a counsel of perfection. What is to encourage the rapid and effective organization of medical facilities? Certainly there is no ground in recent experience to warrant the view that the desired objective will be reached by waiting upon the experiments now in progress. There is as much likelihood that the swirling current of events will lead to the predominance of exploited contract practice as that it will intrench desirable forms of voluntary insurance. Commitment to a voluntary program holds no promise that *it* will bring us to that threshold which would warrant the establishment of a compulsory scheme. There is little evidence in experience, at home or abroad, to indicate that compulsory insurance may be expected to evolve out of the *successes* of voluntary insurance. History is on the other side of the argument.

The reorganization of medical practice which is badly needed will not come of itself, the product of *laissez faire*. It will come—if at all—only as the fruit of strong and directed labors, the product of compelling forces. Of all the forces which society can muster in a program of medical reformation, the strongest is "the power of the purse." Thus, the case is inverted. *Instead of organizing for the payment of medical costs after having achieved improvement of service, society must organize for payment in order to achieve improvement of service.* In our opinion, this conclusion—when taken in conjunction with the strictly economic arguments and with the need for the compulsory principle to give an effective implementation to social insurance—tips the beam of the balance in favor of compulsory, as against voluntary, group payment. It compels us to recognize, however, that a compulsory scheme must be planned in such a way that it calls for contributions and expenditures proportional to the availability of qualified medical facilities. Beyond certain minimum requirements, compulsion should be used in different degrees, calling for larger contributions in one place and for smaller in another, according to local circumstances with respect to the capacity to pay the costs and to furnish good medical care.

Among the essential arguments for compulsory insurance special prominence must be given to the one that voluntary insurance fails to reach the population in need of insurance protection. That voluntary insurance has actually failed in this respect both in foreign countries and in the United States is a matter of record. To be sure, we have seen examples where voluntary insurance has succeeded—as in the case of health insurance in Denmark or in certain industrial establishments in the United States. But we have also noted that these are generally far from being altogether or even largely voluntary. The elements of compulsion may be indirect rather than direct, and economic or social rather than legal, but they are compulsions none the less. Occasion may again be taken to quote the statement of Simons and Sinai:

> Every so-called "voluntary" system is successful in just about the proportion that it contains compulsory features, especially in selling and the collection of premiums.

As between voluntary and compulsory insurance, careful note should be made of the conclusion, recorded in the first Minority Report of the Committee on the Costs of Medical Care (this Minority Report received the formal approval of the American Medical Association and of numerous state and county medical societies), and expressed in the following words:[8]

> It seems clear, then, that if we must adopt in this country either of the methods tried out in Europe, the sensible and logical plan would be to adopt the method to which European countries have come through experience, that is, a compulsory plan under governmental control.

Before leaving this subject, and at the risk of being repetitive, another aspect of the issue between voluntary and compulsory health insurance may be mentioned briefly. At the present time, voluntary insurance is experiencing in the United States what purports to be a new chapter in its history. Under the stimulus of medical associations, apparently because they are fearful that compulsory insurance to which they are opposed may soon be developed in the United States, voluntary health insurance schemes (called "plans") are being contemplated under professional sponsorship and control. The successful development of voluntary insurance to cover large numbers of persons will, they hope, make unnecessary large-scale compulsory insurance. Under this stimulus, a considerable number of plans have been devised and these are receiving much publicity and attention in professional circles.

A recent compilation[9] presents (as of February, 1935) long lists of state and county medical society plans. Upon inspection it is found that a large proportion of the plans listed are "proposed" and not "operating" plans; when plans restricted to the care of indigents or those concerned only with hospital bills are excluded from the count, there are only two state and twenty-two county plans reported as actually operating. Of the actually operating plans for "general" medical care among self-sustaining people, it may be noted that one of these so-called state plans applies to the District of Columbia, and in effect covers little more than a city; the other applies to the State of Washington which also accounts for nine of the twenty-two county plans. Furthermore, those of the county plans which are really insurance plans are generally restricted to the employees of specified large industrial organizations; most of the remaining plans are not insurance but installment-payment plans which distribute the costs of medical care over periods of time but not among groups of people.

The real measure of any "plan" is not its good intentions but its actual accomplishment. Thus far there has been no evidence that strictly voluntary plans under exclusive professional sponsorship and control are proving any more successful than such plans have been in the past, under other sponsorship, in extending coverage to substantial numbers of people. The membership in voluntary plans is still a mere *bagatelle* when measured in terms of the population in need of coverage, and much or most of the present membership goes back to plans inaugurated long ago under local conditions (especially of large-scale employment) which involved either strong economic compulsions or large employer subsidies. It is possible, in spite of both European and American history, that voluntary insurance under professional sponsorship and control in the United States will attain the ends which only compulsory insurance has hitherto succeeded in reaching. Careful, concurrent studies should be conducted under impartial and responsible authorities to record and evaluate developments.

On the basis of the experience accumulated in more than forty countries of the world over a period of more than fifty years, on the grounds of argument which appear to be thoroughly sound, and in accord with all experience in the United States with voluntary insurance and with compulsory insurance (workmen's compensation), one must conclude that the welfare of the public and of the professions requires that group payment of sickness costs should be designed on a compulsory insurance basis.

It is recognized further that a compulsory system of group payment should be flexible; it should provide opportunity for diverse arrangements in the provision of medical services, depending upon local conditions in respect to the availability of professional personnel and facilities and of the people to pay the costs. The system of compulsory insurance should be planned: (a) to provide as complete care as possible; (b) to effect economy and efficiency by utilizing, so far as may be practical, proper organization of the practitioners and agencies furnishing service; and (c) to assure that the quality of service rendered shall be high so far as it can be assured through the joint professional responsibility of the groups of practitioners rendering the service.

REFERENCES AND NOTES

1. The subjects are thoroughly treated in two major volumes published by the International Labour Office: COMPULSORY SICKNESS INSURANCE, Report No. 6, and VOLUNTARY SICKNESS INSURANCE, Report No. 7 (see page 70).

2. Simons, A. M. and Sinai, Nathan: THE WAY OF HEALTH INSURANCE. Chicago, The University of Chicago Press, 1932, p. 205.

3. MEDICAL CARE FOR THE AMERICAN PEOPLE (Final Report of the Committee on the Costs of Medical Care). Chicago, The University of Chicago Press, 1932, 240 pp.

4. Ibid, p. 127; passim.

5. MEDICAL CARE FOR THE AMERICAN PEOPLE (Minority Report No. 1), op. cit., p. 167.

6. Warren, Earl: The Health Insurance Racket in the State of California. Western Hospital Review, May, 1934, xxii, p. 9; also notes in various issues of California and Western Medicine.

7. This and the four following arguments are quoted from the recommendations presented by a fraction of the majority of The Committee on the Costs of Medical Care, MEDICAL CARE FOR THE AMERICAN PEOPLE, op. cit., pp. 131–132. Differences of opinion over voluntary or compulsory insurance were expressed both within the majority and minority reports.

8. MEDICAL CARE FOR THE AMERICAN PEOPLE (Minority Report No. 1), op. cit., p. 164.

9. Special Report of the Bureau of Medical Economics of the American Medical Association. American Medical Association Bulletin, June, 1935, xxx, pp. 81–91.

CHAPTER XVI

SOME BASIC PRINCIPLES FOR AN AMERICAN PROGRAM OF GROUP PAYMENT

I T is a matter of record that most of the population fails to obtain the full benefits of adequate medical care.[1] This state of affairs cannot be wholly or mainly charged against public ignorance, for people are generally aware of the need for more and better care than they receive. Nor can it be charged to any important deficiency in the supply of professional practitioners and institutions, for the United States has an approximately sufficient number of competent medical agencies. The facts in the case show that an economic barrier stands between those who need and those who are prepared to furnish medical service. This barrier of costs rests principally upon two traditions: individual arrangements for the purchase of medical service, and fee-for-service payment by the individual patient. The outstanding characteristic of medical costs is not that they are high, but that they come unexpectedly and fall so unevenly that they cannot generally be budgeted by the individual or the family.

The existing method of buying and paying for medical care is inadequate both for those who need care and for those who furnish it. New arrangements are needed—arrangements whereby medical service will be purchased by groups of people rather than by individuals and medical expenditures will be made from pooled funds rather than from individual resources. Group budgeting and group payment should be designed not only to solve recognized problems in medical costs, but also to stimulate broad improvements in the quality of medical service and to make the improved service available to all who need it.

Furthermore, economic insecurity which arises out of loss of earnings is like insecurity against medical costs in that group budgeting can give to the individual the protection which he cannot provide for himself. While the loss of earnings in times of sickness involves less money than the costs of medical care, it is a risk of nearly the same magnitude. An adequate program of group payment must deal with both classes of financial risk arising out of illness, but—as we have seen—there are cogent reasons why a scheme of group payment for medical costs should not be too intimately interlocked with a scheme of insurance against wage-loss.

How shall a program be formulated to furnish security against the costs of sickness? Our objective is to suggest in general terms, and only in broad outline, the principles which should be taken into full account in any program which may be seriously proposed for group payment appropriate to American needs. As the first step, it is useful to recognize certain fundamental principles which are generally accepted.

1. *So far as may be practical, economic security should be assured against the costs of medical care and against the loss of earnings caused by disability.*

This principle we propose to accept at this stage of the discussion without further argument or evidence.

2. *The provision of good medical care to all of the population is essential to the nation's well-being.*

This principle is so widely accepted as to be almost axiomatic. Yet it is significant to recall this social concept, for often it seems to be forgotten. It is sometimes argued, especially in discussions of medical economics, that organized society does not owe anyone medical care; but a moment's reflection will dissipate whatever force may be alleged for this position.

Long ago it was recognized that the health and vitality of the people are of fundamental concern to the state. Political, economic, and social considerations are in accord on this point. National strength and well-being demand that the population be healthy and vigorous; economic stability and progress depend upon virility.

Many centuries ago the police power of the state was invoked to guard society against contagious diseases. Public health administration was grounded on the effort to protect one person against the communicable disease which afflicts another. Later came sanitation and the protection of community water and food supplies and the collective disposal of waste.

More recently, public health measures have been extended further because it has become increasingly difficult to separate economic from other consequences of disease and disability. Society recognizes that life is precious and that illness is wasteful. Society guards the life of each of its members even to the point of supplying—at public cost—food, shelter, clothing, and medical care for those who are indigent and unable to supply themselves with these necessities of life and of the pursuit of happiness. Society accepts broad responsibilities for the practice of preventive medicine; society pays the cost of guarding and preserving the public health.

Modern society has learned that it has a large stake in the provision of medical service. In normal times, illness is one of the leading causes of dependency; and the cost of supporting those who become dependent falls upon the common purse. The health of the public is just as important to the state as is the education of its citizens. An analogy between health and education—in respect to public concern in them—is sound in every essential. To be sure, medical care and education are not in equal measure public services in the United States. Tax funds are used (or are available) to furnish education for everyone, but medical care only for the indigent poor. But this is due not to any real difference in society's stake in medicine and in education, but to a difference in the extent to which it has been necessary for society to provide service lest it be not otherwise provided adequately or at all.

The principle stated above does not declare that society accepts an obligation to furnish medical care for everybody; it merely states that the provision of medical care is a public concern, and that good medical care for the poor—as well as for the rich—is a public concern. Indeed, without being facetious, one might argue that society has a greater concern in furnishing good medical care to the poor than to the rich; for there is less likelihood that illness will create dependency and will entail public expense if it falls among those who are well-to-do than if it afflicts those of small means.

There is probably no important difference of opinion on the public interest in the general provision of good medical care. But there is room for wide difference of opinion on the extent to which the practice of medicine should be made a public function and medical service should be provided by public servants. For the moment, it is sufficient to recognize society's stake in the public health and in the availability and provision of good medical care. Whether medical service should be furnished by private practitioners or by public servants is an entirely separate issue.

3. *The costs of sickness (medical care and loss of earnings) should be distributed among groups of people and over periods of time.*

This principle recognizes the need to replace the variable costs for individuals by the fixed contributions for members of a group. The reasons which justify this principle have already been reviewed. In modern society, group purchase of medical care and group budgeting of the costs of illness are necessary for the effective provision of service and for the protection of family income. Plans designed to these ends should be in a fundamental way, not means of exploiting the public to whom they apply, but procedures designed to reduce for the individual the burden of costs and to contribute in the largest possible extent to improvement of health.

4. *Those who render medical care should be adequately remunerated.*

Medical practitioners and institutions must be adequately remunerated and supported if their services are to be effective and of high quality. The economic incentive plays a large and significant rôle in medicine, though perhaps less than in most other fields of human endeavor. The maintenance of strong medical professions is in the public interest. And this requires appropriate remuneration of those already in practice and reasonable financial attraction to prospective students of ability. Stable and reasonably assured income is also essential to the efficient operation of hospitals and clinics.

Unfortunate consequences flow from inadequate financial support of desirable forms of medical practice. The purchase of medical services by the individual patient on a fee-for-service basis at the time the services are needed rests upon an old custom. But increasingly it has become an anachronism in modern society. It needs to be replaced by some more appropriate and more equable means of remunerating the physician for his service. It needs to be replaced by some procedure which will enable people to spend more money than they now spend for medical care and which will provide better assurance to the practitioner than he now has that his professional service will give him a fair living.

In devising a satisfactory solution to the problem of paying for medical care, it is essential always to remember that any practice which tends to pauperize the professions or which introduces or fosters commercial practices in medicine is injurious to professional ideals and is antagonistic to the public welfare.

Adequate remuneration involves: (a) an adequate *scale* of remuneration; and (b) an appropriate *procedure* of remuneration. Both the scale and the procedure must be developed in accordance with existing conditions and must be adapted to other essential characteristics of a program of group payment.

As a postulate of the third and fourth principles, it should be recognized that a plan to distribute costs among groups of people and over periods of time should be so designed as to enable the purchase of medical care as adequate as the financial means of the community will permit.

5. *Quality in medical care should not be sacrificed to economy in cost.*

Good medical care is worth what it costs; poor medical care may be worth little and may even be of less than doubtful value. A system of group payment would be a dangerous social instrument unless it were organized and administered with constant watchfulness for the quality of service. Public groups must, even in their own interest, be extremely careful that the desire for economy and reduction of costs is not forged into a weapon to pauperize the professions and the medical institutions. Though economic incentives can operate to encourage improvement in professional competence, they must not be permitted to introduce undesirable competition among medical agencies. Reasonable economies should be encouraged, but not at the price of quality in medical service.

In addition to these five basic principles, it is useful to recognize certain others which are widely accepted by society and which should be utilized, so far as is possible and desirable, in any program of group payment which may be designed for a large fraction of the population. They may be stated as four additional principles:

6. *Regulation and supervision of the qualifications of medical practitioners and institutions are public functions.*

7. *The provision of medical care for the dependent or indigent sick is an obligation of society.*

8. *The medical care of non-indigent persons afflicted with serious mental disorder or with tuberculosis, or with any other disease dangerous to the public health (such as syphilis or gonorrhea), is a concern of society and falls within the domain of public health practice.*

9. *The medical care of non-indigent persons afflicted with other diseases (for example, cancer or orthopedic defects) has tended increasingly to become a public responsibility when elaborate or expensive facilities are required for their diagnosis or treatment.*

These obligations and responsibilities are assumed by society for a variety of reasons: (a) to guard the public interest in health, to assure so far as possible the ethical conduct and the professional competence of practitioners, and to protect the public against incompetent and dangerous healers; (b) to protect the public against communicable and other preventable diseases; (c) to relieve suffering among sick persons when the private purchase of medical care is inadequate or would lead to dependency or to disruption of family life; (d) to provide highly specialized treatment when this is not otherwise available or when the capital investment or the complexity of the medical facilities exceeds the means of private resources; and (e) to provide medical service where private facilities are either entirely lacking or grossly inadequate.

These principles and practices mark the vague lines which divide public from private interest, public from private responsibility, and public from private assumption of costs. It is obviously desirable that these principles shall be incorporated in the foundations for a group-payment plan, or at least that the plan shall not run counter to them unless it provides appropriate substitutes.

The seventh principle—social responsibility for the provision of medical service to the dependent or indigent sick—needs further comment. For many centuries it has been customary for the medical profession to assume responsibility for the sick poor. Indeed, the Principles of Ethics of the American Medical Association declares explicitly:

> The poverty of a patient . . . should command the gratuitous services of a physician.

This principle is grounded in an ancient tradition of the physician: Service to each according to his need; payment from each according to his means. But times have changed, and a doctrine which was conceived in the spirit of highest social morality of other times has now become anti-social in many of its consequences. Though still formally retained in the code of ethics, it has been repudiated both by society and by a large part of the medical profession. Medical service for the poor is an economic responsibility of society, not of the physician. In New York State, for example, the Public Welfare Act and the Emergency Relief Act list medical care and medical supplies along with food, shelter, and clothing, the provision of which to the necessitous poor is incumbent upon the state. The Federal

Emergency Relief Act accepts medical services among the necessities of life and lays down the far-reaching policy that the physician shall be compensated for his service to the unemployed and their families. The federal program for medical care under relief was given specific formulation in July, 1933, when RULES AND REGULATIONS NO. 7 was issued. By December 1st, a majority of states had made some progress toward providing care; by May, 1934, the program was operating more or less successfully in twenty-five states. The services of the physician, dentist, and nurse were placed in the same legal category (in respect to public responsibility of the costs) which has long embraced hospital care for the indigent and the insane. (When the F.E.R.A. program gave way to a program of work-relief, the scheme of medical care for the relief population gave way in substantially the same degree.)

State and county medical societies have become increasingly vocal in their complaints against the burden of "medical charity" in a period of economic depression. The following quotation from the editorial columns of the *West Virginia Medical Journal* (October, 1933) gives a fair picture of current professional views which have led to the establishment of medical contracts and schedules of remuneration for services rendered to the poor who have been receiving financial assistance from official federal, state or local relief agencies.

> Why should medical charity be dispensed on a different basis than other commodities? All the people, including the doctors, contribute to a common fund through taxation to provide food and clothing. But medical treatment is still saddled onto the doctor and he must make the most of it. It does not seem at all fair.
>
> Five years ago, when times were good, we heard little about medical charity. That was because there was little medical charity work to do, and it was handled by the medical profession with little trouble and less credit. Today, when we have millions on the roster of unemployed, the problem becomes a proposition of staggering proportions because the doctors have had less

and less pay work and more and more charity work. Now, at long last, the medical profession is beginning to make itself heard. In many states, including West Virginia, a schedule of allowances has been adopted for doctors attending charity patients. This fee schedule is approximately one-half the amount generally charged in rural sections. In other words, it is better than nothing. At least it is supposed to be.

Let us look at the general plan of medical practice as it has been handed down to us over a period of several hundred years. Under that plan we have charged our patients just about what we thought they were able to pay. The excessively rich have paid thousands of dollars for the same operation that would cost a laboring man less than a hundred. Well-to-do business and office executives have been called on for much higher fees than clerks and carpenters and butchers. This plan, tried out by untold generations of medical men, has been remarkably successful. It has pleased the doctor and has pleased the doctor's patients. It has become so much a part of medical economics that the plan has been recognized time and time again by the courts throughout this country. The doctors have prospered under this plan, and, until a few short years ago, they have been glad to follow it.

The doctors asked for some relief from the great burden of medical charity. In making that request, it seems to us that they implied a willingness to throw overboard their time-tried system of charging according to the incomes of their patients. There is only one justification for charging high fees against the rich. That justification is found in the free work that is given to the poor. Once the doctors start collecting for their poor work, there is no longer any justification for the marked difference in the charges.

The Judicial Council of the American Medical Association does not go quite so far. In its report of May 5, 1934, it says:

> . . . Perhaps the time has come when the profession should distinguish between the temporary and the chronic indigent and demand that the community relieve the private practitioner from furnishing free care to the chronically indigent. But the temporarily indigent, those who when able paid for medical care according to their ability to pay, should still be the charge of the medical profession in their period of distress.

The sliding scale of medical fees was discussed in Chapter III. In the present connection it will be illuminating to consider from another viewpoint the observations of an economist, Professor Douglass V. Brown of Harvard University, quoted by Dr. Hugh Cabot.[2]

> Isn't the sliding-scale a complete anomaly? Given,—a necessary corollary—the payment, by the community or otherwise, for work now done on a charity basis by doctors and hospitals, why should a patient's income be considered? It isn't considered in buying anything else. If the money has been "honestly" acquired, why should *the doctor* penalize the patient for having been successful? If "dishonestly" acquired, why should *the doctor* be the individual chosen to redress social wrongs? The whole thing seems utterly illogical to me. The hospital has more justification than the doctor, inasmuch as the commodity furnished is not the same in all cases.
>
> The whole thing, moreover, works very unfairly in practice. In O.P.D.'s* for example, I have seen John Jones admitted because he had to keep up a heavy mortgage on his house, while Thomas Smith was refused because he had fully paid for his house; the family incomes were almost exactly the same. I have seen Pete Robinson admitted because he had eight children, and Andrew King refused because, by limiting his family to two children, he had rather hoped to get the boy to college. I have seen one person admitted because, while his income was larger by far than that of another, he "had to maintain a higher standard of living." It would be easy to multiply instances of the same sort with respect to physicians' charges. Even granting the necessity for some distribution according to needs, I wonder if this is an intelligent way of going about it.

Medical charity and the sliding scale of fees have ceased to be altogether instruments of social justice. Their persistence is irksome to the profession and irritating to the public, especially in a complex, urban society where continuing personal relationships between doctor and patient are proportionately much less frequent than they once were and where financial inquiries by the doctor into the patient's financial affairs tend to place him on par with a tradesman or an

*Out-patient departments.

installment salesman. Only tradition, inertia, and occasional utility give a continuing lease on life to outworn practices. Both the public and the professions were well rid of them. The seventh principle stated on page 343 expresses the modern viewpoint—*the provision of medical care for the dependent or indigent sick is an obligation of society.*

Further analysis of principles which should be taken into account in any program for group payment may begin with consideration of the unit of population which should be included in a plan. For obvious reasons, it is desirable that the unit should be small enough to embrace only persons who reside in a well-defined geographical area and who are substantially homogeneous in respect to race, social characteristics, and economic circumstance. These requirements would tend to insure that the type of service desired by the bene-ficiaries of the plan and the costs and administrative procedures will be, as nearly as possible, uniform and simple. From this point of view, the plan might be conceived for a few hundred or a few thousand persons or families.

There are important reasons, however, why the unit of population should be large. Up to certain limits, the risks and the guarantees under the plan will have actuarial stability which is proportional to the size of the population covered. The average incidence of sickness and the fluctuations in this average are, on the whole, predictable for large but not for small groups. Though the costs of medical service are highly variable and are essentially non-predictable for the in-dividual or for the family, they are known, predictable, and budget-able for groups of individuals or for groups of families. And the larger the group, the more reliable is the prediction of medical costs. Experience with group-payment plans in the United States and in other countries shows that the finances are usually very seriously lacking in stability when less than 5,000 or 10,000 persons are covered. Surveys of the incidence of sickness and of the variations in medical costs indicate that an actuarial basis is uncertain until *at least* 30,000 or 40,000 persons are included. Some who have studied this problem closely would place the lower limit even as high as 50,000 persons. Reasoning along this line, the plan should be designed for the largest practical unit of population. (It should be made clear that this refers to the *actuarial* unit; the administrative unit of population may be much smaller.)

A third type of consideration suggests an important compromise between these first two. If a group-payment plan is to have actuarial soundness, *at least* some 40,000 or 50,000 persons should be included. Probably even a larger minimum would be deduced if consideration were focussed upon the size of population sufficiently large to need and to support a full complement of medical agencies. If the plan is to be independent of local and temporary fluctuations in employment and income, still larger units must be accepted. If the plan is to be accommodated to accepted practices, it must be coördinated with medical and welfare programs in which the city, the county, or the state is the unit.

Finally, if the plan should or must have compulsory features, the state becomes the logical unit of population because in the United States the compulsory (that is, the legally required) distribution of costs for most public health and public welfare activities and for most of the institutional care of the sick has long been established on a state-wide (not on a city or county or federal) basis. Laws which may have to be established to safeguard the administration of group-payment plans must at the outset be expected to extend on a state-wide scale. From these points of view, the state is the logical *legal* unit for the protection of group-payment plans designed to meet sickness costs. For the people who are subject to the Federal Government in such matters as workmen's compensation (i.e., for the District of Columbia, wards and employees of the United States, those engaged in certain classes of interstate commerce, etc.), federal legislation would be required.

Thus, we may add to the nine principles already stated:

10. *If a group-payment plan is to reach the people who need its*

benefits and if it is to have financial stability, it should be planned for a population which is sufficiently large to support a full complement of necessary medical facilities, and preferably should be planned on a state-wide basis.

Next, there are summarized in the following group of nine principles the conclusions derived from the studies of European experience, of American experience with voluntary insurance and with compulsory insurance under the workmen's compensation laws, and from the available evidence on American needs.

11. *So far as is practicable, group payment of medical costs should not be combined with insurance against the loss of wages during a period of illness (except perhaps to remunerate employed women for wage-loss preceding and following confinement for childbirth).*

12. *The group payment of sickness costs should embrace all economic groups in the population to whom the private purchase of medical care and the loss of wages on account of sickness bring variable costs which are burdensome and which cannot be budgeted on an individual or family basis.*

13. *The group purchase of medical care should provide, as far as possible, complete home, office and hospital service, including necessary health examinations and other preventive care.*

14. *A system (or systems) for the group payment of sickness costs should not include or permit the operation of proprietary or profit-making administrative agencies or of any independent intermediary between the potential patient and the medical agencies.*

15. *Administrative procedures concerned with the delivery of medical service should be determined by the joint action of professional and lay representatives, and the plan should provide for professional administration of professional personnel and activities.*

16. *A system of group payment for medical care should provide for maximum coördination of the medical provisions with the work of public health and other governmental authorities engaged in health, medical or welfare activities.*

17. *Experience indicates, and the welfare of the public and of the*

professions requires, that group payment of sickness costs should be grounded on a compulsory basis.

18. *A compulsory system of group payment for medical care should provide opportunity for diverse arrangements in the provision of medical service, depending upon local conditions in respect to availability of facilities and the ability of the people to pay, except that the system should be planned: (a) to provide as complete care as possible; (b) to effect economy and efficiency by utilizing proper organization of the practitioners and agencies furnishing service; and (c) to assure that the quality of service rendered shall be high so far as it can be assured through the joint professional responsibility of the groups of practitioners rendering the service.*

19. *Preventive and curative measures should be correlated in policy and administration.*

In a measure, the eighteenth principle introduces an essential element of flexibility where otherwise the seventeenth might seem to call for rigidity. The diversity of existing conditions renders impractical any proposal which would even imply uniformity in the scope of medical service to be provided by a compulsory group-payment plan. The eighteenth principle recognizes that there is large diversity in needs and that in each community or for each geographical area the plan should be adaptable to local circumstances. Thus, it is complementary to the twelfth and thirteenth principles.

It would be easy to misunderstand the significance of the eighteenth principle, especially if it were interpreted in such a way as to excuse the development of heterogeneous, inadequate, or poorly designed programs of group payment. Nothing could be further from the intent. Our conception of a sound plan requires that it should be in accord with the general principles which have been formulated and that it should be so designed that in the least favored communities not less than essential services, and in the most privileged areas complete medical services, are provided. The desirable plan will provide not only for such differences in scope, but will contain within itself the mechanism whereby changes in scope may be readily made, either by increasing or reducing the variety of services furnished.

Obviously, such conceptions as are embraced in these nineteen principles entail the development of appropriate administrative machinery. The tenth principle (*a group-payment plan . . . should be planned for a population which is sufficiently large to support a full complement of necessary medical facilities, and preferably should be planned on a state-wide basis*) has already foreshadowed an essential characteristic of the administrative process. It is desirable that large units of population, especially units as large as the population of a state, should be considered when designing a group-payment plan. The adoption of the seventeenth principle (i.e., a compulsory basis) suggests that a compulsory system of group payment should be administered by a legally constituted state agency with executive authority to adapt the flexible provisions in the plan (according to the eighteenth principle) to the different conditions which might prevail in local areas within a state. In accordance with the seventeenth and eighteenth principles, the state executive body might authorize a uniform plan for the entire state. Or, if circumstances did not justify this, it might authorize quite a different program: a general plan of minimum essential services for the state as a whole and, in each local area, additional medical service of such scope as local facilities and ability to pay would justify. The seventeenth and eighteenth principles are not incompatible; they are mutually supplementary.

Legislative enactments and executive developments might lead to the establishment of state systems of group payment and these might come into existence rapidly or slowly. The history of workmen's compensation indicates that a program of the kind under analysis moves very rapidly after it has first been adopted in two or three states; within a few years after the first enactments many states follow suit. Forty-eight states and the Federal Government may go their own ways and bring into being forty-nine insurance systems. Many students of the subject hold that such an outlook has its virtues: each state becomes a laboratory in which a particular plan is subjected to experiment, and each state may benefit from the experiences of the others. Glamorous as this may seem in theory, in practice it may be futile. Although a common thread may run through all the systems, the results obtained in one state may be (and probably would be) secured under conditions which cannot be evaluated against those which prevail in another. Forty-nine systems may bring into being a maze of practice and procedure—further confounded by thousands of local variations on the themes—in which neither the courts, nor the administrative authorities, nor the professions, nor the public, can find their way. In such a vast conglomeration only one conclusion may stand out in sharp relief: a system of some particular sort tends to remain fixed and invariable in a state because the authorities who are accustomed to administer it oppose change. The lessons learned under one plan may batter in vain against the walls of inertia which support another.

Far more important than freedom to experiment is assurance that in each state the plan which is adopted will be designed toward the essential objectives and will embrace those practices which are a common necessity everywhere. There should still be room for experimentation in administrative practice; but if the experimentation is to yield results of value there must be some basic uniformity among various systems in respect to essentials. Uniformity of this kind has often been sought and sometimes attained, in both criminal and civil codes, through the influence of so-called "standard bills," developed often by national agencies. Experience of recent years suggests an effective means of attaining this end, namely, through the influence of permissive federal legislation. This *modus operandi* is especially significant for our purposes because it is just as important that the Federal Government should sponsor group payment of sickness costs for those who are subject to federal legislation as that state governments should provide for the citizens of the several states. The same arguments which call for action by a state government call for action by the Federal Government. And there are many obvious reasons why a plan established by federal legislation—

primarily for the half million people residing in the District of
Columbia, for other wards of the United States, for those engaged
in interstate commerce, and for others—should lay down basic
standards of practice which might be emulated by the states.

Other lines of reasoning also urge federal standards. First, there is
the necessity that in a plan for the group payment of medical costs
the medical services which are furnished for the diagnosis and care
of the sick should be closely integrated with preventive services for
the well. Increasingly, public health practice in the states and local
areas is becoming integrated with the federal public health machinery. In the circumstances of the present economic emergency
there is every indication that this trend will gain momentum, especially through the influence of the various federal relief and control
agencies and of the Social Security Act. There is much to be gained
by a similar national coördination of medical practices generally,
especially in respect to encouraging the formulation of standards of
practice (as is now being done by certain national professional
agencies). It is perhaps no exaggeration to say that one of the greatest contributions which a nationally recognized plan for group payment could make would be encouragement and strengthening of
those groups which are establishing high standards of professional
practice and which are stimulating educational institutions, postgraduate schools, hospitals, clinics and other organized facilities to
improve the quality of medical service. *Group-payment plans can
contribute in this direction by requiring that those who furnish
medical care for the people covered by the plans shall meet the
specifications of approved standards with respect to education, experience, periodic postgraduate training, consultative practice, etc.* A
group-payment plan whose standards were sponsored by the Federal
Government could give a national impetus to the movement for
improved professional practice.

Second, another type of consideration argues for an integrated
relation between federal and state legislation. The ability to purchase
good medical care depends upon spendable wealth. There are not

only thousands of local areas but even some entire states in which average income is insufficient to enable people to purchase adequate medical service. *The provision of good medical care to all of the population is essential to the nation's well-being* (the second principle). Federal subsidy to less favored areas is essential and unavoidable in group payment for medical care even as in the public health programs of states and local areas and in certain other fields of national interest. If it should become necessary to use tax funds to finance, in part or in whole, compulsory group payment of medical costs, the taxing powers of the Federal Government may be essential in many states to supplement local resources or local means of collecting funds.

Thus, financial as well as professional considerations suggest a rôle for the Federal Government which should be dictated by the following objectives:

a. A federal plan of group payment for the people who are subject to the federal authority;

b. Federal specification of standards of practice and administration designed to improve the quality of medical and public health service;

c. The development of a federal agency which will constantly accumulate information on national health, and which will be available to federal and local authorities, in a consultative and advisory capacity, on needs for the development of health and medical agencies, on economical and efficient means of building hospitals and other institutions, and of operating health and medical programs; and

d. Federal subsidies to states and (through the states) to local governments which are in need of such assistance and which establish group payment of sickness costs in accordance with federal minimum specifications and which continue to meet federal minimum standards for medical and public health service.

It may be emphasized that these conclusions arise out of considerations which are equally sound whether group payment operates through insurance or through taxation.

These arguments lead logically to the proposal that the acts of the Federal Government and of state and local governments should be part of a clear and concerted national program. Less than this would lead to confused, inconsistent and uneven developments. If the group payment of sickness costs is to be developed rationally and efficiently, if prevention and cure of disease are to be raised to that high level which is made possible by modern science, and if administration is to be effective, all activities should be directed toward the objectives of a health program for the nation. Such a view of the immediate future requires a courageous and broad-gauged recasting of health and medical relationships. Furthermore, it means that compulsory insurance or other compulsory provision against the costs of sickness should be envisaged as an essential part of a modernized program of public health.

Even casual inspection of the foregoing nineteen principles emphasizes that they deal far more with provision against the costs of medical care than against loss of earnings caused by the disabling illness of employed persons. In the nature of the case this was inevitable. Having established in respect to loss of earnings that protection of the individual is needed and can be effected through group budgeting, nearly all other features of that subject are details. The exact size of the losses, the average loss, and the average cost of protection, the precise definition of the population which needs protection and of the benefits which should be provided by insurance— these and numerous other questions deal with ways and means rather than with fundamental principles. And this study has been deliberately restricted to the analysis of principles rather than of procedures.

In respect to insurance for cash benefit to furnish partial replacement of wages lost on account of disability, it should be remembered that there must be a medical certification that a disability exists. In countries which practice sickness insurance against wages lost through disability, the procedure followed in furnishing this certification is intimately related to the procedures followed in furnishing medical service. Our studies have convinced us that these two medical functions—certification of disability, and medical service—should be separated administratively as widely as possible. But it would still remain a fact that insurance against loss of earnings would have profoundly important relation to insurance for medical service.

It has been evident from the outset that in respect to the costs of medical care this study dealt with a larger and far more complex problem than in respect to loss of earnings. Protection of the worker is not the only objective. Protection of his family, provision of good service, fair and equitable arrangements with the practitioners who furnish service, prevention of disease, and a number of other issues are also very important. It is not sufficient that there should be financial protection against the costs of medical care. The protection must be sound, and it must not be anti-social in respect to the proper interests of the medical agencies. In the long run, any system of budgeting medical costs which resulted in wasteful expenditures, or in inadequate remuneration of the professions, or in degrading the standards of medical practice, or in interfering with the independence of the professions in respect to professional service, would be very harmful to society. Society cannot afford to give security to one essential group at a serious cost to another, least of all when it need not. The principles which have been laid down as a guide for insurance against the costs of medical care attempt to provide the basis for a program which may deal adequately with the needs both of those who receive medical service and of those who furnish it.

Attention may again be called to the fact that the nineteen principles developed in the preceding chapters have a firm foundation in broad experience. In respect to the costs of medical care in the United States and the problems which arise out of these costs, these principles utilize the facts collected by the Committee on the Costs of Medical Care and which have never been seriously challenged by any responsible authority. In respect to broader questions of policy, the principles depend upon experience with voluntary and compulsory systems of health and sickness insurance in the United States and in European countries. It is therefore not surprising that there are fundamental agreements between these principles and those which have been laid down by various labor organizations, and by professional associations interested in health insurance and in the relations of medical practice to insurance against the costs of sickness. More specifically, attention may be called to the fact that there are many fundamental agreements between the principles which are laid down here and those which have been proposed by the General Conference of the International Labour Organization, by the International Professional Association of Physicians, by various state medical societies, the American Hospital Association, the Western Hospital Association, the American College of Surgeons, the American Medical Association, the Committee on Economics of the Canadian Medical Association, and the American Dental Association, and, more recently, by the President's Committee on Economic Security. To assist the interested student of the subject in discovering the points of agreement and disagreement, the several series of principles and resolutions have been brought together in an Appendix to this volume.

There is no quarrel between the public in search of security against the consequences of ill health and the professions whose first interest has always been the prevention and cure of illness. Both have common opportunities and common interests in developing a broad program to prevent disease and to mitigate the economic consequences of illness. Fortunately, the same basic procedures which will distribute sickness costs among those who must bear them, will operate to alleviate the burden of these costs, will enable people to budget them and therefore spend more money for useful health and medical services, and will also provide larger and more assured incomes for those who render medical services.

These observations are especially significant because the facts in the case have shown that while sickness costs are burdensome to people of small means, the ordinary pay-as-you-go expenditures for medical care furnish unsatisfactory remuneration to the practitioners and the hospitals. Group budgeting of sickness costs in advance of the actual need can solve both of these problems simultaneously. It can assure the family that provision is being made against the costs of sickness through periodic payments before the emergency arises; it can assure the medical agencies that the funds are being regularly accumulated so that remuneration for medical services is guaranteed.

Furthermore, large-scale experience has shown that the remuneration of the medical agencies can be placed upon a sound and adequate basis if a system of insurance is not a poor-man's system. Where the insured population is restricted to the poor, only large financial contributions from employers or from governments or from both can save the schedule of medical remuneration from being poor-man's fees. A system of group budgeting which would provide adequately against loss of earnings and against medical costs, and which would provide fair remuneration to physicians, dentists, nurses, and hospitals must include more than the poor. It should embrace all to whom the costs of sickness are seriously burdensome and whose incomes are insufficient to permit individual budgeting against the variable and uncertain costs which arise out of illness.

Not uncommonly, the mention of health insurance raises in the minds of medical practitioners the bogey of "state medicine" or "public medicine" or "socialized medicine." This fear rests upon a misunderstanding of the relation of medical practitioners to health insurance.

Health insurance is not a system of medical practice. It is a system of paying the costs of sickness through budgeting and prepayment. It is always and everywhere consistent with the private practice of medicine. Indeed, so far as medical practitioners are concerned, health insurance as actually practised in European countries and in the United States is almost the antithesis to "state medicine" because it is a system of accumulating a financial pool from which to remunerate private practitioners. In modern systems like that of Great

Britain, professional matters are under professional control, all licensed practitioners have the privilege of being insurance practitioners or not, as they choose, and the method of remuneration (salary, fee, or per-capita payment) is a choice left to the professions. The 18,000 physicians engaged in British insurance practice are not employed by a government agency; they are private practitioners who have chosen to engage in insurance practice while also carrying on their other private practice among non-insured persons. They and the British Medical Association have repeatedly endorsed health insurance and have recorded their considered opinion that the scope of the system should be enlarged in respect to both the insured population and the medical benefits. Neither in Great Britain nor in any other insurance country has any responsible group, public or professional, ever seriously proposed the abandonment of health insurance.

In this volume, the practical questions which would arise in planning for the United States a system of insurance against sickness have been scarcely touched. The objective has been to examine needs and experience, and to submit for further study and consideration a series of principles upon which such a system should be based. Nor has the subject of taxation been explored as a method of paying for medical care, except incidentally as tax support has appeared as a complement—and not as a mutually exclusive alternative—to insurance. These subjects wait on further studies.

This volume may be closed by expressing the hope that these studies will contribute to a further understanding of the economic problems which arise out of illness and of measures which may be designed to deal with these problems. The fundamental need is to transform costs which are burdensome to individuals into costs which are budgeted by large groups of people and which are distributed over periods of time. Group payment of the costs of sickness would contribute to the economic security of a large majority of the people and would open new possibilities for the improvement of the nation's health.

References and Notes

1. Falk, I. S., Rorem, C. Rufus and Ring, Martha D.: THE COSTS OF MEDICAL CARE. Chicago, The University of Chicago Press, 1933, 648 pp.; MEDICAL CARE FOR THE AMERICAN PEOPLE (Final Report of the Committee on the Costs of Medical Care). Chicago, The University of Chicago Press, 1932, 240 pp.

2. Cabot, Hugh: THE DOCTOR'S BILL. New York, Columbia University Press, 1935, pp. 270–271.

PART FOUR

APPENDICES

APPENDIX 1

An Extract from the Report of the President's Committee on
Economic Security
(Report to the President, January 15, 1935)*

HEALTH INSURANCE

The development of more adequate public-health services is the first
and most inexpensive step in furnishing economic security against illness.
There remains the problem of enabling self-supporting families of small
and moderate means to budget against the loss of wages on account of
illness and against the costs of medical services needed by their members.
The nature of this problem and the nature of the risks which it involves
calls for an application of the insurance principle to replace the variable
and uncertain costs for individuals by the fixed and predictable costs for
large groups of individuals.

Insurance against the costs of sickness is neither new nor novel. In the
United States we have had a long experience with sickness insurance both
on a nonprofit and commercial basis. Both forms have been inadequate
in respect to the protection they furnish, and the latter—commercial insurance—has in addition been too expensive for people of small means.
Voluntary insurance holds no promise of being much more effective in
the near future than it has been in the past. Our only form of compulsory
insurance has been that which is provided against industrial accidents
and occupational diseases under the workmen's compensation laws. In
contrast other countries of the world have had experience with compulsory health or sickness insurance applied to over a hundred million persons and running over a period of more than 50 years. Nearly every large
and industrial country of the world except the United States has applied
the principle of insurance to the economic risks of illness.

The committee's staff has made an extensive review of insurance against
the risks of illness, including the experience which has accumulated in

*Report to the President of the Committee on Economic Security. Washington,
Government Printing Office, January 15, 1935, pp. 41–43.

365

the United States and in other countries of the world. Based upon these studies the staff has prepared a tentative plan of insurance believed adequate for the needs of American citizens with small means and appropriate to existing conditions in the United States. From the very outset, however, our committee and its staff have recognized that the successful operation of any such plan will depend in large measure upon the provision of sound relations between the insured population and the professional practitioners or institutions furnishing medical services under the insurance plan. We have accordingly submitted this tentative plan to our several professional advisory groups organized for this purpose. These advisory groups have requested an extension of time for the further consideration of these tentative proposals, and such an extension has been granted until March 1, 1935. In addition, arrangements have been effected for close coöperative study between the committee's technical staff and the technical experts of the American Medical Association.

Until the results of these further studies are available, we cannot present a specific plan of health insurance. It seems desirable, however, to advise the professions concerned and the general public of the main lines along which the studies are proceeding. These may be indicated by the following broad principles and general observations which appear to be fundamental to the design of a sound plan of health insurance.

1. The fundamental goals of health insurance are: (a) The provision of adequate health and medical services to the insured population and their families; (b) the development of a system whereby people are enabled to budget the costs of wage loss and of medical costs; (c) the assurance of reasonably adequate remuneration to medical practitioners and institutions; (d) the development under professional auspices of new incentives for improvement in the quality of medical services.

2. In the administration of the services the medical professions should be accorded responsibility for the control of professional personnel and procedures and for the maintenance and improvement of the quality of service; practitioners should have broad freedom to engage in insurance practice, to accept or reject patients, and to choose the procedure of remuneration for their services; insured persons should have freedom to choose their physicians and institutions; and the insurance plan shall recognize the continuance of the private practice of medicine and of the allied professions.

3. Health insurance should exclude commercial or other inter-

mediary agents between the insured population and the professional agencies which serve them.

4. The insurance benefits must be considered in two broad classes: (a) Cash payments in partial replacement of wage-loss due to sickness and for maternity cases, and (b) health and medical services.

5. The administration of cash payments should be designed along the same general lines as for unemployment insurance and, so far as may be practical, should be linked with the administration of unemployment benefits.

6. The administration of health and medical services should be designed on a State-wide basis, under a Federal law of a permissive character. The administrative provisions should be adapted to agricultural and sparsely settled areas as well as to industrial sections, through the use of alternative procedures in raising the funds and furnishing the services.

7. The costs of cash payments to serve in partial replacement of wage loss are estimated as from 1 to $1\frac{1}{4}$ percent of pay roll.

8. The cost of health and medical services, under health insurance, for the employed population with family earnings up to $3,000 a year, is not primarily a problem of finding new funds, but of budgeting present expenditures so that each family or worker carries an average risk rather than an uncertain risk. The population to be covered is accustomed to expend, on the average, about $4\frac{1}{2}$ percent of its income for medical care.

9. Existing health and medical services provided by public funds for certain diseases or for entire populations should be correlated with the services required under the contributory plan of health insurance.

10. Health and medical services for persons without income, now mainly provided by public funds, could be absorbed into a contributory insurance system through the payment by relief or other public agencies of adjusted contributions for these classes.

11. The role of the Federal Government is conceived to be principally (a) to establish minimum standards for health insurance practice, and (b) to provide subsidies, grants, or other financial aids or incentives to States which undertake the development of health insurance systems which meet the Federal standards.

APPENDIX 2

PRINCIPLES ADOPTED BY THE AMERICAN MEDICAL ASSOCIATION

1. ADOPTIONS OF JUNE, 1934*

The delegates [of the House of Delegates of the American Medical Association] have in their hands a pamphlet entitled "Sickness Insurance Problems in the United States" as presented by the Board of Trustees.

Your committee does not recommend any plan, but has abstracted from the pamphlet the following principles and suggests that they be followed by all constituent bodies of the American Medical Association as bases for the conduct of any social experiments that may be contemplated by them:

First: All features of medical service in any method of medical practice should be under the control of the medical profession. No other body or individual is legally or educationally equipped to exercise such control.

Second: No third party must be permitted to come between the patient and his physician in any medical relation. All responsibility for the character of medical service must be borne by the profession.

Third: Patients must have absolute freedom to choose a duly qualified doctor of medicine who will serve from among all those qualified to practice and who are willing to give service.

Fourth: The method of giving the service must retain a permanent confidential relation between the patient and a "family physician." This relation must be the fundamental and dominating feature of any system.

Fifth: All medical phases of all institutions involved in the medical service should be under professional control, it being understood that hospital service and medical service should be considered separately. These institutions are but expansions of the equipment of the physician. He is the only one whom the laws of all nations recognize as competent to use them in the delivery of service. The medical profession alone can determine the adequacy and character of such institutions. Their value depends on their operation according to medical standards.

Sixth: However the cost of medical service may be distributed, the

---

*American Medical Association Bulletin, June, 1934, pp. 98–99; also Journal of the American Medical Association, June 30, 1934, p. 2199.

immediate cost should be borne by the patient if able to pay at the time the service is rendered.

Seventh: Medical service must have no connection with any cash benefits.

Eighth: Any form of medical service should include within its scope all qualified physicians of the locality covered by its operation who wish to give service under the conditions established.

Ninth: Systems for the relief of low income classes should be limited strictly to those below the "comfort level" standard of incomes.

Tenth: There should be no restrictions on treatment or prescribing not formulated and enforced by the organized medical profession.

2. INTERPRETATION OF THE SIXTH PRINCIPLE*

(March, 1935)

The *sixth* principle was given the following interpretation by the Bureau of Medical Economics of the American Medical Association:

Sixth: However the cost of medical service may be distributed, the immediate cost should be borne by the patient if able to pay at the time the service is rendered. ("Immediate" in this connection is here interpreted as meaning that at least a part of the medical service should be paid for by the patient at the time the service is rendered.)

3. REVISIONS OF JUNE, 1935†

The *Special Report of the Bureau of Medical Economics of the American Medical Association*† presents the ten principles of the Association with some changes from the text cited above. The principles which have been amended are the following:

Third: Patients must have absolute freedom to choose a legally qualified doctor of medicine who will serve them from among all those qualified to practice and who are willing to give service.

Sixth: In whatever way the cost of medical service may be distributed, it should be paid for by the patient in accordance with his income status and in a manner that is mutually satisfactory.

Eighth: Any form of medical service should include within its scope all legally qualified doctors of medicine of the locality covered by its operation who wish to give service under the conditions established.

*American Medical Association Bulletin, March, 1935, xxx, p. 42.

†American Medical Association Bulletin, June, 1935, xxx, pp. 90–91. It is recorded that: "This Report as printed includes changes and additions adopted by the House of Delegates." (Footnote, p. 81.)

APPENDIX 3

PRINCIPLES OF THE MEDICAL SERVICE BOARD OF THE AMERICAN
COLLEGE OF SURGEONS

REPORT TO THE BOARD OF REGENTS OF THE AMERICAN COLLEGE OF
SURGEONS, APPROVED BY THE BOARD OF REGENTS,
JUNE, 1934*

The Medical Service Board of the American College of Surgeons respectfully submits the following report to the Board of Regents.

1. The American College of Surgeons affirms its interest and its desire to co-operate with other agencies looking toward the provision of more adequate medical service to the whole community.
2. The College believes that it is the duty of the medical profession to assume leadership in this movement and to take control of all measures directed to this end.
3. Encouragement should be given to the trial of new methods of practice designed to meet these needs, and a careful evaluation of their success should be the duty of the medical profession before they are offered for general adoption. All such new and experimental methods of practice must be conducted strictly in accordance with the accepted code of ethics of the medical profession in order that the interests of the patient and of the community may be protected.
4. The College recognizes for immediate study four groups of the population for whom more adequate medical service should be made available, as follows:

   a. The indigent.
   b. The uneducated and credulous members of the community.
   c. Those who because of limited resources are unable, unaided, to meet the costs of serious illness and hospitalization.
   d. Those living in remote districts where adequate medical service is not obtainable.

5. The care of the indigent sick should be a direct obligation upon the community and (unless otherwise compensated by intangible benefits such as staff and teaching appointments, opportunity and experience) physicians fulfilling this public service should receive remuneration.

*Bulletin of the American College of Surgeons, June, 1934, xviii, No. 2, pp. 3–5.

6. The College should work in co-operation with other medical groups in order to dispel the ignorance and credulity of the public, and to bring the people to a proper realization of the protective and curative resources of modern medicine.

7. The American College of Surgeons recognizes that the periodic pre-payment plan providing for the costs of medical care of illness and injury of individuals and of families of moderate means offers a reasonable expectation of providing them with more effective methods of securing adequate medical service.

A number of different plans for the organization of such services have been proposed, although few have been in operation long enough to permit definite conclusions in regard to their success. It is to be desired that these experiments be continued. Conditions differ to such a degree in different parts of the country that a specific plan which is practicable in one place may require modification of details in other communities. The varying restrictions imposed by present insurance laws in different states further complicate the problem.

Periodic pre-payment plans providing for the costs of medical service may be divided into two classes:

A. Payment for medical service.

B. Payment for hospitalization.

Plans for the payment of hospitalization alone (Class B) without provision for payment for medical service, may be considered the first project to be undertaken in the average community.

The American College of Surgeons believes that certain general principles can and should be established, the observance of which will tend to obviate known difficulties and dangers which may threaten the success of these special forms of medical service. These principles are as follows:

a. Periodic pre-payment plans for medical service should be free from the intervention of commercial intermediary organizations operating for profit. After deduction of the clerical costs of operation of the fund and such accumulation of reserve as may be advisable in the interest of the contributors or may be legally imposed, the full amount paid by the contributors should be available for medical and hospital services.

b. In the interest of the patient, the organization of plans for the periodic payment of medical and hospital costs must be under the control of the medical profession. The medical profession must act in concert with the hospitals and such other allied services as may be involved in the individual project, together with a group of citizens representative of the whole community and of industry who are interested in the successful operation of the plan.

c. The principle of free choice of the physician and hospital by the patient must be assured to the end that the responsibility of the individual physician to the individual patient shall always be maintained. When hospitalization is required, this choice must of necessity be limited to the physicians and surgeons who hold appointments on the staffs of the hospitals participating in the plan or to those physicians and surgeons who are acceptable to the hospital. It is further recommended that only approved hospitals be admitted to participation in such a plan.

d. The compensation of the physician and of the hospital should be estimated with due regard to the resources available in the periodic payment fund and should be based upon the specific services rendered.

e. The organization and operation of any plan of this type must be free from any features not in accordance with the code of ethics of the medical profession which code has been established for the protection of the patient.

f. The medical organizations participating in such a plan must assume the responsibility for the quality of service rendered.

8. Periodic pre-payment plans for medical and hospital service should eliminate many of the conditions which have brought about the development of industrial contract practice. Until such plans have been more widely established certain general principles are here formulated with a view to the elimination of the commercial features of such forms of medical service.

a. The Minimum Standard for Industrial Medicine and Traumatic Surgery of the American College of Surgeons should be accepted.

b. Physicians and surgeons, qualified as in paragraph 2 of the above [following] Minimum Standard may properly be employed on a full-time or a part-time basis by industrial organizations to provide medical and surgical service for their employees, as follows:

i. To provide emergency service and first aid in injury or disease, and to provide adequate medical or surgical care for industrial injuries and diseases. Medical and surgical care of the families of employees, and of employees themselves, except for emergency and industrial injuries and diseases, should be provided by the industrial physician only in remote districts where other adequate medical service is not available.

ii. To provide pre-employment and periodic physical examinations.

iii. To study the hazards of the particular industry and to co-operate with other agencies in effecting such measures as may be needed for the prevention of injury and disease.

iv. To keep accurate records such as may be required by local Workmen's Compensation laws, and so complete as to serve for scientific investigation of industrial hazards with a view to their further prevention. These records are privileged communications, subject always to due process of law.

c. The sale of a contract by an industrial organization to an individual physician or group of physicians for medical and/or hospital service for its employees encourages commercial competition and is to be condemned.

d. Unethical practices in publicity, advertising, solicitation, and competition, either of a professional or of a financial nature, must be eliminated.

e. The accepted code of ethics of the medical profession, which is designed to protect the best interests of the patient, should apply to industrial medical service as to all other forms of medical practice.

Following is the Minimum Standard for Industrial Medicine and Traumatic Surgery of the American College of Surgeons:

1. That the industry shall have an organized medical department, or service, with competent medical staff including consultants and adequate emergency dispensary and hospital facilities and personnel to assure efficient care of the ill and injured.

2. That membership on the medical staff shall be restricted to physicians and surgeons who are (a) graduates of scientific medicine holding the degree of Doctor of Medicine, in good standing and licensed to practice in their respective states or provinces; (b) competent in the field of industrial medicine and traumatic surgery; (c) worthy in character and in matters of professional ethics, that in the latter connection, the practice of the division of fees under any guise whatsoever be prohibited.

3. That there shall be a system of accurate and complete records filed in an accessible manner—a complete record being one which includes identification data; cause of illness or injury; nature and extent of illness or injury; detailed description of physical findings; special examinations such as consultations, clinical laboratory and X-ray; tentative or provisional diagnosis; treatment; prognosis with estimated period of disability; progress of illness or injury; final diagnosis; condition on discharge; and results, and such additional information as may be required by statute for Workmen's Compensation claims or for other purposes.
4. That all patients requiring hospitalization shall be sent to institutions approved by the American College of Surgeons.
5. That the medical department shall have general supervision over the sanitation of the plant and the health of all employees.

APPENDIX 4

PRINCIPLES SUBMITTED BY THE COMMITTEE ON ECONOMICS OF THE CANADIAN MEDICAL ASSOCIATION

(As presented at the Annual Meeting, June 18–22, 1934.)*

1. That, in the provinces where state health insurance is established, it be administered by the departments of public health (whether or not under a Commission) in order to co-ordinate the organized preventive and curative medical services.
2. That a Central Health Insurance Board and Local Insurance Boards be appointed, representative of all interested, to advise the responsible administrative authority.
3. That the professional side of health insurance medical service be the responsibility of the organized medical profession through the appointment, by the medical societies, of a Central Medical Services Committee and Local Medical Services Committees to consider and advise on all questions affecting the administration of the medical benefit.
4. That local areas for health insurance administration correspond to urban municipalities and rural health unit areas.
5. That the whole province be served by adequate departments of public health, organized on the basis of provision of individual health supervision by the health insurance general practitioner.

*Report of the Committee on Economics of the Canadian Medical Association, pp. 37–38.

6. That there be a State Health Insurance Fund, provincially controlled, and that "Regional Officers", to act as supervisors and referees, be appointed, paid and controlled by the provincial department of Public Health.

7. That medical care for indigents be provided under the Plan, the State to pay the premiums of the indigent, who then receive medical care under exactly the same conditions as the insured person.

8. That the Plan be compulsory for persons, with dependents, having an income of less than $2,500 per annum; and for persons, without dependents, having an income of $1,200 and less per annum.

9. That the dependents of insured persons be eligible for the medical benefit.

10. That there be offered, on a voluntary basis, to those with incomes above the health insurance level, Hospital Care Insurance, and that this be administered as part of the State Health Insurance Plan.

11. That the only benefit under the Plan be the medical benefit.

12. That the medical benefit be organized as follows:

   (a) Every qualified licensed practitioner to be eligible to practise under the Plan;
   (b) The insured person to have freedom of choice of general practitioner;
   (c) The medical service to be based upon making available to all a general practitioner service for health supervision and the treatment of disease;
   (d) Additional services to be secured normally through the general practitioner:
       (1) Specialist and consultant medical service (only those so designated to be eligible to practise as specialist and consultant);
       (2) Visiting-nurse service in the home;
       (3) Hospital care;
       (4) Auxiliary services—usually in hospital;
       (5) Pharmaceutical service.
   (e) Dental service, arranged direct with dentist or upon reference.

13. That the Insurance Fund should receive contributions from the insured, the employers of the insured, and the State.

14. That the medical practitioners of each local area be remunerated according to the method of payment which they select.

15. That the Central Medical Services Committee decide the relation-

ship between specialist and general practitioner fees, and between medical and surgical fees.

16. That contract-salary service be limited to areas with a population insufficient to maintain a general practitioner in the area without additional support from the Insurance Fund.

17. That no economic barrier be imposed between doctor and patient, but that the insured be required to pay a part of the cost of medicines.

APPENDIX 5

Resolutions of the American Hospital Association

1. Periodic Payment Plan for the Purchase of Hospital Care*
Adopted September, 1933

WHEREAS, our prevailing hospital system does not relieve the paying patient of a financial burden which is frequently beyond his ability to pay and which comes when he is least able to pay such expense, and

WHEREAS, experience has proved that the principle of group hospitalization insurance can be operated to the benefit of both the public and the hospitals if developed upon a sound basis and if surrounded with the necessary safeguards, and

WHEREAS, the adoption of some plan which would distribute the costs of sickness and benefit the sick individual would be one of the most effective ways to offset the increasing demand for more radical and potentially dangerous forms of national or state medicine, and

WHEREAS, the Board of Trustees of this Association has endorsed the principle of periodic payments for the purchase of hospital care and its Council on Community Relations and Administrative Practice has prepared suggested safeguards and recommended a basis of such plan,

BE IT RESOLVED, that the American Hospital Association in convention assembled endorse the basic principle of periodic payment for the purchase of hospital care and urge that our Council continue to study existing plans both here and abroad in order to make available to our hospitals reliable data on this subject and in order that our hospitals themselves may provide leadership in this phase of public service.

*From *American Hospital Association Proceedings,* Thirty-Fifth Annual Convention, Milwaukee, Wisconsin, September 11–15, 1933, p. 737.

2. GROUP HOSPITALIZATION*

WHEREAS, the American Hospital Association has approved the principle of group hospitalization whereby persons of moderate means may by small regular payments into a common fund assure themselves against the cost of hospital care when they need it, and

WHEREAS, more than forty cities have put such plans into operation or into process of organization, and

WHEREAS, the principle has received public endorsement by the American College of Surgeons and other national professional bodies, and of a number of state and local medical societies, and

WHEREAS, there is need for such a plan among large numbers of people even in normal times, a need that is increasing under present economic conditions,

THEREFORE, BE IT RESOLVED that the American Hospital Association reaffirm its approval of group hospitalization under the standards laid down by the Association designed to assure that it shall be conducted for public service rather than for profit, shall be consistent with legal requirements, high standards of professional care, and the traditions of the medical profession, and

BE IT FURTHER RESOLVED that the Association will continue to promote public knowledge concerning such plans and to assist their establishment through the dissemination of information and advice in cooperation with civic and professional organizations, and

BE IT FURTHER RESOLVED that experience having shown that there is a strong demand that group hospitalization plans should cover the dependents of members, and that such extension is often practicable, the Association urges communities which have adopted less inclusive plans to consider further the project with a view to such an extension whenever locally feasible.

APPENDIX 6

PRINCIPLES ADOPTED BY THE AMERICAN DENTAL ASSOCIATION

1. ADOPTION OF AUGUST, 1934†

The Special Committee on Dental Economics [of the House of Delegates of the American Dental Association] believes there is a possibility

*Resolution passed by American Hospital Association in convention at Philadelphia, Pennsylvania, September, 1934.

†*Journal of the American Dental Association,* October, 1934, pp. 1847–1848.

that some form of legislation will be presented to the people of this country, dealing with what is called "Economic Security" which will provide old age pensions and benefits for unemployment and health.

Therefore, we wish to place before the American Dental Association before such legislation becomes an actuality, the following principles, believing them to safeguard the best interests of all concerned.

1. In all conferences that may lead to the formation of a plan relative to this subject, there must be participation by authorized dental representatives.
2. The plans should provide dental care for indigents and needy children.
3. The plans should give careful consideration to the needs of the people, the obligation to the taxpayer and the interests of the profession.
4. The plans should be flexible so as to be adaptable to local conditions.
5. There must be complete exclusion of proprietary or profit-making agencies.
6. All features of dental service in any method of dental practice shall be under the control of the dental profession, as no other body or individual is educationally equipped to exercise such control.
7. All legally licensed dentists of a locality should be eligible to serve under such regulations as may be adopted.
8. Persons eligible to such service should be free to choose their dentist from the list of those who have agreed to furnish service under the adopted regulations.
9. Freedom of practitioners to accept or reject patients and freedom of all persons, who so prefer, to obtain dental service other than that provided by such plans, must be assured.
10. An adequate program should be provided for public education on the need of and the opportunities for dental care.

2. ADOPTION OF NOVEMBER, 1935*

The House of Delegates of the American Dental Association adopted the following resolution regarding dental service plans:

WHEREAS, for the past few years there has been considerable agitation concerning changes in medical and dental practices; and
WHEREAS, out of this discussion has come no concrete expression of

*Journal of the American Dental Association, January, 1936, p. 164.

opinion as how best to furnish health service to all the people that
would be at once fair and equitable to all parties concerned; and
WHEREAS, the Board of Trustees of the American Dental Association
have gone on record as opposing the socializing of the dental profession and all plans of compulsory health insurance; and
WHEREAS, the Committee on Economics of the American Dental Association believes the most effective opposition to such forms of
practice would be a system under full control of the organized health
professions, which will supply health service to all of the people; and
WHEREAS, it has been the custom of our people, when seeking health
service to pay for what they get and get what they pay for, we
recognize the fact that health service must be provided for the
indigent and those whose income is insufficient to pay customary
fees for dental care; and
WHEREAS, to meet these conditions health services for the low income
groups should be supplied at fees which are within the limits of
their ability to pay, and the care of the indigent must be, as it always
has been, a charity problem of each community; therefore be it
Resolved, that the American Dental Association in annual session
assembled approve of further study and experimentation with plans
to furnish such services as have been established in Washington, D. C. and St. Louis, Missouri, as we believe that the outcome of
such practical research might terminate in a satisfactory solution to
the vexing problems of providing adequate dental service to the
low income group.

APPENDIX 7

PROGRAM OF THE MEDICAL LEAGUE FOR SOCIALIZED MEDICINE*

. . . The Medical League for Socialized Medicine submits the following Platform or Program of measures and means to be developed into
law, and to serve as a basis upon which to establish an adequate system
of Socialized Medicine, with adequate care of the people by the doctors,
and adequate care of the doctors by the people:

PROGRAM

1. Adequate medical care of the sick and injured as a social function,
   right and duty, and not as a private or public charity. Curative

*Medical League for Socialized Medicine: Platform or Statement of Principles and
Programme, pp. 3–4.*

as well as preventive means, measures, and agencies to be included.
2. A socialized system of medical care in health, illness and injury, free of fees.

(a) Under the auspices and with the subsidy of the state.
(b) Financed by taxation, similar to the public educational system or other governmental functions.
(c) Operated and regulated by the organized medical and allied professions, the medical and dental colleges and the officials of existing public health agencies.
(d) This system to include all dental, pharmaceutical, nursing and allied services and personnel.

3. All hospitals, clinics, laboratories, pharmacies, etc., to be publicly owned and operated institutions, accessible to the sick free of charge. The hospitals and clinics to be the medical centers for ward and ambulatory cases, and to be properly organized, coordinated and geographically distributed. House sick calls to be received at these centers and to be assigned to local or neighborhood physicians designated to cover specific local territories.
4. All equipment, supplies, laboratory and other facilities of a medical, surgical, dental, pharmaceutical, nursing or other nature, to be furnished free by the state.
5. All medical, dental, pharmaceutical, nursing and allied education to be furnished free by the state.
6. All duly licensed or registered pharmacists, dentists, druggists, nurses, etc., to be legally entitled to practice under the system as full time practitioners or workers.

(a) Subject to established rules and regulations of admission and practice.
(b) Proper safeguards of their rights and privileges under the system and the law.
(c) With representation and a voice in the operation of the system.

7. Compensation to be adequate:

(a) Graded according to time of graduation, length of service in the system, rank held, and type of work.
(b) Salary increases and promotion to higher ranks to be based on similar considerations and to be automatically enforced.
(c) Pensions, sickness, old age and other disability and social insurance to be included and applied.

8. Hours of work to be assigned and regulated and scheduled so as to provide:

(a) Adequate medical care for the sick and injured at all times.
(b) Adequate time and opportunity for the physicians and allied workers for rest, recreation, vacations, and further professional study—with pay.

9. Organized cooperative groups and group methods to be employed under the system wherever possible. Special provisions to be made for rural and other territories inaccessible to regularly organized medical centers.

10. Individual private medical practice permissible under the same conditions and regulations as in private education, plus existing licenses and requirements by the state.

APPENDIX 8

DRAFT CONVENTION ADOPTED BY THE INTERNATIONAL LABOUR OFFICE

Draft Convention [No. 24] concerning sickness insurance[1] for workers in industry and commerce and domestic servants.

(Geneva, May 25–June 16, 1927)*

The General Conference of the International Labour Organisation of the League of Nations,

Having been convened at Geneva by the Governing Body of the International Labour Office, and having met in its Tenth Session on 25 May 1927, and

Having decided upon the adoption of certain proposals with regard to sickness insurance for workers in industry and commerce and domestic servants, which is included in the first item of the Agenda of the Session, and

Having determined that these proposals shall take the form of a draft international convention,

---

[1] This Convention came into force on 15 July 1928. It had been ratified on 1 September 1934 by Austria, Bulgaria, Chile, Colombia, Czechoslovakia, Germany, Great Britain, Hungary, Latvia, Lithuania, Luxemburg, Nicaragua, Rumania, Spain, Uruguay and Yugoslavia.

*From *Draft Conventions and Recommendations adopted by the International Labour Conference at its Eighteen Sessions held 1919–1934.* Geneva, International Labour Office, 1934, pp. 134–138.

adopts, this fifteenth day of June of the year one thousand nine hundred and twenty-seven, the following Draft Convention for ratification by the Members of the International Labour Organisation, in accordance with the provisions of Part XIII of the Treaty of Versailles and of the corresponding Parts of the other Treaties of Peace:

ARTICLE 1.

Each Member of the International Labour Organisation which ratifies this Convention undertakes to set up a system of compulsory sickness insurance which shall be based on provisions at least equivalent to those contained in this Convention.

ARTICLE 2.

The compulsory sickness insurance system shall apply to manual and non-manual workers, including apprentices, employed by industrial undertakings and commercial undertakings, out-workers and domestic servants.

It shall, nevertheless, be open to any Member to make such exceptions in its national laws or regulations as it deems necessary in respect of:

(a) Temporary employment which lasts for less than a period to be determined by national laws or regulations, casual employment not for the purpose of the employer's trade or business, occasional employment and subsidiary employment;

(b) Workers whose wages or income exceed an amount to be determined by national laws or regulations;

(c) Workers who are not paid a money wage;

(d) Out-workers whose conditions of work are not of a like nature to those of ordinary wage-earners;

(e) Workers below or above age-limits to be determined by national laws or regulations;

(f) Members of the employer's family.

It shall further be open to exempt from the compulsory sickness insurance system persons who in case of sickness are entitled by virtue of any laws or regulations, or of a special scheme, to advantages at least equivalent on the whole to those provided for in this Convention.

This Convention shall not apply to seamen and sea fishermen for whose insurance against sickness provision may be made by a decision of a later Session of the Conference.

ARTICLE 3.

An insured person who is rendered incapable of work by reason of the abnormal state of his bodily or mental health shall be entitled to a cash benefit for at least the first twenty-six weeks of incapacity from and including the first day for which benefit is payable.

The payment of this benefit may be made conditional on the insured person having first complied with a qualifying period and, on the expiry of the same, with a waiting period of not more than three days.

Cash benefit may be withheld in the following cases:

(a) Where in respect of the same illness the insured person receives compensation from another source to which he is entitled by law; benefit shall only be wholly or partially withheld in so far as such compensation is equal to or less than the amount of the benefit provided by the present Article;

(b) As long as the insured person does not by the fact of his incapacity suffer any loss of the normal product of his labour, or is maintained at the expense of the insurance funds or from public funds; nevertheless, cash benefits shall only partially be withheld when the insured person, although thus personally maintained, has family responsibilities;

(c) As long as the insured person while ill refuses, without valid reason, to comply with the doctor's orders, or the instructions relating to the conduct of insured persons while ill, or voluntarily and without authorisation removes himself from the supervision of the insurance institutions.

Cash benefit may be reduced or refused in the case of sickness caused by the insured person's wilful misconduct.

ARTICLE 4.

The insured person shall be entitled free of charge, as from the commencement of his illness and at least until the period prescribed for the grant of sickness benefit expires, to medical treatment by a fully qualified medical man and to the supply of proper and sufficient medicines and appliances.

Nevertheless, the insured person may be required to pay such part of the cost of medical benefit as may be prescribed by national laws or regulations.

Medical benefit may be withheld as long as the insured person refuses, without valid reason, to comply with the doctor's orders or the instructions relating to the conduct of insured persons while ill, or neglects to make use of the facilities placed at his disposal by the insurance institution.

ARTICLE 5.

National laws or regulations may authorise or prescribe the grant of medical benefit to members of an insured person's family living in his household and dependent upon him, and shall determine the conditions under which such benefit shall be administered.

ARTICLE 6.

Sickness insurance shall be administered by self-governing institutions, which shall be under the administrative and financial supervision of the competent public authority and shall not be carried on with a view of profit. Institutions founded by private initiative must be specially approved by the competent public authority.

The insured persons shall participate in the management of the self-governing insurance institutions on such conditions as may be prescribed by national laws or regulations.

The administration of sickness insurance may, nevertheless, be undertaken directly by the State where and as long as its administration is rendered difficult or impossible or inappropriate by reason of national conditions, and particularly by the insufficient development of the employers' and workers' organisations.

ARTICLE 7.

The insured persons and their employers shall share in providing the financial resources of the sickness insurance system.

It is open to national laws or regulations to decide as to a financial contribution by the competent public authority.

ARTICLE 8.

This Convention does not in any respect affect the obligations arising out of the Convention concerning the employment of women before and after childbirth, adopted by the International Labour Conference at its First Session.

ARTICLE 9.

A right of appeal shall be granted to the insured person in case of dispute concerning his right to benefit.

ARTICLE 10.

It shall be open to States which comprise large and very thinly populated areas not to apply the Convention in districts where, by reason of the small density and wide dispersion of the population and the inadequacy of the means of communication, the organisation of sickness insurance, in accordance with this Convention, is impossible.

The States which intend to avail themselves of the exception provided by this Article shall give notice of their intention when communicating their formal ratification to the Secretary-General of the League of Nations. They shall inform the International Labour Office as to what districts they apply the exception and indicate their reasons therefor.

In Europe it shall be open only to Finland to avail itself of the exception contained in this Article.

ARTICLE 11.

The formal ratifications of this Convention under the conditions set forth in Part XIII of the Treaty of Versailles and in the corresponding Parts of the other Treaties of Peace shall be communicated to the Secretary-General of the League of Nations for registration.

ARTICLE 12.

This Convention shall come into force ninety days after the date on which the ratifications of two Members of the International Labour Organisation have been registered by the Secretary-General.

It shall be binding only upon those Members whose ratifications have been registered with the Secretariat.

Thereafter, the Convention shall come into force for any Member ninety days after the date on which its ratification has been registered with the Secretariat.

ARTICLE 13.

As soon as the ratifications of two Members of the International Labour Organisation have been registered with the Secretariat, the Secretary-General of the League of Nations shall so notify all the Members of the International Labour Organisation. He shall likewise notify them of the registration of ratifications which may be communicated subsequently by other Members of the Organisation.

ARTICLE 14.

Subject to the provisions of Article 12, each Member which ratifies this Convention agrees to bring the provisions of Articles 1, 2, 3, 4, 5, 6, 7, 8, 9 and 10 into operation not later than 1 January 1929, and to take such action as may be necessary to make these provisions effective.

ARTICLE 15.

Each Member of the International Labour Organisation which ratifies this Convention engages to apply it to its colonies, possessions and protectorates, in accordance with the provisions of Article 421 of the Treaty of Versailles and of the corresponding Articles of the other Treaties of Peace.

ARTICLE 16.

A Member which has ratified this Convention may denounce it after the expiration of ten years from the date on which the Convention first comes into force, by an act communicated to the Secretary-General of the League of Nations for registration. Such denunciation shall not take effect until one year after the date on which it is registered with the Secretariat.

ARTICLE 17.

At least once in ten years, the Governing Body of the International Labour Office shall present to the General Conference a report on the working of this Convention and shall consider the desirability of placing on the Agenda of the Conference the question of its revision or modification.

ARTICLE 18.

The French and English texts of this Convention shall both be authentic.

APPENDIX 9

DRAFT CONVENTION ADOPTED BY THE INTERNATIONAL LABOUR OFFICE

Draft Convention [No. 25] concerning sickness
insurance for agricultural workers.[1]

(Geneva, May 25–June 16, 1927)*

The General Conference of the International Labour Organisation of the League of Nations,

[1] This Convention came into force on 13 July 1928. It had been ratified on 1 September 1934 by Austria, Bulgaria, Chile, Colombia, Czechoslovakia, Germany, Great Britain, Luxemburg, Nicaragua, Spain and Uruguay.

*From *Draft Conventions and Recommendations adopted by the International Labour Conference at its Eighteen Sessions held 1919–1934.* Geneva, International Labour Office, 1934, pp. 139–143.

Having been convened at Geneva by the Governing Body of the International Labour Office, and having met in its Tenth Session on 25 May 1927, and

Having decided upon the adoption of certain proposals with regard to sickness insurance for agricultural workers, which is included in the first item of the Agenda of the Session, and

Having determined that these proposals shall take the form of a draft international convention,

adopts, this fifteenth day of June of the year one thousand nine hundred and twenty-seven, the following Draft Convention for ratification by the Members of the International Labour Organisation, in accordance with the provisions of Part XIII of the Treaty of Versailles and of the corresponding Parts of the other Treaties of Peace:

ARTICLE 1.

Each member of the International Labour Organisation which ratifies this Convention undertakes to set up a system of compulsory sickness insurance for agricultural workers, which shall be based on provisions at least equivalent to those contained in this Convention.

ARTICLE 2.

The compulsory sickness insurance system shall apply to manual and non-manual workers, including apprentices, employed by agricultural undertakings.

It shall, nevertheless, be open to any Member to make such exceptions in its national laws or regulations as it deems necessary in respect of:

(a) Temporary employment which lasts for less than a period to be determined by national laws or regulations, casual employment not for the purpose of the employer's trade or business, occasional employment and subsidiary employment;

(b) Workers whose wages or income exceed an amount to be determined by national laws or regulations;

(c) Workers who are not paid a money wage;

(d) Out-workers whose conditions of work are not of a like nature to those of ordinary wage-earners;

(e) Workers below or above age-limits to be determined by national laws or regulations;

(f) Members of the employer's family.

It shall further be open to exempt from the compulsory sickness insurance system persons who in case of sickness are entitled by virtue of any laws or regulations, or of a special scheme, to advantages at least equivalent on the whole to those provided for in this Convention.

ARTICLE 3.

An insured person who is rendered incapable of work by reason of the abnormal state of his bodily or mental health shall be entitled to a cash benefit for at least the first twenty-six weeks of incapacity from and including the first day for which benefit is payable.

The payment of this benefit may be made conditional on the insured person having first complied with a qualifying period and, on the expiry of the same, with a waiting period of not more than three days. Cash benefit may be withheld in the following cases:

(a) Where in respect of the same illness the insured person receives compensation from another source to which he is entitled by law; benefit shall only be wholly or partially withheld in so far as such compensation is equal to or less than the amount of the benefit provided by the present Article;

(b) As long as the insured person does not by the fact of his incapacity suffer any loss of the normal product of his labour, or is maintained at the expense of the insurance funds or from public funds; nevertheless, cash benefit shall only partially be withheld when the insured person, although thus personally maintained, has family responsibilities.

(c) As long as the insured person while ill refuses, without valid reason, to comply with the doctor's orders, or the instructions relating to the conduct of insured persons while ill, or voluntarily and without authorisation removes himself from the supervision of the insurance institutions.

Cash benefit may be reduced or refused in the case of sickness caused by the insured person's wilful misconduct.

ARTICLE 4.

The insured person shall be entitled free of charge, as from the commencement of his illness and at least until the period prescribed for the grant of sickness benefit expires, to medical treatment by a fully qualified medical man and to the supply of proper and sufficient medicines and appliances.

Nevertheless, the insured person may be required to pay such part of the cost of medical benefit as may be prescribed by national laws or regulations.

Medical benefit may be withheld as long as the insured person refuses, without valid reason, to comply with the doctor's orders or the instructions relating to the conduct of insured persons while ill, or neglects to make use of the facilities placed at his disposal by the insurance institution.

ARTICLE 5.

National laws or regulations may authorise or prescribe the grant of medical benefit to members of an insured person's family living in his household and dependent upon him, and shall determine the conditions under which such benefit shall be administered.

ARTICLE 6.

Sickness insurance shall be administered by self-governing institutions, which shall be under the administrative and financial supervision of the competent public authority and shall not be carried on with a view of profit. Institutions founded by private initiative must be specially approved by the competent public authority.

The insured persons shall participate in the management of the self-governing insurance institutions on such conditions as may be prescribed by national laws or regulations.

The administration of sickness insurance may, nevertheless, be undertaken directly by the State where and as long as its administration is rendered difficult or impossible or inappropriate by reason of national conditions, and particularly by the insufficient development of the employers' and workers' organisations.

ARTICLE 7.

The insured persons and their employers shall share in providing the financial resources of the sickness insurance system.

It is open to national laws or regulations to decide as to a financial contribution by the competent public authority.

ARTICLE 8.

A right of appeal shall be granted to the insured person in case of dispute concerning his right to benefit.

ARTICLE 9.

It shall be open to States which comprise large and very thinly populated areas not to apply the Convention in districts where, by reason of the small density and wide dispersion of the population and the inadequacy of the means of communication, the organisation of sickness insurance, in accordance with this Convention, is impossible.

The States which intend to avail themselves of the exception provided by this Article shall give notice of their intention when communicating their formal ratification to the Secretary-General of the League of Nations. They shall inform the International Labour Office as to what districts they apply the exception and indicate their reasons therefor.

In Europe it shall be open only to Finland to avail itself of the exception contained in this Article.

ARTICLE 10.

The formal ratifications of this Convention under the conditions set forth in Part XIII of the Treaty of Versailles and in the corresponding Parts of the other Treaties of Peace shall be communicated to the Secretary-General of the League of Nations for registration.

ARTICLE 11.

This Convention shall come into force ninety days after the date on which the ratifications of two Members of the International Labour Organisation have been registered by the Secretary-General.

It shall be binding only upon those Members whose ratifications have been registered with the Secretariat.

Thereafter, the Convention shall come into force for any Member ninety days after the date on which its ratification has been registered with the Secretariat.

ARTICLE 12.

As soon as the ratifications of two Members of the International Labour Organisation have been registered with the Secretariat, the Secretary-General of the League of Nations shall so notify all the Members of the International Labour Organisation. He shall likewise notify them of the registration of ratifications which may be communicated subsequently by other Members of the Organisation.

ARTICLE 13.

Subject to the provisions of Article 11, each Member which ratifies this Convention agrees to bring the provisions of Articles 1, 2, 3, 4, 5, 6, 7, 8, and 9 into operation not later than 1 January 1929, and to take such action as may be necessary to make these provisions effective.

ARTICLE 14.

Each Member of the International Labour Organisation which ratifies this Convention engages to apply it to its colonies, possessions and protectorates, in accordance with the provisions of Article 421 of the Treaty of Versailles and of the corresponding Articles of the other Treaties of Peace.

ARTICLE 15.

A Member which has ratified this Convention may denounce it after the expiration of ten years from the date on which the Convention first comes into force, by an act communicated to the Secretary-General of the League of Nations for registration. Such denunciation shall not take effect until one year after the date on which it is registered with the Secretariat.

ARTICLE 16.

At least once in ten years, the Governing Body of the International Labour Office shall present to the General Conference a report on the working of this Convention and shall consider the desirability of placing on the Agenda of the Conference the question of its revision or modification.

ARTICLE 17.

The French and English texts of this Convention shall both be authentic.

APPENDIX 10

GENERAL PRINCIPLES OF HEALTH INSURANCE OF THE INTERNATIONAL LABOUR OFFICE

Recommendation [No. 29] concerning the general principles of sickness insurance.

(Geneva, May 25–June 16, 1927)*

The General Conference of the International Labour Organisation of the League of Nations,

Having been convened at Geneva by the Governing Body of the International Labour Office, and having met in its Tenth Session on 25 May 1927, and
Having decided upon the adoption of certain proposals with

---

*From *Draft Conventions and Recommendations adopted by the International Labour Conference at its Eighteen Sessions held 1919–1934.* Geneva, International Labour Office, 1934, pp. 144–148.

regard to the principles of sickness insurance, the first item on
the Agenda of the Session, and

Having determined that these proposals should take the form
of a recommendation,

adopts this fifteenth day of June of the year one thousand nine hundred
and twenty-seven, the following Recommendation, to be submitted to
the Members of the International Labour Organisation for consideration
with a view to effect being given to it by national legislation or otherwise,
in accordance with the provisions of Part XIII of the Treaty of Versailles
and of the corresponding Parts of the other Treaties of Peace:

Whereas the maintenance of a healthy and vigorous labour supply is
of capital importance not only for the workers themselves, but also for
communities which desire to develop their productive capacity; and

Whereas this development is only attainable by constantly and
systematically applying provident measures to obviate or make good
any loss of the workers' productive efficiency; and

Whereas the best provident measure for these purposes is to establish a system of social insurance which confers clearly defined rights
on the persons to whom it applies;

Therefore the General Conference of the International Labour
Organisation,

Having adopted Draft Conventions concerning, of the one part,
sickness insurance for workers in industry and commerce and domestic
servants, and, of the other part, sickness insurance for agricultural
workers, drafts which lay down minimum conditions which must
be complied with from the beginning by every system of sickness insurance, and

Considering that, in order to put the experience already gained at
the disposal of the Members with a view to assisting them in the
institution or completion of their sickness insurance services, it is
desirable to indicate a number of the general principles which practice shows to be the best calculated to promote a just, effective and
appropriate organisation of sickness insurance,

Recommends that each Member should take the following principles
and rules into consideration:

I. SCOPE OF APPLICATION.

1. Sickness insurance should include within its scope, without dis-
crimination as to age or sex, every person who performs work by way
of his occupation and under a contract of service or apprenticeship.

2. If, however, it is considered desirable to fix age-limits by reason

of the fact that workers above or below such limits are already protected by law or otherwise, such limits should not apply to young persons who cannot normally be considered as dependent upon their family or to workers who have not reached the old-age pension age; and

If exceptions are made in respect of workers whose earnings or income exceed a specified amount, such exceptions should only apply to workers whose earnings or income are such that they may reasonably be expected to make their own provision for sickness.

II.   BENEFITS.

A. *Cash Benefits.*

3. In order to secure that an insured person who is rendered incapable of work by sickness may recover his health as early as possible, the cash benefit representing compensation for lost wages should be adequate.

For this purpose the statutory scale of benefit should ordinarily be fixed in relation to the normal wage which is taken into account for the purposes of compulsory insurance, and should be a substantial proportion of such wage, regard being had to family responsibilities; but in countries where the workers have adequate facilities, of which they are accustomed to take advantage to procure for themselves additional benefit by other means, a uniform scale of benefit may be appropriate.

4. The statutory benefit should be paid for at least the first twenty-six weeks of incapacity as from and including the first day for which benefit is payable; nevertheless, the period for which benefit is payable should be increased to one year in cases of serious and chronic illness and for insured persons who will not receive any invalidity benefit on the expiry of their right to sickness benefit.

5. An insurance institution which can show that it is in a sound financial position should be authorised:

> (a) To increase the statutory scale of benefit up to specified amounts either for all insured persons or for certain groups of the same, in particular insured persons with family responsibilities;
>
> (b) To prolong the statutory period during which benefit is payable.

6. In countries where burial expenses are not, customarily or by law, covered by some other insurance, sickness insurance institutions should, on the death of an insured person, pay a benefit in respect of the cost of decent burial; they should also be empowered to pay such

a benefit in respect of the burial expenses of the insured person's dependants.

B. *Benefits in Kind*.

7. Treatment by a fully qualified doctor and the supply of proper and sufficient medicines and appliances should be granted to an insured person from the beginning of his illness and for so long as the state of his health requires it; the insured person should be entitled to these benefits free of charge from the beginning of his illness and at least until the expiry of the period prescribed for the grant of sickness benefit.

8. In addition to treatment by a fully qualified doctor and the supply of proper and sufficient medicines and appliances, there should be available for the insured person, as and when local and financial conditions admit, facilities for specialist services, as well as dental treatment, and for treatment in hospital, where his family circumstances necessitate it or his illness requires a mode of treatment which can only be given in hospital.

9. While an insured person is maintained in hospital, the insurance institution should pay to his dependants the whole or a part of the sickness benefit which would have been payable to him had he not been so maintained.

10. With a view to ensuring good conditions for the maintenance in health of the insured person and his family, members of the insured person's family living in his home and dependent upon him should be furnished with medical benefit, as and when it may be possible and practicable to do so.

11. Insurance institutions should be empowered to avail themselves, on equitable conditions, of the services of such doctors as they need.

In urban centres, and within specified geographical limits, an insured person should be entitled to choose a doctor from among those at the disposal of the insurance institution, unless this would involve considerable extra expense to the institution.

C. *Sickness Prevention*.

12. As most diseases can be prevented, an alert policy of prevention is calculated to avert loss of productive efficiency, to render available for other purposes the financial resources which are absorbed by avoidable illness, and to promote the material, intellectual and moral well-being of the community.

Sickness insurance should assist in inculcating the practice of the rules of hygiene among the workers. It should give preventive treatment and grant the same to as large a number of individuals as possible as soon as the premonitory symptoms of disease appear. It should be capable of contributing towards the prevention of the spread of disease and the improvement of the national health, in pursuance of a general policy co-ordinating all the various activities towards these ends.

III. ORGANISATION OF INSURANCE.

13. Insurance institutions should be administered, under the supervision of the competent public authority in accordance with the principles of self-government, and shall not be carried on for profit. The insured persons being those who are the most directly interested in the working of the insurance scheme should, through elected representatives, have an important part in the management of the insurance system.

14. A good organisation of medical benefit and, in particular, the efficient provision and utilisation of medical equipment embodying the results of scientific progress can be most easily secured—except in certain special circumstances—by concentrating action on a territorial basis.

IV. FINANCIAL RESOURCES.

15. The financial resources for the insurance scheme should be provided by contributions from the insured persons and contributions from employers. The provision thus jointly made can be supplemented to advantage by contributions from public funds, especially for the purpose of improving the health of the people.

With a view to securing the stability of the insurance system, reserve funds, appropriate to the peculiar circumstances of the system, should be constituted.

V. SETTLEMENT OF DISPUTES.

16. With a view to their being settled rapidly and inexpensively, disputes as to benefits between insured persons and insurance institutions should be referred to special tribunals, the members of which include judges or assessors who are specially cognisant of the purposes of insurance and the needs of insured persons.

VI. EXCEPTION FOR SPARSELY POPULATED TERRITORIES

17. States which, by reason of the small density of their population or of the inadequacy of the means of communication, cannot organise sickness insurance in certain parts of their territory should:

(a) Establish in such parts of their territory a sanitary service adequate to the local conditions;

(b) Examine periodically whether the conditions required for the introduction of compulsory sickness insurance in the parts of their territory previously excepted from the compulsory scheme are fulfilled.

VII. SEAMEN AND SEA FISHERMEN.

18. This Recommendation shall not apply to seamen and sea fishermen.

APPENDIX 11

RESOLUTIONS OF THE INTERNATIONAL PROFESSIONAL ASSOCIATION OF PHYSICIANS

(Association professionelle internationale des médecins)

ADOPTED BY THE COUNCIL OF THE ASSOCIATION, SEPTEMBER, 1931*

PREAMBLE

I. The International Professional Association of Physicians fully approves, for the economically weak class of society, the principle of social insurance, which constitutes a great social advance, as well as a powerful factor in the prosperity and well being of the nations.

II. The principles herewith set forth represent only those provisions which, by the very fact of its fundamental rôle in the operation of sickness insurance, the medical corps has a right to insist on.

III. In formulating these principles, as the result of long and comprehensive investigations, and as conclusions based on these investigations, the International Professional Association of Physicians has been guided, not alone by solicitude for the special interests of the medical corps, but above all by its duty toward all the sick, and by the necessities for the proper functioning of the insurance societies.

But it maintains that *only the closest cooperation* between the insurance societies and all other institutions of social insurance with the representatives of the organized medical corps guarantees the proper functioning of sickness insurance and its development.

IV. It is necessary that the practicing physicians be heard, through their professional associations, in the preparation of laws and regulations concerning sickness insurance and also in all modifications in the course of their application. The physicians are the natural pillars of sickness insurance; they have a full *right to be heard* on this subject. The International Professional Association of Physicians insists on this

*From the *American Medical Association Bulletin,* April, 1934, xxix, pp. 74–75.

point with all its energy, backed by the indisputable defects—becoming more and more evident—committed by the majority of existing legislation, as a result of the absence of the practicing physicians.

V. The International Professional Association of Physicians also emphatically demands the autonomy of the medical service, including the material and moral *independence* of the physician, and this in the interest of the patients themselves.

It is proper, to be sure, that the medical corps remain always outside all conflicts of a political or religious character that may arise within the directing committee of the societies and that the position of the medical corps and the physicians shall not be affected by any changes whatever in the composition of the directing committees. Moreover, experience has shown that in those countries where the physician is given a dignified, honorable and influential position in relation to the sickness societies, and where the medical profession preserves the liberal and independent character of the practice of medicine, there is the most fruitful development of sickness insurance.

VI. The International Professional Association of Physicians is of the opinion that sickness insurance, whether compulsory or voluntary, ought, from the social point of view, to be applied only to those persons who are incapable of meeting the necessary costs of medical care in cases of sickness from their own resources. The field of insurance ought, therefore, to be limited by a maximum income, which is determined by the conditions of living in each country, with due consideration of all interests, including those of the medical corps.

VII. The socially insured in every country should be entitled to receive medical care up to the age limit which entitles them to old-age insurance or to care by analogous institutes.

It is also clear that the idea of social insurance cannot be realized if the *members of the family* of the insured (direct members: wife and minor children) do not share the benefits of sickness insurance.

VIII. In order not to remove the moral responsibility of the insured in his daily life, in order to secure a normal and healthy practice of medicine, and even in the interest of the sick, insurance legislation should always require the *insured to share* in the cost of medical care and drugs, which share may be very modest, but a share fixed by the law. The application of this principle should be adjusted to the special conditions and needs of each country, but it should not result in a situation where those who have the greatest need of the relief furnished by the societies are deprived of help. (Subsidiary aid to the indigents should be furnished by some organization.)

For the same reason the cash payments during sickness should be so calculated as to exclude the temptation of the insured to abuse the benefits of insurance. But it is to be understood that the application of these principles should be varied to meet the special conditions and needs of each country.

ORGANIZATION OF MEDICAL SERVICE UNDER SICKNESS INSURANCE

IX. The International Professional Association of Physicians declares that its first duty is to proclaim that one of the principal factors in healing is mutual confidence between the patient and his physician. This implies the free choice of physician by the patient. (Freedom of confidence.) The International Professional Association of Physicians therefore demands, as a condition sine qua non of good functioning of medical service in sickness insurance that free choice be written into the text of legislation in all countries.

This free choice implies that "all" physicians authorized to practice in the country shall be qualified to care for the insured, subject to the reservation that they adhere to the agreements concluded in each country between the societies and the organized medical corps of which every physician ought to be a member.

The principle of free choice shall be considered as maintained even if, in the rural sections, in consideration of special situations, choice is restricted to the nearest physician.

X. At all times, in general, in order to determine the relations between the societies and the medical corps, it is necessary to conclude *collective contracts* between the regional or local societies and the corresponding professional medical groups.

In those countries where the law requires that contracts be made between the societies and the organized medical corps, it is desirable that the respective delegates deal directly among themselves, without the intervention of any so-called impartial body, the members of which are too often incompetent to deal with the matter and are apt to rest their decisions on insufficiently justifiable bases, thereby not only endangering the interests of one of the contracting parties but also damaging the later good functioning of sickness insurance.

If such organizations as committees of arbitration do, nevertheless, exist in certain countries, the physicians should have equal representation on these, appointed exclusively by the organized medical corps.

XI. Every physician accepting the terms of the contract shall have the right to care for the patients of the society, without the latter having the power to designate certain special physicians, which would be contrary to freedom of confidence and free choice of physician by the patient, which should be limited only for very special and grave reasons, such as the proved unworthiness of the physician.

It is necessary to guard with jealous care to see that *professional secrecy* is observed in sickness insurance. In the interest of the good functioning of the societies it is useful for the physician to state the causes of the days of sickness. But the medical corps of each country should determine the regulations on this point with the government or with the organizations according to national customs.

XII. The care of medical specialists, as well as hospitalization of the sick in case of need and according to the course of the sickness, should be guaranteed to the insured.

The latter should also, if the budget permits, be given the benefit of further medical treatments and all therapeutic agencies.

XIII. In the interest of the sick, and in order to assure them of the most efficient care, the physicians cannot accept any restrictions on their *right to prescribe* and must have the power to order all useful and *irreplaceable* medicaments. The medical organizations should always, on the other hand, seek to suppress all expensive and superfluous medication, or what might be called "luxury treatment."

As to the duration of the care given to the insured the International Professional Association of Physicians is of the opinion that the medical services of insurance should be extended to cover the *total* duration of illness, or of an accident and its results, up to recovery or decease, or until the moment when the insured is admitted to a home or other social institution (old age or invalidity insurance).

XIV. It is contrary to a proper practice of medicine that the payment of physicians should be by a fixed sum to a group (au forfait global), or by a fixed amount as a salary without regard to the service given. As to the other modes of payment of the physician, such as according to the medical act, or according to the number of insured on the physician's list, whether payment is by the society (third party payment), or by the patient (direct payment) it is necessary to leave the choice to each nation, according to the desires of each professional medical group, which thus follows the customs of each national collectivity.*

XV. The *administrative control* of the patients should be conducted by the care of the societies. The *professional medical control* should

*All of the sections in the text were adopted unanimously. The section which follows failed to receive a unanimous vote, as Dr. Cox of the British Medical Association expressly declared that he voted against it: "Direct payment of the physician by the patient guarantees a healthy and moral practice of medicine and tends to be extended little by little in the countries having systems of sickness insurance. The insured and the physicians who have lived for decades under a régime of payment through a third party may not always pass to this new method of paying medical honorariums, without a slow and methodical preliminary preparation of the public mind, which will be all the more necessary in those countries where the grave results of the world crisis cause especial resistance to the sudden introduction of any change, and it is the opinion of the General Council of the International Professional Association of Physicians that a disturbance of the relations between patients and physicians might aggravate the social sickness."

be exercised by the physicians, or by the medical councils approved by the societies in agreement with the medical group. The *technical control*, wherever it is indispensable, may be exercised only by a physician, under the form of a consultation between confrères, permitting the treating physician to explain his position with complete frankness and freedom and with perfect equality.

But it is to be emphasized that the physicians charged with the control of sickness insurance can successfully fulfil their rôle only if they possess the confidence of the treating physician, if they have an extensive experience with the problems of social medicine, and if they show great tact in the exercise of their functions. Moreover, only these qualities will assure them that cordial cooperation which is legally due them from the practicing physicians.

XVI. On the subject of legal control of professional relations the International Professional Association of Physicians is of the opinion that, since certain countries have established "medical institutions," charged with supervision of such work of the physicians engaged in insurance practice as deals with certificates of incapacity for work, economical prescribing, furnishing special appliances, etc., these institutions ought to be chosen in agreement with the professional medical groups and be sufficiently independent of the insurance organizations to be able to base their decisions exclusively on technical considerations. The participation of laymen in this work of control is not acceptable, since their decisions would lack technical judgment.

XVII. The better the administration of the society is organized from the medical points of view, the more useful and effective will be the medical service supplied to the insured. To secure this object, in the special interest of the patients, the International Professional Association of Physicians believes it to be natural and equitable that whatever is related to the medical service should be studied and regulated in agreements between the societies and the delegates of the medical groups. It follows that the medical corps should be represented in all phases of the administration that affect medical service.

The International Professional Association of Physicians declares that the insurance societies should act only as *intermediaries* between the patients and the physicians, pharmacists, hospitals, clinics, dispensaries, sanatoriums and preventoriums, but that they ought not themselves to operate either the factories producing pharmaceuticals, nor the hospitals, dispensaries, sanatoriums, preventoriums, etc.

XVIII. For all disputes and litigation, whether between society and physician or between the insured and the physician, there should be established special tribunals in which the interests of the disputants are equally represented, with the right of appeal, either to a special higher judicdiction or to the ordinary tribunals.

XIX. The International Professional Association of Physicians approves the equal representation of employers, insured and physicians in the institutions of sickness insurance wherever these deal with questions of a medical character.

The International Professional Association of Physicians maintains in the very interest of social insurance that not only those who contribute by their payments should participate in the administration of social insurance, but also those who by their work assure not simply the operation, but the very existence of these institutions.

CONCLUSION

The International Professional Association of Physicians has kept in view, not only the professional and ethical interests of the physicians, but, above all, the interests of the sick, all of whom should, whether rich or poor, be assured of receiving the best of care.

That the representatives of the insurance societies should respect the rightful interests of the physicians, as well as those of the patients, and that the physicians respect, along with the interest of the patients, the rightful interests of the insurance societies, constitute the indispensable conditions for any proper solution of the problem of sickness insurance.

APPENDIX 12

RESOLUTIONS OF THE FIFTH INTERNATIONAL CONFERENCE OF NATIONAL ASSOCIATIONS OF HEALTH INSURANCE FUNDS AND MUTUAL AID SOCIETIES

September, 1933*

GENERAL RESOLUTION

The Sixth Meeting of the International Conference, having approved the report of the Chairman of the International Committee on its work and having noted the views expressed by the accredited representatives of health insurance schemes in various countries,

(1) Reiterates its unaltered belief in the principle of compulsory insurance, which is the only sound basis for a completely effective social insurance system, able to survive any test, in all circumstances and for workers in every occupation;

*From *Industrial and Labour Information* (International Labour Office, Geneva), 30 October 1933, xlviii, No. 5, pp. 144–149.

(2) Expresses the opinion that even the best health insurance schemes to be met with in any country at present guarantee only a minimum subsistence level by their cash benefits and a minimum of medical protection by their curative and preventive measures, and therefore emphasises the danger of any restriction of the basic benefits;

(3) Stresses the capital importance of social insurance, more especially in times of economic depression which lead to a decline in the general standard of living and a reduction in the physical resistance and the purchasing power of insured persons and their families;

(4) Emphasises the urgent social and economic necessity for maintaining the insured status of workers who have become unemployed, and requests the public authorities to provide financial assistance to enable the rights of workers who have long been out of employment to be guaranteed;

(5) Notes the withdrawal of the German National Federation of Health Insurance Funds by decision of the Government Commissioner appointed to manage the Association after the former autonomous bodies had been dissolved;

(6) Decides to prosecute more intensively its efforts to defend and develop social insurance by tightening the bonds between those federations and institutions in every country which, by word and deed, are serving the cause of international collaboration and understanding.

THE POSITION OF MEDICAL PRACTITIONERS UNDER HEALTH INSURANCE

Responsibility for the Organisation of Benefits in Kind. (1) The Conference is of the opinion that insured persons should receive adequate and appropriate curative and preventive treatment free of charge, subject to the possibility of their being required to bear a fraction of the medical expenses. When the legislation holds the insurance funds responsible for the quality and extent of the medical treatment, the funds should themselves organise and provide medical benefits in kind.

(2) The Conference confirms its view that the insurance should cover the sickness risk as completely and as economically as possible. The great majority of the federations and institutions affiliated to the Conference further believe that this can best be achieved by making the insurance funds responsible for the provision of medical benefits in kind.

Qualifications of Doctors Attending Insured Persons. (3) The grant of benefits in cash and in kind depends on the doctor in attendance, who must often possess very wide and highly specialised knowledge in order to be able to decide on applications for benefits and determine whether the worker is incapacitated for employment. He must therefore have a certain experience of his profession so as to be in a position to fulfil the special duties devolving on him.

(4) Wherever the insurance funds are empowered to exercise discretion in the recognition of medical practitioners they should have the right to demand that recognition be made dependent on at least one year's hospital experience and one year's experience in general practice. Special regulations should be drawn up defining the training required for appointment as confidential medical consultant, chief medical officer or specialist.

Selection of Doctors to Attend Insured Persons. (5) The Conference, believing that the selection of doctors to attend insured persons must depend not only on considerations of maximum efficiency but also on other factors varying from country to country, such as the mentality of the population and more particularly of the insured population, the financial situation of the health insurance scheme, the comparative strength of the interests involved, etc., considers it wiser, for the time being at least, to refrain from laying down binding international rules on this subject.

(6) Nevertheless, a large number of the affiliated federations and institutions which are obliged to provide benefits in kind are of the opinion that the best system, in view of the collective nature of social insurance, is for the funds to select the doctors called upon to attend insured persons.

Contracts with Medical Practitioners. (7) The Conference considers that the medical service provided by health insurance cannot be adequately guaranteed save by long-term agreements between doctors and insurance funds, these agreements being freely drawn up by the parties concerned.

Such negotiations being more successful if carried through in the general interest and not for the benefit of any single fund or individual practitioner, the Conference recommends that the relations between funds and doctors should be governed by collective agreements between associations of funds and organisations of the medical profession, subject to adaptations to meet local conditions.

(8) When it proves impossible to conclude such agreements because of differences of opinion, and when the medical service is not in the hands of doctors acting as officials of the insurance funds, the funds should have legal power to substitute specified cash benefits for benefits in kind.

Treatment of Insured Persons. (9) The doctor in attendance must be free to decide on the treatment of the patient, but this does not preclude the requirement that the treatment should be economical and should not involve any useless expenditure on benefits in cash or in kind.

(10) General rules should be laid down for economy of treatment under social insurance. These rules should deal not only with prescriptions for drugs but also with every other method of treatment, diagnosis, hospital care, rest cures, etc. They should indicate treatments which are at once effective and economical.

(11) To prescribe unnecessary drugs or treatment does the patient no good and is a source of loss to the fund. Therefore it should be made legally compulsory for the doctor to follow the rules for economical treatment, in the interest both of the social insurance scheme and of the nation as a whole. The rules should give practical hints on treatment which will give the best results at the lowest cost. When two methods are of equal value, the doctor must choose the more economical.

(12) The rules should be drawn up by representatives of the fund and of the doctors, with the help of expert pharmacists.

(13) Patent medicines and proprietary drugs often increase the cost of treatment with no advantage to the patient.

(14) Patent medicines should as a rule not be prescribed unless no substitute can be made up more cheaply from the pharmacopoeia. Patent or proprietary medicines which have not been sufficiently tested or which merely contain well-known drugs in a new wrapping or whose composition is unknown should be excluded from use in social insurance.

Since there are, however, proprietary medicines which have great therapeutic value and cannot be replaced, Governments should see that they are not sold at excessive prices.

(15) The rules for prescribing patent or proprietary medicines should be drawn up by representatives of the funds and of doctors, with the help of expert pharmacists.

(16) The Conference considers that no satisfactory solution of the problem of proprietary medicines can be reached until the official pharmacopoeias have been entirely and radically revised and the manufacture of drugs put under systematic supervision.

Medical Certificates. (17) The medical attendant must be free to decide whether the insured person is or is not fit for work. Reasonable, carefully thought-out rules do not restrict this freedom, but help him in this most difficult and extremely responsible task.

(18) These rules should define clearly the concept of incapacity for work for the purpose of social insurance, taking as a basis the wide experience of the insurance institutions. The commoner groups of diseases, such as tuberculosis, rheumatic troubles, etc., should be treated separately, as should also the main occupational subdivisions.

The rules should indicate reliable scientific methods of detecting malingering, but they should also warn doctors of the danger of suspecting a malingerer in every case.

(19) The Conference is of opinion that the best of rules can never be a substitute for experience, thorough examination and the investigation of each individual case in all its aspects. At the same time, rules are a useful and indispensable guide for beginners and also even for experienced practitioners.

Professional Secrecy. (20) The legal provisions concerning professional secrecy for doctors were drawn up in the interest of the patient, and such protection must be fully afforded to insured persons. But long experience shows that the sense of responsibility and discretion imposed on the staffs of insurance funds are a sufficient guarantee for the insured person, even when the diagnosis is communicated to the fund.

(21) Sickness insurance cannot fight against social diseases or prevent occupational diseases unless it has a knowledge of their causes, based on sound statistics. Unless the diagnosis is known to the insurance fund it cannot carry out this very important part of its duties, nor can it prevent abuses and unreasonable demands for medical attendance.

(22) The Conference considers that it would be desirable for every country to find suitable means and methods for giving the health insurance funds free access to information concerning diagnoses, so that the provisions drawn up in the interest of the patient with regard to professional secrecy do not prove an obstacle to the building up of a really social health insurance scheme able to combat disease.

(23) When the insurance scheme refunds the cost of treatment, the necessary information should be supplied to the medical services of the funds.

(24) A diagnosis communicated to a fund should be accessible only to the officials and services to whom the knowledge is necessary in order to safeguard the health and economic interests of the insured persons and the fund. The diagnosis should be communicated by means of symbols (figures).

(25) The legislative provisions relating to professional secrecy should apply to the staffs of insurance funds in the same way as to doctors, with severe punishments for breach of secrecy. In addition, officials who knowingly reveal professional secrets should be dismissed.

Remuneration of Medical Practitioners. (26) In general health insurance schemes in which medical benefits are provided in kind by the funds, the system of remunerating the medical practitioner at a fixed rate per insured person is the most satisfactory in view of the collective nature of insurance.

When circumstances permit, payment may well be made through the medical association.

(27) In countries where the law prescribes that the cost of medical benefits shall be refunded by the funds, the rates which they have to pay and the rates normally charged by the doctors engaging in insurance work should coincide.

Participation of Insured Persons in the Cost of Medical Attendance and Drugs. (28) The necessity for paying a share of the cost of medical treatment and drugs may inflict a grave wrong, more especially on those insured persons who are in a particularly precarious financial situation, and may endanger their proper treatment. For this reason the proportion payable by the insured person should be low.

(29) No provision for such participation should be made in countries where insurance is so organised that overfrequent recourse to doctors and the immoderate use of pharmaceutical benefits are checked by other means.

Supervision of the Doctor. (30) There must be systematic supervision of the work of the medical practitioner; most of the supervision must be exercised by the confidential medical adviser to the fund.

(31) Arbitration boards or committees should deal with disputes concerning the grant of benefits in cash or in kind. In countries which have adopted the system of free choice, much of the supervision can be left to the medical association concerned, but even then the funds must necessarily have the assistance of a confidential medical adviser who is an expert in such work.

(32) Supervision should be restricted to economy in treatment and checking the existence and duration of incapacity for work, to the exclusion of all other matters. The correctness of the diagnosis or the plan of treatment cannot be checked in every case, for the medical attendant, while exercising his purely medical functions, must be entirely free; he is and must remain wholly responsible for the treatment. If in any particular case the process of supervision reveals some medical error which must be put right in the interest of the patient, the matter must be considered as a purely medical one to be settled by the doctors concerned to the exclusion of any other person or body acting for the fund.

Special Training of Doctors. (33) Every student of medicine should receive systematic training in the aims and tasks of the insurance scheme and in the special duties of doctors attending insured patients.

(34) In countries where extensive systematic training is given to medical students, no special courses of training for health insurance work are necessary; but as such training is rarely given at universities, special courses are desirable in the interest both of the doctors and of the insured persons.

(35) These courses should include at least the following points: (a) social legislation, with special reference to national and international social insurance; (b) the social causes of and prophylactic measures for combating social diseases, such as tuberculosis, alcoholism, infantile mortality, acute infectious diseases, etc.; (c) labour hygiene, occupational diseases, industrial accidents, accident prevention and the protection of workers; (d) medical problems which are of special importance in health insurance work and are not adequately dealt with at universities, more particularly economical methods of treatment and methods of proving malingering. Attention should also be devoted to certain selected aspects of the pathology, therapeutic treatment and prophylaxis of those diseases which are most widespread among workers.

(36) These courses will have no practical value unless combined with practical work. That means that the students must have an opportunity of seeing the working of a fund, its medical establishments and the consulting rooms of the medical practitioners attending insured patients. They must also visit specimens of healthy and unhealthy workplaces and have practice in prescribing economical drugs and determining carefully when a person is unfit for employment.

(37) The funds must assist in the work of these courses through their experts and their most experienced doctors; otherwise the courses cannot be really successful.

(38) Supplementary courses of instruction are necessary and useful for health insurance work as for all other departments of medical work. They should be of short duration, so that doctors practising in country districts can easily attend. They should be held, so far as possible, concurrently with other refresher courses for doctors in university towns, so that the health insurance doctors can have an opportunity of bringing their knowledge up to date in other branches of their profession. The curriculum should cover, generally speaking, the latest progress in the four branches of training mentioned above as being of special importance for health insurance work.

(39) The funds should collaborate as far as possible with associations of doctors and with medical faculties in the organisation of these courses. They should help their doctors to attend by contributing to their expenses. They should also place their medical establishments and their specialists at the disposal of the organisers of the courses.

PARTICIPATION OF ACCUMULATION FUNDS IN THE SUPPLY OF MEDICAL EQUIPMENT

(1) Invalidity, old-age and widows' and orphans' insurance funds must be entirely free to decide on the investment of their funds, pro-

vided always that they observe the statutory provisions governing the degree of safety and rate of interest.

(2) In planning their investments these funds should not overlook the fact that they must supply capital for various medical and social institutions. Whenever a fraction of the investments must be in public funds, subscription to municipal loans should be considered equivalent to the purchase of Government securities.

(3) The provision and development of medical equipment is one of the most important of all the social activities which these insurance funds should endeavour to promote by their investments.

(4) The social insurance scheme is the principal user of medical equipment, but the provision of loans by accumulation funds for the development of existing equipment is permissible only if the equipment is of undoubted technical value, if the loan will produce a marked improvement or extension of the services available for the insured persons and if the insurance institutions, in return for their assistance, receive certain powers of supervision and guarantees of efficient working.

(5) When the above conditions cannot be fulfilled and when the financial situation of the institutions permits and the desired result depends upon it, the institutions should endeavour to provide and maintain their own medical equipment. The question then arises of the share in this work to be taken by the health insurance and the invalidity, old-age and widows' and orphans' insurance schemes respectively.

To a great extent the proportion in which they share is determined by the obligations imposed by law on the funds concerning the curative and preventive benefits which they must provide.

If the health insurance funds undertake the provision of curative and preventive benefits for insured persons and their families not only in case of sickness but also in the event of invalidity, then these funds must provide the whole medical equipment of the insurance scheme. For this purpose they must obtain the necessary loans from the invalidity, old-age and widows' and orphans' insurance funds.

If, on the other hand, these latter funds are legally responsible for preventive and curative measures in the event of invalidity, there must necessarily be a division of the cost between them and the health insurance funds. The latter will set up clinics, dispensaries, convalescent homes, etc.; the former will set up establishments for the treatment of lingering diseases and those affections which most generally lead to invalidity.

(6) When the insurance institutions participate in the development of medical equipment either in the form of loans to public bodies or establishments or by setting up their own equipment, they should do

so in collaboration with all the other bodies responsible for protecting public health.

In the comprehensive plan which must be drawn up, the insurance scheme must be given its due place, not merely in return for its financial contribution in the form of loans, subsidies, etc., but also on account of the great influence which its benefits have on public health and its position in the first rank of those who use the medical services in question.

INDEX

INDEX

Abortion, 169
Accidents, 267
  Industrial, 92, 291–293, 295–297, 299–300, 308, 311, 317–318
  Prevention, 304–305, 316
Acts:
  British Columbia, 281
  Denmark, 241–242, 244–245, 248–249, 257, 261–262
  F.E.R.A., 344–345
  France, 209, 234
  Germany, 117, 135–137
  Japan, 62
  Medical, 128
  New York State, 294, 311
  Public welfare, 344
Additional benefits (see British health insurance)
Administration, 67, 274, 277, 281, 303
  British dental benefits, 165
  British health insurance, 147–154, 182–184
  British insurance benefits, 163–167, 186
  British medical benefits, 154–161
  Costs, 122, 165, 254–256
  Denmark, 255, 260–262
  France, 228–239
  German sickness insurance, 73, 96–97, 104–105, 122–125, 127, 135–137
  Public health, 276, 340
  Workmen's compensation, 295, 297, 299–301, 303–304, 308–309, 317–318, 325, 329, 349–351
Agriculture, 18, 142, 210–211, 214, 221, 242
Agricultural workers, 207–208, 210, 220, 289
Alberta, 62
Alsace and Lorraine, 206–207, 209
Ambulance services, 170
Amendment, Thoumyre, 230
America (see also United States), 324
American College of Surgeons, 358, 370–374
American Dental Association, 358, 377–379
American Hospital Association, 358, 376–377

American Medical Association, 42, 54, 290, 298, 307, 315, 334, 337, 344, 346, 358, 368–369
American Public Health Association, 320
Amtliche Nachrichten für Reichsversicherung, 97, 99
Anaesthesia, 169
Anderson, G. C., 204
Andrews, J. B., 319
Annual reports (see Ministry of Health)
Annuity, 118, 214
Antonelli, Etienne, 218, 239
Approved Institutions, 159
Approved Societies, 143–144, 147–148, 150–153, 155, 163–167, 172, 176, 178, 183, 186–187, 192–193, 195, 199, 280, 285–286
Argentina, 63
Arkansas, 45, 293
Armstrong, D. B., 35
"Arrangers, own," 158–159
Assessments, 152–153, 221
Attendance system, 155
Australia, 63
Austria, 61, 63, 326

Basic wage, 81
Belgium, 63
Benefit associations, 147
Benefit period:
  Denmark, 247–248
  France, 213–216
  Germany, 112–114
  Great Britain, 144–145
Benefit society, 65, 74
Benefits (see also cash, dental, disability, funeral, home, hospital, insurance, maternity, medical, nursing, ophthalmic, pharmaceutical, service, sickness, statutory, treatment and unemployment benefits), 283, 285, 288
Assessment (France), 221
British Columbia, 62
Costs:
  Denmark, 245–246, 261
  France, 222
  Great Britain, 142, 174–175

413